Teacher's Guide for AP* Calculus

To accompany

CALCULUS
Single Variable

Fourth Edition

Deborah Hughes-Hallett
University of Arizona

Andrew M. Gleason
Harvard University

William G. McCallum
University of Arizona

et al.

Written by:

Benita Albert
Oak Ridge High School

Raymond J. Cannon
Baylor University

Mark J. Howell
Gonzaga College High School

Steven Olson
Hingham High School and
Northeastern University

Edited by:

Ann Davidian
Gen. Douglas MacArthur High School

With contributions from:

Deborah Hughes-Hallett
University of Arizona

Sarah S. Latham
Princeton Day School

Michael Sherman
Belmont Hill School

WILEY
John Wiley & Sons, Inc.

To order books or for customer service please, call 1-800-CALL WILEY (225-5945).

ISBN-13 978- 0-471-71481-1
ISBN-10 0-471-71481-X

Printed in the United States of America

10 9 8 7 6 5 4 3 2 1

Printed and bound by Malloy Lithographing, Inc.

Introduction

This *Teacher's Guide for AP* Calculus* has been prepared to provide you with a variety of resources to assist you in teaching AP Calculus. All four authors have been members of the AP Calculus Test Development Committee at various times. They are master teachers who have a great deal of expertise with teachers' needs in teaching the AP Curriculum.

The first sections of the Guide are syllabi that provide section-by-section and day-to-day plans for Calculus AB and Calculus BC. The *Syllabus by Section* provides teachers with an overview of the course, and a general idea of the amount of time to spend on each chapter. The *Daily Plan* includes a list of text problems to be assigned for each day. At the end of each chapter, there is a list of suggested AP problems that can be assigned after a topic is studied.

This is followed by a correlation of Free Response questions to the chapters of the text. Every AP Calculus Free Response question from 1969-2004 is included in this correlation.

Each Chapter begins with AP Teacher Tips. This is followed by multiple choice questions and answers, and free response questions and solutions. Calculator active, calculator inactive, and calculator neutral questions are included.

Laboratory experiments are provided to enable students to discover calculus concepts independently. Some of these labs are spreadsheet applications. Others rely heavily on students' use of a graphing calculator. Still others require students to expand on the concepts covered in the course.

For teachers of Calculus BC, a section on vectors has been included. Sections 13.1 and 17.2 from the Multivariable text have been modified to provide teachers with material appropriate for a vector unit in the BC curriculum.

Acknowledgements

Many people helped to put this project together. David Lovelock devoted considerable time and effort to critically examining various drafts of the guide. His contributions were invaluable. The project also benefited from the many careful suggestions of Patti Frazer Lock, Andrew M. Gleason, David O. Lomen, Carl Swenson, and Thomas W. Tucker. Elliot J. Marks provided invaluable technical assistance. Frank Virga added to this project by processing parts of the manuscript.

Finally, working with Kelly Boyle, Michael Boezi and Laurie Rosatone at John Wiley and Sons was a pleasure.

Ann Davidian

Table of Contents

Syllabus for Calculus AB

By Section

Section	CH. 1: A LIBRARY OF FUNCTIONS	Days	Cum. Days
1.1	Functions & Change	1	1
1.2	Exponential Functions	2	3
1.3	New Functions From Old	2	5
1.4	Logarithmic Functions	3	8
1.5	Trigonometric Functions	2	10
1.6	Powers, Polynomials, & Rational Functions	2	12
1.7	Introduction to Continuity	1	13
1.8	Limits	3	16
	Review - AP Questions - Test	4	20
	Total Days	**20**	
	CH. 2: KEY CONCEPT: THE DERIVATIVE		
2.1	How Do We Measure Speed?	2	22
2.2	The Derivative at a Point	2	24
2.3	The Derivative Function	2	26
2.4	Interpretations of the Derivative	0.5	26.5
2.5	The Second Derivative	1	27.5
2.6	Differentiability	0.5	28
	Review - AP Questions - Test	5	33
	Total Days	**13**	
	CH 3: SHORT-CUTS TO DIFFERRENTIATION		
3.1	Powers and Polynomials	2	35
3.2	The Exponential Function	2	37
3.3	The Product and Quotient Rules	2	39
3.4	The Chain Rule	3	42
3.5	The Trigonometric Functions	3	45
3.6	The Chain Rule and Inverse Functions	3	48
3.7	Implicit Functions	2	50
3.8	Hyperbolic Functions	0	50
3.9	Linear Approximation and the Derivative	1	51
3.10	Theorems About Differentiable Functions	1	52
	Review - AP Questions - Test	6	58
	Total Days	**25**	

Section	CH 8: USING THE DEFINITE INTEGRAL		
8.1	Areas and Volumes	3	113
8.2	Applications to Geometry	2	115
8.3	Area and Arc Length in Polar Coordinates	0	115
8.4	Density and Center of Mass	2	117
8.5	Applications to Physics	0	117
8.6	Applications to Economics	0	117
8.7	Distribution Functions	0	117
8.8	Probability, Mean, and Median	0	117
	Review - AP Questions - Test	4	121
	Total Days	**11**	
	CH 9:SEQUENCES AND SERIES		
9.1	Sequences	0	121
9.2	Geometric Series	0	121
9.3	Convergence of Series	0	121
9.4	Tests for Convergence	0	121
9.5	Power Series and Interval of Convergence	0	121
	Review - AP Questions - Test	0	121
	Total Days	**0**	
	CH 10: APPROXIMATING FUNCTIONS USING SERIES		
10.1	Taylor Polynomials	0	121
10.2	Taylor Series	0	121
10.3	Finding and Using Taylor Series	0	121
10.4	The Error in Taylor Polynomial Approximations	0	121
10.5	Fourier Series	0	121
	Review - AP Questions - Test	0	121
	Total Days	**0**	
	CH 11:DIFFERENTIAL EQUATIONS		
11.1	What is a Differential Equation?	2	123
11.2	Slope Fields	2	125
11.3	Euler's Method	0	125
11.4	Separation of Variables	3	128
11.5	Growth and Decay	2	130
11.6	Applications and Modeling	1	131
11.7	Models of Population Growth	0	131
11.8	Systems of Differential Equations	0	131
11.9	Analyzing the Phase Plane	0	131
11.10	Second-Order Differential Equations: Oscillations	0	131
11.11	Linear Second-Order Differential Equations	0	131
	Review - AP Questions - Test	5	136
	Total Days	**15**	

4

Syllabus for Calculus BC

By Section

Section	CH. 1: A LIBRARY OF FUNCTIONS	Days	Cum. Days
1.1	Functions & Change	0	0
1.2	Exponential Functions	0	0
1.3	New Functions From Old	0	0
1.4	Logarithmic Functions	0	0
1.5	Trigonometric Functions	0	0
1.6	Powers, Polynomials, & Rational Functions	0	0
1.7	Introduction to Continuity	1	1
1.8	Limits	2	3
	Review - AP Questions - Test	0	3
	Total Days	3	
	CH. 2: KEY CONCEPT: THE DERIVATIVE		
2.1	How Do We Measure Speed?	1	4
2.2	The Derivative at a Point	1	5
2.3	The Derivative Function	2	7
2.4	Interpretations of the Derivative	0.5	7.5
2.5	The Second Derivative	1	8.5
2.6	Differentiability	0.5	9
	Review - AP Questions - Test	5	14
	Total Days	11	
	CH 3: SHORT-CUTS TO DIFFERRENTIATION		
3.1	Powers and Polynomials	2	16
3.2	The Exponential Function	2	18
3.3	The Product and Quotient Rules	2	20
3.4	The Chain Rule	2	22
3.5	The Trigonometric Functions	2	24
3.6	The Chain Rule and Inverse Functions	2	26
3.7	Implicit Functions	1	27
3.8	Hyperbolic Functions	0	27
3.9	Linear Approximation and the Derivative	1	28
3.10	Theorems About Differentiable Functions	1	29
	Review - AP Questions - Test	5	34
	Total Days	20	

Section	CH 4: USING THE DERIVATIVE		
4.1	Using First and Second Derivatives	2	36
4.2	Families of Curves	1	37
4.3	Optimization	2	39
4.4	Applications to Marginality	0	39
4.5	Optimization and Modeling	2	41
4.6	Rates and Related Rates	2	43
4.7	L'Hopital's Rule, Growth, and Dominance	1	44
4.8	Parametric Equations	2	46
	Review - AP Questions - Test	5	51
	Total Days	**17**	
	CH. 5: KEY CONCEPT: THE DEFINITE INTEGRAL		
5.1	How Do We Measure Distance Traveled?	1	52
5.2	The Definite Integral	1	53
5.3	The Fundamental Theorem and Interpretations	2	55
5.4	Theorems About Definite Integrals	2	57
	Review - AP Questions - Test	4	61
	Total Days	**10**	
	CH. 6: CONSTRUCTING ANTIDERIVATIVES		
6.1	Antiderivatives Graphically and Numerically	1	62
6.2	Constructing Antiderivatives Analytically	2	64
6.3	Differential Equations	1	65
6.4	Second Fundamental Theorem of Calculus	1	66
6.5	The Equations of Motion	0	66
	Review - AP Questions - Test	5	71
	Total Days	**10**	
	CH 7: INTEGRATION		
7.1	Integration By Substitution	2	73
7.2	Integration By Parts	2	75
7.3	Tables of Integrals	1	76
7.4	Algebraic Identities and Trigonometric Substitutions	1	77
7.5	Approximating Definite Integrals	1	78
7.6	Approximation Errors and Simpson's Rule	1	79
7.7	Improper Integrals	1	80
7.8	Comparison of Improper Integrals	1	81
	Review - AP Questions - Test	5	86
	Total Days	**15**	

Syllabus for Calculus AB

Daily Plans

Day	Total	Section	Problems
1	1	1.1	p. 7: 1, 3, 7, 11, 13, 17, 25, 28, 36
2	2	1.2	p. 14: 1, 3, 6, 11, 13, 17, 36
3	3	1.2	p. 14: 18-21, 23, 28, 35
4	4	1.3	p. 21: 2,3,5-8,14,20-22,26-28
5	5	1.3	p. 21: 30, 39-44, 52, 54
6	6	1.4	p. 27: 1-7, 9, 11, 12, 14, 16
7	7	1.4	p. 27: 19, 27, 29, 31, 39
8	8	1.4	p. 27: 33-36, 39-41, 44
9	9	1.5	p. 35: 7,9-11, 13, 18-20, 25
10	10	1.5	p. 35: 29, 30, 38, 40, 46
11	11	1.6	p. 42: 1, 2, 5, 7, 10, 11, 13, 14
12	12	1.6	p. 42: 16, 19, 20, 22, 29, 31
13	13	1.7	p. 47: 1-9 odd, 17, 19, 20, 22
14	14	1.8	p. 55: 1, 2, 9, 11, 13, 14, 15, 16
15	15	1.8	p. 55: 17-22
16	16	1.8	p. 55: 30, 32, 34, 36, 37, 39, 41
17	17	Review	p. 58: 1, 4, 7, 10, 11, 15-17, 19, 34, 38, 46, 47
18	18	Ck. Und.	p. 62: All
19	19	AP Q.	69AB1, 70AB2, 75AB1, 80AB3
20	20	Test	
1	21	2.1	p. 71: 1, 3, 5-10
2	22	2.1	p. 71: 11-21
3	23	2.2	p. 78: 1, 3, 7-13
4	24	2.2	p. 78: 14-18, 29. 33, 37, 42
5	25	2.3	p. 86: 1-9, 11, 14
6	26	2.3	p. 86: 15, 21, 33, 37, 38, 40
7	27	2.4 & 2.5	p. 91: 1-4; p. 97: 2, 4-9, 13
8	28	2.5 & 2.6	p. 91: 5; p. 93: 15, 16, 19-23; p. 101: 1, 2, 7, 10, 12
9	29	Review	p. 103: 3, 5, 8, 9, 15, 18, 21, 23, 28; p. 91: 8-12, 19
10	30	Ck. Und.	p. 106: All
11	31	AP Q.	Possible questions to select from: 76AB2, 76AB7-BC6, 78AB3, 81AB5-BC2, 82BC7,
12	32	AP Q.	86AB4, 86BC6(a,b), 89BC6, 93BC6(a,b), 97AB2(a,b,c), 98AB3(a,b,c)
13	33	Test	
1	34	3.1	p. 115: 3-43 odd
2	35	3.1	p. 115: 45-50, 53,55,57,62,65
3	36	3.2	p. 120: 1-25 odd, 27, 28
4	37	3.2	p. 120: 29, 30, 35, 37, 40-42, 45, 46
5	38	3.3	p. 124: 3, 4, 5, 8 ,10, 11, 13, 16, 19, 20, 23, 30, 31, 33
6	39	3.3	p. 124: 35, 37, 42-45, 47, 49, 50, 52, 53

7	40	3.4	p. 130: 1-25 odd
8	41	3.4	p. 130: 27-51 odd
9	42	3.4	p. 130: 53, 55, 57, 59, 61, 63, 68, 69, 81, 84
10	43	3.5	p. 136: 3-25 odd
11	44	3.5	p. 136: 27-39 odd, 40, 41
12	45	3.5	p. 136: 42-44, 46, 47, 48, 50
13	46	3.6	p. 141: 1-17 odd, 35, 37, 39, 40
14	47	3.6	p. 141: 19-33 odd, 41-43
15	48	3.6	p. 141: 45-63 odd
16	49	3.7	p. 145: 1-17 odd
17	50	3.7	p. 145: 19-31 odd
18	51	3.9	p. 154: 1, 3, 5, 10, 11, 19, 21
19	52	3.10	p. 158: 1-10
20	53	Review	p. 159: 3-60 every third problem
21	54	Review	p. 159: 67-81odd, 84, 89, 97, 99, 101
22	55	Ck. Und.	p. 163: All
23	56	AP Q.	Possible questions to select from: 77AB4-BC2, 77AB7-BC6, 78AB5-BC1, 80AB6-BC4, 81AB1,
24	57	AP Q.	85AB1, 88AB1, 90AB2, 91AB3, 92AB4-BC1, 94AB3, 95AB3, 95AB5-BC3, 96AB6, 98AB6, 2000AB5-BC5
25	58	Test	
1	59	4.1	p. 172: 1, 2, 6-13
2	60	4.1	p. 172: 14-20, 24, 27
3	61	4.1	p. 172: 28, 34, 35, 39, 42, 43, 47
4	62	4.2	p. 179: 2, 3, 4, 16, 21-23, 33, 37
5	63	4.3	p. 186: 1, 2, 4, 6, 7, 9, 11
6	64	4.3	p. 186: 14, 17, 20-24
7	65	4.3	p. 186: 28, 33, 35, 37-39
8	66	4.5	p. 202: 1, 4, 6, 10, 11, 16, 17
9	67	4.5	p. 202: 18-24
10	68	4.5	p. 202: 25-28, 32, 34
11	69	4.6	p. 210: 1, 8, 11, 12, 16, 17, 18
12	70	4.6	p. 210: 19, 23, 24, 25, 26, 27, 31, 33
13	71	4.7	p. 218: 1-17 odd
14	72	Review	p. 229: 1-19 odd, 22, 25, 29, 30
13	73	Review	p. 229: 31, 32, 35, 37, 39, 51-54
14	74	Ck. Und.	p. 234: All
15	75	AP Q.	Possible questions to select from: 75AB7-BC5, 76AB4, 78AB7-BC6, 80BC7, 82AB4
16	76	AP Q.	82AB6-BC3, 84AB5, 85AB5-BC2, 85AB6, 87BC2, 88BC1, 88BC3, 89AB5, 90AB4, 90BC3, 91AB5, 91AB6, 94AB5-BC2, 94BC4, 95BC5, 96AB1, 96AB4-BC4
17	77	Test	
1	78	5.1	p. 246: 1, 7, 9, 11, 15, 16, 22
2	79	5.2	p. 253: 1, 2, 7, 8, 9, 12, 14, 15, 17
3	80	5.2	p. 253: 19, 21, 24, 25, 27, 28, 29
4	81	5.3	p. 261: 1-9, 13
5	82	5.3	p. 261: 15, 18, 20, 22, 27, 34
6	83	5.4	p. 270: 1-11 odd, 14-19

7	84	5.4	p. 270: 21, 23, 26, 31, 34-39
8	85	Review	p. 272: 4, 10, 14, 15, 18, 34, 35, 38, 45, 36-39
9	86	Ck. Und.	p. 278: All
10	87	AP Q.	Possible questions to select from: 81AB7, 90BC6, 97AB4, 98AB3, 99AB3-BC3, 99AB4, 2000AB2-BC2
11	88	Test	
1	89	6.1	p. 285: 1-4, 11-13, 16, 18, 23
2	90	6.2	p. 292: 1-21
3	91	6.2	p. 292: 34-51
4	92	6.2	p. 292: 55, 59-73, 77
5	93	6.3	p. 297: 1, 2, 5-10
6	94	6.3	p. 297: 11, 13, 15, 16, 18
7	95	6.4	p. 302: 1-4, 8, 9, 11, 13, 14
8	96	6.4	p. 302: 15-19, 21-23
9	97	Review	p. 306: 4, 7-10, 12-14, 17, 18, 22, 40
10	98	Review	p. 306: 42-44, 47-49, 51, 52, 62, 68
11	99	Ck. Und.	p. 309: All
12	100	AP Q.	Possible questions to select from: 86BC6, 87BC6, 91AB1, 94AB6, 95AB6, 95BC6, 97AB1
13	101	AP Q.	97AB3, 97AB5-BC5, 99AB1, 99AB5-BC5, 2000AB4
14	102	Test	
1	103	7.1	p. 318: 1-18
2	104	7.1	p. 318: 19-38
3	105	7.1	p. 318: 45-59
4	106	7.1	p. 318: 60-65, 77, 80
5	107	7.5	p. 342: 1-4, 8, 9, 22, 23
6	108	Review	p. 361: 21-29, 33, 34, 40, 117, 118, 151, 152
7	109	AP Q.	Possible questions to select from: 85AB4-BC3, 86AB5-BC2, 88AB2, 88AB5, 94AB6, 96AB3-BC3, 97BC4
8	110	Test	
1	111	8.1	p. 372: 1-10
2	112	8.1	p. 372: 11-18
3	113	8.1	p. 372: 19-22, 24-27
4	114	8.2	p. 380: 1-7, 9, 10
5	115	8.2	p. 380: 29-32, 34, 36
6	116	8.4	p. 397: 1-6, 10
7	117	8.4	p. 397: 11, 16; p. 428: 1-5
8	118	Review	p. 428: 6, 7, 11, 23, 32, 33
9	119	AP Q.	Possible questions to select from: 69BC1, 81BC6, 83AB4, 88BC5, 91BC3
10	120	AP Q.	91BC4 ,92AB5-BC2, 94AB2-BC1, 95AB4-BC2, 96AB2, 96AB5, 97AB2, 92BC3, 98AB5-BC5, 98BC1
11	121	Test	
1	122	11.1	p. 525: 1-8
2	123	11.1	p. 525: 9, 10, 13, 15, 16
3	124	11.2	p. 529: 1-5
4	125	11.2	p. 529: 6-10
5	126	11.4	p. 539: 2, 7, 9, 12, 17, 19
6	127	11.4	p. 539: 16, 20, 21, 24, 25, 33

7	128	11.4	p. 539: 36, 37, 40, 41, 45
8	129	11.5	p. 546: 1-3, 5, 7, 9
9	130	11.5	p. 546: 11, 12, 15, 19, 21, 22
10	131	11.6	p. 555: 4, 7, 8, 9, 11, 13
11	132	Review	p. 595: 3, 7, 8, 9, 19
12	133	Review	p. 595: 20, 31, 33, 35
14	134	AP Q.	Possible questions to select from: 85BC4, 87BC1, 88BC6, 89AB6, 92AB6, 93AB6, 93BC6
15	135	AP Q.	94BC6, 97AB6-BC6, 98AB4, 2000AB6, 2000BC6
16	136	Test	
1	137	Review	Materials for Review:
2	138	Review	Released Exams: 2003, 1998, 1997, 1993, 1988, 1985 Multiple Choice & Free Response
3	139	Review	Free-Response Sections of the three most recent AP Examinations
4	140	Review	Preparing for the AP Calculus(AB) Examination by George W. Best & J. Richard Lux,
5	141	Review	Venture Publishing.
6	142	Review	
7	143	Review	
8	144	Review	
9	145	Review	
10	146	Review	
11	147	Review	
12	148	Review	
13	149	Review	
14	150	Review	

Daily Plans

For Calculus BC

Day	Total	Section	Problems
1	1	1.7	p. 47:1-9 odd, 17,19,20,22
2	2	1.8	p. 55: 1,2,9,11,14,15,17,21
3	3	1.8	p. 55: 28,31-43 odd
4	4	2.1	p. 71: 1,2,5,7,9,10,14,15,16
5	5	2.2	p. 78: 8,9,10,11-16,20,35,37,42
6	6	2.3	p. 86: 1-9, 11,14
7	7	2.3	p. 86: 15,21,33,37,38,40
8	8	2.4 & 2.5	p. 91: 1-4; p. 97: 3-8,13
9	9	2.5 & 2.6	p. 91: 5; p. 97: 15,16,21,22,23: p. 101: 1,2,7,10,12
10	10	Review	p. 103: 3,5,8,11,15,18,21,23,28; p. 91: 6-12, 19
11	11	Ck. Und.	p. 106: All
12	12	AP Q.	Possible questions to select from: 76AB2, 76AB7-BC6, 78AB3, 81AB5-BC2, 82BC7,
13	13	AP Q.	86AB4, 86BC6(a,b), 89BC6, 93BC6(a,b), 97AB2(a,b,c), 98AB3(a,b,c)
14	14	Test	
1	15	3.1	p. 115: 3-43 odd
2	16	3.1	p. 115: 45-50, 53,55,57,62,65
3	17	3.2	p. 120: 1-25 odd, 27, 28
4	18	3.2	p. 120: 29, 30, 35, 37, 40-42, 45, 46
5	19	3.3	p. 124: 3, 4, 5, 8 ,10, 11, 13, 16, 19, 20, 23, 30, 31, 33
6	20	3.3	p. 124: 35, 37, 42-45, 47, 49, 50, 52, 53
7	21	3.4	p. 130: 3, 6, 9,…,52 every 3rd problem
8	22	3.4	p. 130: 53-63 odd, 68,69,81,84
9	23	3.5	p. 136: 3-25 odd
10	24	3.5	p. 136: 27-39 odd, 40, 41
11	25	3.6	p. 141: 3, 6, 9,…,33 every 3rd problem
12	26	3.6	p. 141: 35-63 odd
13	27	3.7	p. 145: 1-27 odd
14	28	3.9	p. 154: 1,3,5,10,11,19,21
15	29	3.10	p. 158: 1-10, 14
16	30	Review	p. 159: 1-66 as needed, 83,84,97,99,101
17	31	Ck. Und.	p. 162: All
18	32	AP Q.	Possible questions to select from: 77AB4-BC2, 77AB7-BC6, 78AB5-BC1, 80AB6-BC4, 81AB1, 85AB1, 88AB1, 90AB2, 91AB3, 92AB4-BC1, 94AB3,95AB3, 95AB5-BC3,
19	33	AP Q.	96AB6, 98AB6, 2000AB5-BC5
20	34	Test	
1	35	4.1	p. 172: 1, 2, 6-20
2	36	4.1	p. 172: 24,27,28,34,35,39,42,43,47

3	37	4.2	p. 179: 2, 3, 4, 16, 21-23, 33, 37
4	38	4.3	p. 186: 1, 2, 4, 6, 7, 9, 11,14,17
5	39	4.3	p. 186: 20-24,28,33,35,37,38,39
6	40	4.5	p. 202: 1, 4, 6, 10, 11, 16, 20
7	41	4.5	p. 202: 21-28,32,34
8	42	4.6	p. 210: 1, 8, 11, 12, 16, 17, 18
9	43	4.6	p. 210: 19, 23, 24, 25, 26, 27, 31, 33
10	44	4.7	p. 218: 1-17 odd
11	45	4.8	p. 226: 1,2,5,7,23,24,26,32
12	46	4.8	p. 226: 34,35,36,37,39
13	47	Review	p. 229: 1-19 as needed, 22,25,29-32,35,37,39,51-54
14	48	Ck. Und.	p. 234: All
15	49	AP Q.	Possible questions to select from: 75AB7-BC5, 76AB4, 78AB7-BC6, 80BC7, 82AB4, 84AB5, 84BC2, 85AB5-BC2, 85AB6, 87BC2, 88BC1, 88BC3, 89AB5, 89BC4, 90AB4, 90BC3,
16	50	AP Q.	91AB5, 91AB6, 94AB5-BC2, 94BC3, 94BC4, 95BC5, 96AB1, 96AB4-BC4, 96BC6
17	51	Test	
1	52	5.1	p. 246: 1, 7, 9, 11, 15, 16, 22
2	53	5.2	p. 253: 1,7,9,12,14,24,25,27,28,29
3	54	5.3	p. 261: 1-9, 13
4	55	5.3	p. 261: 15, 18, 20, 22, 27, 34
5	56	5.4	p. 270: 1-11 odd, 14-19
6	57	5.4	p. 270: 21, 23, 26, 31, 34-39
7	58	Review	p. 272: 4, 10, 14, 15, 18, 34, 35, 38, 45, 36-39
8	59	Ck. Und.	p. 278: All
9	60	AP Q.	Possible questions to select from: 81AB7, 90BC6, 97AB4, 98AB3, 99AB3-BC3, 99AB4, 2000AB2-BC2
10	61	Test	
1	62	6.1	p. 285: 1-4, 11-13, 16, 18, 23
2	63	6.2	p. 292: 1-45 odd
3	64	6.2	p. 292: 47-77 odd
4	65	6.3	p. 297: 1, 2, 6, 7, 10, 17, 18, 21
5	66	6.4	p. 302: 1-3, 8, 9, 13-16, 19,35,36
6	67	Review	p. 306: 1-38 as needed, 44, 48, 49, 51,52,62,65,68,70
7	68	Ck. Und.	p. 309: All
8	69	AP Q.	Possible questions to select from: 82BC6, 86BC6, 87BC6, 91AB1, 94AB6, 95AB6,
9	70	AP Q.	95BC6, 97AB1, 97AB3, 97AB5-BC5, 99AB1, 99AB5-BC5, 2000AB4
10	71	Test	
1	72	7.1	p. 318: 1-25
2	73	7.1	p. 318: 26-38, 62,66,84,87
3	74	7.2	p. 325: 1,2,5,9,15,17,22,26
4	75	7.2	p. 325: 30,32,43,52,56
5	76	7.3	p. 330: 13,20,30,32,35,48
6	77	7.4	p. 337: 1,3,9,25,28,32,44,63
7	78	7.5	p. 342: 1-4, 8, 9, 22, 23
8	79	7.6	p. 347: 2,4,5,6
9	80	7.7	p. 355: 8,9,15,17,38

10	81	7.8	p. 359: 12,21,22,23,32
11	82	Review	p. 361: 1-134 as needed, 151, 152
12	83	Ck. Und.	p. 364: All
13	84	AP Q.	Possible questions to select from: 80BC6, 85AB4-BC3, 86AB3-BC1, 86AB5-BC2, 88AB2,
14	85	AP Q.	88AB5, 89AB3, 94AB4, 94AB6, 95AB2, 96AB3-BC3, 96BC1, 97BC4, 98BC6
15	86	Test	
1	87	8.1	p. 372: 2,3,5,7,8,10,12
2	88	8.1	p. 372: 13, 14, 16, 18, 26, 28
3	89	8.2	p. 381: 1, 5, 10, 11, 28,29,31,35
4	90	8.3	p. 389: 1,7,10,15,17,23,24
5	91	8.3	p. 389: 25,27,29,31,36,38
6	92	8.4	p. 397: 1,2,3,5,6,9,10,14
7	93	8.5	p. 406: 1,3,6,8,10,15
8	94	Review	p. 428: 6, 7, 11, 23, 32, 33
9	95	AP Q.	Possible questions to select from: 69BC1, 71BC6, 81BC6, 83AB4, 85BC5, 83BC2, 84BC5,
10	96	AP Q.	87BC3, 88BC5, 90BC4, 91BC3, 91BC4, 92AB5-BC2, 92BC3, 92BC5, 93 BC4, 95AB4-BC2,
11	97	AP Q.	96AB2, 96AB5, 96BC1, 96BC5, 97BC 3, 98AB5-BC5, 98BC1, 2000 AB1-BC1
12	98	Test	
1	99	9.1	p. 441: 1,3,4,7,9,14,16,21,27,29
2	100	9.2	p. 448: 2,3,11-21
3	101	9.2	p. 448: 25,28,29
4	102	9.3	p. 454: 1-4,10-13
5	103	9.3	p. 454: 16-19,24,33
6	104	9.4	p. 462: 4-11,14,15,20,21
7	105	9.4	p. 462: 42,43,44,47,52,55,56,58
8	106	9.5	p. 469: 1-5,7,9,11,12,16,19,24,32
9	107	Review	p. 471: 25,28,29,34,35,39,42-45
10	108	Ck. Und.	p. 474: All
11	109	Test	
1	109	10.1	p. 484: 1,3,5,17-20,22,23
2	110	10.1	p. 484: 13-16,26,28,29,31
3	111	10.2	p. 489: 5,7,9,17,21,23,24
4	112	10.2	p. 489: 25,31,32,34,35,37
5	113	10.3	p. 495: 1,2,6,12,14,16,26,27,35
6	114	10.4	p. 501: 5,9-12,14,17
7	115	Review	p. 514: 1,2,5,9,11,18,19,21,24,30,33
8	116	Ck. Und.	p. 517: All
9	117	AP Q.	Possible questions to select from: 77BC5, 81BC3, 82BC5, 83BC5, 84BC4,
10	118	AP Q.	86BC5, 87BC4, 88BC4, 90BC5, 91BC5, 92BC6, 93BC5, 94BC5,
11	119	AP Q.	85BC4, 96BC2, 97BC2, 98BC3, 99BC2, 2000BC3
12	120	Test	
1	121	11.1	p. 525: 1,7,9,13,14,15
2	122	11.2	p. 529: 1-5,8-10
3	123	11.3	p. 534: 1,2,4,5
4	124	11.4	p. 539: 1,16,19,25,39,44
5	125	11.5	p. 546: 1,2,5,9,21,22

6	126	11.6	p. 555: 4, 7, 8, 9, 11, 13
7	127	11.7	p. 564: 2,3,7,9,14
8	128	Review	p. 595: 7,8,10,16,29,31,35
9	129	AP Q.	Possible questions to select from:
10	130	AP Q.	85BC4, 87BC1, 88BC6, 89AB6, 91BC6, 92AB6, 93AB6, 93BC6, 94BC6
11	131	AP Q.	97AB6-BC6, 98AB4, 98BC4, 99BC6, 2000AB6, 2000BC6
12	132	Test	
1	133	Vectors	Spend 3 days on motion in the plane and vectors using the supplementary material in this guide
2	134	Vectors	(see pages 293 – 320) and AP Problems. Possible questions to select from:
3	135	Vectors	75BC3, 78BC7, 79BC6, 87BC5, 93BC2, 95BC1, 97BC1, 99BC1, 2000BC4
4	136	Test	
1	137	Review	Materials for Review:
2	138	Review	Released Exams: 2003, 1998, 1997, 1993, 1988, 1985 Multiple Choice & Free Response
3	139	Review	Free-Response Sections of the three most recent AP Examinations
4	140	Review	Preparing for the AP Calculus (BC) Examination by George W. Best & J. Richard Lux,
5	141	Review	Venture Publishing
6	142	Review	
7	143	Review	
8	144	Review	
9	145	Review	
10	146	Review	
11	147	Review	
12	148	Review	
13	149	Review	
14	150	Review	

Correlation between AP Questions and
Chapters in the Textbook

Year	Question	Chapter	OK for AB	Notes
1969	AB 1	1		
1969	AB 2, BC 2	3		All AB problems are suitable for AB and BC.
1969	AB 3, BC 3	7		
1969	AB 4, BC 4	4		Only BC problems with a "Yes" in the
1969	AB 5	8		"OK for AB" column are suitable for AB.
1969	AB 6	5		
1969	AB 7	3		Not in CD means that the item is no longer
1969	BC 1	8	Yes	part of the course description.
1969	BC 5	8	Yes	
1969	BC 6	Not in CD		
1969	BC 7	9		
1970	AB 1, BC 1	5		
1970	AB 2	1		
1970	AB 3, BC 2	4		
1970	AB 4	4		
1970	AB 5	4		
1970	AB 6, BC 5	4		
1970	AB 7	7		
1970	BC 3	4	Yes	
1970	BC 4	Not in CD		
1970	BC 6	9		
1970	BC 7	2	Yes	
1971	AB 1	3		
1971	AB 2	7		
1971	AB 3	4		
1971	AB 4, BC 1	4		
1971	AB 5	8		
1971	AB 6	4		
1971	AB 7, BC 3	4		
1971	BC 2	8	Yes	
1971	BC 4	10		
1971	BC 5	7		
1971	BC 6	8		
1971	BC 7	2	Yes	

1972	AB 1	3		
1972	AB 2, BC 1	4		
1972	AB 3, BC 2	7		
1972	AB 4, BC 3	4		
1972	AB 5	4		
1972	AB 6	8		
1972	AB 7	6		
1972	BC 4	9		
1972	BC 5	Not in CD		
1972	BC 6	4	Yes	
1972	BC 7	8		
1973	AB 1	4		
1973	AB 2	6		
1973	AB 3, BC 1	3		
1973	AB 4, BC 2	8		
1973	AB 5, BC 3	4		
1973	AB 6	4		
1973	AB 7	7		
1973	BC 4	4		
1973	BC 5	Not in CD		
1973	BC 6	9		
1973	BC 7	7		
1974	AB 1, BC 1	3		
1974	AB 2	4		
1974	AB 3	3		
1974	AB 4, BC 2	6		
1974	AB 5, BC 4	4		
1974	AB 6	7		
1974	AB 7	11		
1974	BC 3	8	Yes	
1974	BC 5	8		
1974	BC 6	Not in CD		
1974	BC 7	4	Yes	
1975	AB 1	1		
1975	AB 2	4		
1975	AB 3	5		
1975	AB 4, BC 1	4		
1975	AB 5	3		

1975	AB 6, BC 2	8		
1975	AB 7, BC 5	2		
1975	BC 3	Vectors		
1975	BC 4	9		
1975	BC 6	Not in CD		
1975	BC 7	4	Yes	
1976	AB 7, BC 6	2		
1976	BC 1	4	Yes	
1976	BC 4	7		
1976	BC 5	Not in CD		
1976	BC 7	10		
1976	AB 1	3		
1976	AB 2	2		
1976	AB 3, BC 2	8		
1976	AB 4	4		
1976	AB 5, BC 3	4		
1976	AB 6	6		
1977	AB 1	3		
1977	AB 2	4		
1977	AB 3	8		
1977	AB 4, BC 2	3		
1977	AB 5, BC 3	6		
1977	AB 6	4		
1977	AB 7, BC 6	3		
1977	BC 1	7	Yes	
1977	BC 4	Not in CD		
1977	BC 5	9		
1977	BC 7	6	Yes	
1978	AB 1	3		
1978	AB 2	3		
1978	AB 3	2		
1978	AB 4	7		
1978	AB 5, BC 1	3		
1978	AB 6, BC 3	4		
1978	AB 7, BC 6	4		
1978	BC 2	3	Yes	
1978	BC 4	Not in CD		
1978	BC 5	10		

1978	BC 7	Vectors		
1979	AB 1	3		
1979	AB 2	4		
1979	AB 3, BC 3	4		
1979	AB 4, BC 1	4		
1979	AB 5, BC 5	8		
1979	AB 6	2		
1979	AB 7	6		
1979	BC 2	Not in CD		
1979	BC 4	10		
1979	BC 6	Vectors		
1979	BC 7	4	Yes	
1980	AB 1	8		
1980	AB 2	4		
1980	AB 3	1		
1980	AB 4, BC 1	7		
1980	AB 5, BC 2	4		
1980	AB 6, BC 4	3		
1980	AB 7	2		
1980	BC 3	9		
1980	BC 5	Not in CD		
1980	BC 6	8		
1980	BC 7	4	Yes	
1981	AB 1	3		
1981	AB 2	8		
1981	AB 3, BC 1	4		
1981	AB 4	3		
1981	AB 5, BC 2	2		
1981	AB 6, BC 4	4		
1981	AB 7	5		
1981	BC 3	9		
1981	BC 5	Not in CD		
1981	BC 6	8	Yes	
1981	BC 7	4	Yes	
1982	AB 1	7		
1982	AB 2	2		
1982	AB 3, BC 1	8		
1982	AB 4	4		

1982	AB 5, BC 2	4		
1982	AB 6, BC 3	4		
1982	AB 7	3		
1982	BC 4	Not in CD		
1982	BC 5	10		
1982	BC 6	6		
1982	BC 7	2	Yes	
1983	AB 1	3		
1983	AB 2	4		
1983	AB 3, BC 1	4		
1983	AB 4	8		
1983	AB 5, BC 3	11		
1983	BC 2	7		Surface Area
1983	BC 4	Not in CD		
1983	BC 5	10		
1984	BC 5	8		
1984	AB 1	6		
1984	AB 2	3		
1984	AB 3, BC 1	8		
1984	AB 4, BC 3	4		
1984	AB 5	4		
1984	BC 2	4		
1984	BC 4	9		
1985	AB 1	3		
1985	AB 2, BC 1	6		
1985	AB 3	8		
1985	AB 4, BC 3	7		
1985	AB 5, BC 2	4		
1985	AB 6	4		
1985	BC 4	11	Yes	
1985	BC 5	8		
1985	BC 6	4	Yes	
1986	AB 1	4		
1986	AB 2	4		
1986	AB 3, BC 1	7		Parts
1986	AB 4	2		
1986	AB 5, BC 2	7		
1986	AB 6, BC 3	7		

1986	BC 4	Not in CD		
1986	BC 5	10		
1986	BC 6	6	Yes	
1987	AB 1	6		
1987	AB 2	3		
1987	AB 3	8		
1987	AB 4	4		
1987	AB 5	4		
1987	AB 6	5		
1987	BC 1	11	Yes	
1987	BC 2	4	Yes	
1987	BC 3	8		Parts
1987	BC 4	10		
1987	BC 5	Vectors		
1987	BC 6	6	Yes	
1988	AB 1	3		
1988	AB 2	7		
1988	AB 3	8		
1988	AB 4	4		
1988	AB 5	7		
1988	AB 6	6		
1988	BC 1	4	Yes	
1988	BC 2	8	Yes	Shells
1988	BC 3	4	Yes	
1988	BC 4	9		
1988	BC 5	8	Yes	
1988	BC 6	11	Yes	
1989	AB 1	4		
1989	AB 2	8		
1989	AB 3	7		
1989	AB 4	3		
1989	AB 5	4		
1989	AB 6	11		
1989	BC 1	6	Yes	
1989	BC 2	8	Yes	
1989	BC 3	4	Yes	
1989	BC 4	4		
1989	BC 5	Not in CD		

1989	BC 6	2	Yes	
1990	AB 1	6		
1990	AB 2	3		
1990	AB 3	8		
1990	AB 4	4		
1990	AB 5	4		
1990	AB 6	3		
1990	BC 1	4	Yes	
1990	BC 2	8	Yes	
1990	BC 3	4	Yes	
1990	BC 4	8		
1990	BC 5	10		
1990	BC 6	5	Yes	
1991	AB 1	6		
1991	AB 2	8		
1991	AB 3	3		
1991	AB 4	3		
1991	AB 5	4		
1991	AB 6	4		
1991	BC 1	6	Yes	
1991	BC 2	4	Yes	
1991	BC 3	8	Yes	
1991	BC 4	8	All but part(d)	
1991	BC 5	10		
1991	BC6	11		
1992	AB 1	4		
1992	AB 2	6		
1992	AB 3	4		
1992	AB 4, BC 1	3		
1992	AB 5, BC 2	8		
1992	AB 6	11		
1992	BC 3	8		
1992	BC 4	4	Yes	
1992	BC 5	8		
1992	BC 6	9		
1993	AB 1	4		
1993	AB 2	4		
1993	AB 3, BC 1	8		

1993	AB 4, BC 3	4		
1993	AB 5	6		
1993	AB 6	11		
1993	BC 2	Vectors		
1993	BC 4	8		
1993	BC 5	10		
1993	BC 6	11	Yes	
1994	AB 1	4		
1994	AB 2, BC 1	8		
1994	AB 3	3		
1994	AB 4	7		Parts
1994	AB5, BC 2	4		
1994	AB 6	7		
1994	BC 3	4		
1994	BC 4	4	Yes	
1994	BC 5	10		
1994	BC 6	11	Yes	
1995	AB1	4		
1995	AB2	7		Parts
1995	AB3	3		
1995	AB4, BC2	8		
1995	AB5, BC3	3		
1995	AB6	6		
1995	BC 1	Vectors		
1995	BC 4	10		
1995	BC 5	4	Yes	
1995	BC 6	6	Yes	
1996	AB1	4		
1996	AB2	8		
1996	AB3 – BC3	7		
1996	AB4 – BC4	4		
1996	AB5	4		
1996	AB6	3		
1996	BC1	7		
1996	BC2	10		
1996	BC5	8		
1996	BC6	4		
1997	AB 1	6		

1997	AB 2	8		
1997	AB 3	6		
1997	AB 4	5		
1997	AB 5 – BC 5	6		
1997	AB 6 – BC 6	11		
1997	BC 1	Vectors		
1997	BC 2	10		
1997	BC 3	8		
1997	BC 4	7	Yes	
1998	AB 1	8		
1998	AB 2, BC 2	4		
1998	AB 3	5		
1998	AB 4	11		
1998	AB 5, BC 5	8		
1998	AB 6	3		
1998	BC 1	8	Yes	
1998	BC 3	10		
1998	BC 4	11	Euler	
1998	BC 6	7		
1999	AB 1	7		
1999	AB 2, BC 2	8		
1999	AB 3, BC 3	5		
1999	AB 4	4		
1999	AB 5, BC 5	6		
1999	AB 6	4		
1999	BC 1	Vectors		
1999	BC 4	10		
1999	BC 6	11	Euler	
2000	AB 1, BC 1	8		
2000	AB 2, BC 2	5		
2000	AB 3	4		
2000	AB 4	6		
2000	AB 5, BC 5	3		
2000	AB 6	11		
2000	BC 3	10		
2000	BC 4	Vectors		
2000	BC 6	11	Yes	
2001	AB 1	8		

2001	AB 2, BC 2	6		
2001	AB 3, BC 3	5		
2001	AB 4, BC 4	4		
2001	AB 5	6		
2001	AB 6	11		
2001	BC 1	8		
2001	BC 5	11		
2001	BC 6	10		
2002	AB 1, BC 1	8		
2002	AB 2, BC 2	6		
2002	AB 3	6		
2002	AB 4, BC 4	6		
2002	AB 5	4		
2002	AB 6	4		
2002	BC 3	Vectors		
2002	BC 5	11		
2002	BC 6	10		
2002(B)	AB 1	8		
2002(B)	AB 2, BC 2	4		
2002(B)	AB 3	6		
2002(B)	AB 4, BC 4	7		
2002(B)	AB 5, BC 5	11		
2002(B)	AB 6	4		
2002(B)	BC 1	8		
2002(B)	BC 3	8		
2002(B)	BC 6	9		
2003	AB 1, BC 1	8		
2003	AB 2	8		
2003	AB 3	5		
2003	AB 4, BC 4	6		
2003	AB 5, BC 5	11		
2003	AB 6	6		
2003	BC 2	Vectors		
2003	BC 3	8		
2003	BC 6	10		
2003(B)	AB 1, BC 1	8		
2003(B)	AB 2	6		
2003(B)	AB 3, BC 3	5		

2003(B)	AB 4	8		
2003(B)	AB 5, BC 5	6		
2003(B)	AB 6	11		
2003(B)	BC 2	8		
2003(B)	BC 4	Vectors		
2003(B)	BC 6	10		
2004	AB 1, BC 1	5		
2004	AB 2, BC 2	8		
2004	AB 3	6		
2004	AB 4, BC 4	5		
2004	AB 5	6		
2004	AB 6	11		
2004	BC 3	Vectors		
2004	BC 5	11		
2004	BC 6	10		
2004(B)	AB 1	8		
2004(B)	AB 2	5		
2004(B)	AB 3, BC 3	7		
2004(B)	AB 4, BC 4	6		
2004(B)	AB 5	11		
2004(B)	AB 6, BC 6	5		
2004(B)	BC 1	Vectors		
2004(B)	BC 2	10		
2004(B)	BC 5	8		

AP Teacher Tips
Chapter 1: A Library of Functions

This chapter lays the foundation for calculus by reviewing the most common functions, including linear, exponential, logarithmic, trigonometric, power, polynomial, and rational functions. These functions are presented using the "Rule of Four", i.e., graphically, numerically, algebraically, and verbally.

Hopefully, your students received this background in their precalculus course. Since precalculus is no longer tested directly on the Advanced Placement examination, you must decide how best to cover this material.

Some teachers use parts of this chapter as a summer assignment for their students. Others use the first six sections as a brief review during the first few days of school. Still others refer back to appropriate sections of the chapter as the need arises during the school year.

Sections 1.7 and 1.8 cover the topics of continuity and limits, as well as the Intermediate Value Theorem. All of these topics are included in the AP Calculus course description. The more formal definition of limit, as well as one-sided limits and limits at infinity, are discussed. Be sure your students also see the definition of infinite limits. These ideas should be linked to horizontal and vertical asymptotes.   These sections contain a wealth of ideas, and you may want to spend extra time developing the concepts. They can all be reviewed later in the course when the students have more computational skill and you are covering "curve-sketching".

Since the material in the first six sections of this chapter is not directly tested on the AP Calculus examination, there are no appropriate "AP type" questions provided. However, in an effort to familiarize students with short answer questions, we have provided you with twenty questions in a multiple-choice format. These questions appear in the *ConcepTests* book,[1] which you may want to look at throughout the year.

Note that the format of the *ConcepTests* is different from that of the AP exam. Questions may have four or five answer choices, matching and true-false questions appear, and some questions may have more than one correct answer.

We have included eight additional multiple-choice questions based on material that is tested on the AP Calculus examination. These questions are similar to the type of questions that students might see on an AP Calculus examination. Since answering multiple-choice questions is a bit of an art, we hope that these questions will help students begin to develop their test-taking skills.

---

[1] *ConcepTests to Accompany Calculus*, Fourth Edition, John Wiley and Sons, Inc., 2005.

Problems for Chapter One

Exercises

1. Which of the following functions has its domain identical with its range?
    (a) $f(x) = x^2$
    (b) $g(x) = \sqrt{x}$
    (c) $h(x) = x^3$
    (d) $i(x) = |x|$

2. Put the following linear functions in order of increasing slope.

    (a) $y = \pi x + 9$
    (b) $y = 3x + 1$
    (c) $y = -10x$
    (d) $y = x$
    (e) $y = \dfrac{x}{10} + 7$
    (f) $y = -100$

3. List the lines in the figure below in the order of increasing slope. (The graphs are shown in identical windows.)

(a)

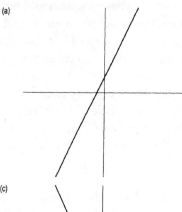

(b)

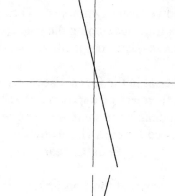

(c)

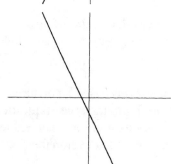

(d)

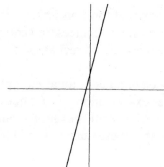

4. Which of the graphs represents the position of an object that is speeding up and then slowing down?

(a) distance

(b) distance

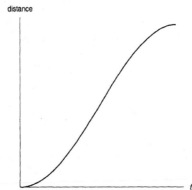

(c) distance

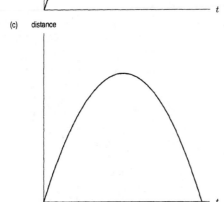

(d) distance

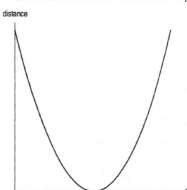

5. Which of the following tables could represent an exponential function?

(a)

x	$f(x)$
1	1/16
2	1/8
3	1/4
4	1/2

(b)

x	$g(x)$
1	9
2	-3
3	1
4	$-1/3$

(c)

x	$h(x)$
1	1
2	4
4	16
8	64

(d)

x	$k(x)$
1	10
2	5
3	2
4	1

6. Let $f(x) = ab^x$, $b > 0$. Then $\dfrac{f(x+h)}{f(x)} =$

(a) b^h

(b) h

(c) $b^{x+h} - b^x$

(d) a

7. Estimate the doubling time for the exponential growth shown in Figure 1.1.

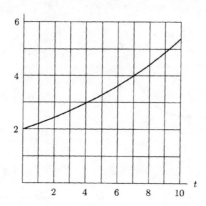

Figure 1.1

8. If $f(x) = \sqrt{x^2 + 1}$ and $g(x) = e^{x^2}$ then $f(g(x)) =$

   (a) $e^{(x^2+1)}$

   (b) $\sqrt{e^{2x^2} + 1}$

   (c) $e^{\sqrt{x^2+1}}$

   (d) $\sqrt{e^{x^4} + 1}$

9. Which of the following could describe the graph in Figure 1.2.

   (a) $y = 3\sin\left(\dfrac{x}{2} + \dfrac{\pi}{2}\right)$ (b) $y = 3\sin\left(2x + \dfrac{\pi}{2}\right)$ (c) $y = 3\cos(2x)$

   (d) $y = 3\cos\left(\dfrac{x}{2}\right)$ (e) $y = 3\sin(2x)$ (f) $y = 3\sin\left(\dfrac{x}{2}\right)$

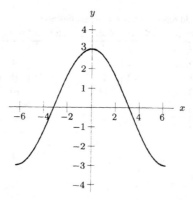

Figure 1.2

For Problems 10–11, consider the four graphs.

(I)

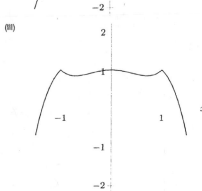

(II)

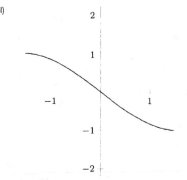

(III)

(IV)

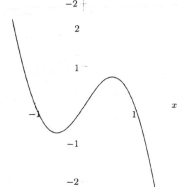

10. Which of these graphs could represent even functions?

11. Which of these graphs could represent odd functions?

12. Use the properties of logarithms to decide which of the following is largest.

    (a) $\ln(30) - \ln(2)$
    (b) $2\ln 4$
    (c) $\ln 3 + \ln 4$
    (d) $\dfrac{\ln 4}{\ln 2}$

13. Which of the following functions are increasing and concave up?

    (a) 3^{-x}
    (b) 3^{x}
    (c) $\ln x$
    (d) $-\ln x$

14. Which of the following graphs represents the inverse of the function graphed in Figure 1.3?

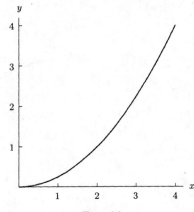

Figure 1.3

(a)
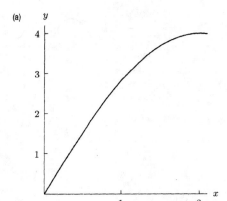

(b)
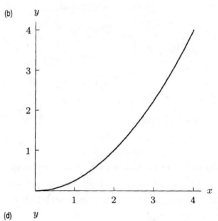

(c)
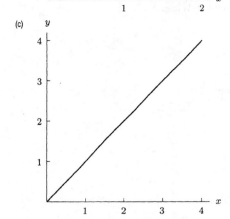

(d)
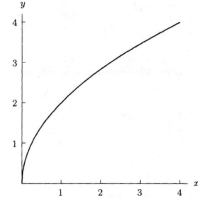

15. What is the degree of the graph of the polynomial in Figure 1.4?

   (a) 3
   (b) 5
   (c) Either (a) or (b)
   (d) Neither (a) nor (b)
   (e) Any polynomial of degree greater than 2

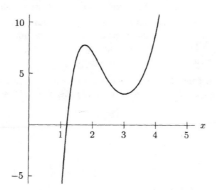

Figure 1.4

16. Which of the graphs represents $y = \dfrac{2x^2}{x^2 + x - 2}$?

(a)

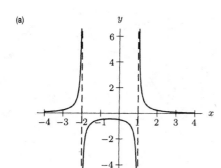

(b)

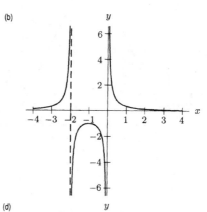

(c)

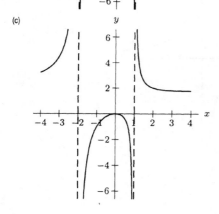

(d)

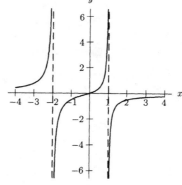

35

For Problems 17–18, decide whether the function is continuous on the given interval.

17. $f(x) = \dfrac{1}{x-2}$ on $[0,3]$

18. $f(x) = \dfrac{1}{x-2}$ on $[-1,0]$

19. Possible criteria for a limit: *As you get closer and closer to the limit point the function gets closer and closer to the limit value.* Which of the following is an example that meets the criteria but does not have the stated limit?

  (a) As x increases to 2, $f(x) = x^2$ gets closer and closer to 4, so the limit at $x = 2$ of $f(x)$ is 4.

  (b) As x increases to 100, $f(x) = 1/x$ gets closer and closer to 0, so the limit as x goes to 100 of $f(x)$ is 0.

  (c) As x increases to 3, $f(x) = (1+x)^2$ gets closer and closer to 16, so the limit as x goes to 3 of $f(x)$ is 16.

  (d) None of these show a problem with this criteria for a limit.

20. Definition of continuity of a function at a point: *If the limit of the function exists at a point and is equal to the function evaluated at that point, then the function is continuous at that point.* Which of the following is not continuous at $x = c$?

  (a) (I) only

  (b) (II) only

  (c) (III) only

  (d) (I) and (II)

  (e) (I) and (III)

  (f) (II) and (III)

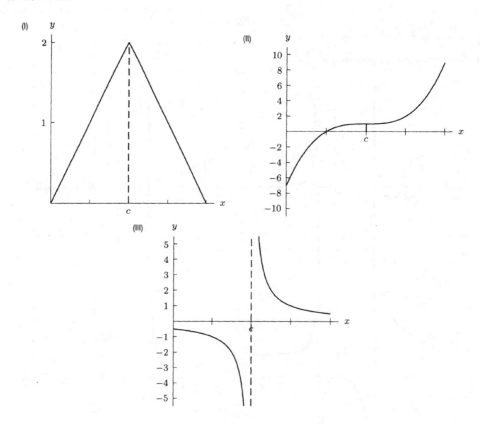

Solutions to Problems for Chapter One

Exercises

1. (b) and (c). For $g(x) = \sqrt{x}$, the domain and range are all nonnegative numbers, and for $h(x) = x^3$, the domain and range are all real numbers.

2. (c), (f), (e), (d), (b), (a). In order to put the lines in the correct order, consider the slope of each function.

3. (b), (c), (a), (d).

4. (b). The graph has a positive slope everywhere, which is increasing for t near zero and decreasing for larger times.

5. (a). In (a) each term in this table is found by multiplying the previous term by 2. In fact the entries in this table have the form $(1/16)2^{x-1}$. Answer (b) is incorrect since each term in this table is found by multiplying the previous term by $-1/3$, but exponential functions need ab^x, where $b > 0$. Although in (c) the ratio of adjacent terms is constant, the x values do not change by a constant amount. Answer (d) is incorrect since the ratio between adjacent terms is not constant.

6. (a), since $f(x + h) = ab^{x+h} = ab^x b^h = f(x)b^h$.

7. 7

8. (b)

9. (a) and (d). Note that (b), (c), and (e) have period π, with the rest having period 4π. Answer (f) has $y(0) = 0$. (a) and (d) could describe the graph.

10. (III) could be the graph of an even function.

11. (II) and (IV) could be graphs of odd functions.

12. (b). $\ln(30) - \ln(2) = \ln(15)$, $2\ln(4) = \ln(16)$, $\ln(3) + \ln(4) = \ln(12)$, and $\frac{\ln(4)}{\ln(2)} = \frac{\ln(2^2)}{\ln 2} = \frac{2\ln 2}{\ln 2} = 2 = \ln(e^2)$. Since $e^2 < 9$ and $\ln x$ is an increasing function, $\ln(16)$ is the largest number.

13. (b). Note that (a) and (d) are decreasing, and (c) is concave down.

14. (d). The graph of the inverse is a reflection of the function across the line $y = x$.

15. (e). The graph could represent any such polynomial. The window may not show all the crucial behavior of the polynomial.

16. (c). The graph goes through the origin and has vertical asymptotes at $x = 1$ and -2. It is negative for $0 < x < 1$, and the function is positive for large x. Alternatively, the function has a horizontal asymptote $y = 2$.

17. $f(x)$ is not continuous because $f(2)$ is not defined.

18. $f(x)$ is continuous.

19. (b) meets this criteria, but this limit is $1/100$, not 0.

20. (c)

Chapter 1 Multiple Choice Questions

1. Among the following choices, the largest value of h which ensures that $3x + 1$ is within 0.5 of 7 when x is within h of 2 is $h =$

(A) 0.01   (B) 0.05   (C) 0.1   (D) 0.2   (E) 0.25

2. Let $f(x) = \begin{cases} x^2 - 4 & \text{for } x < 3 \\ 7 & \text{for } x = 3 \\ 2x + 4 & \text{for } x > 3 \end{cases}$

Then $\lim\limits_{x \to 3^+} f(x) =$

(A) 2   (B) 5   (C) 7   (D) 10   (E) Does not exist

3. $\lim\limits_{x \to \infty} \dfrac{x^2 + 3x + 5}{2x^2 - 7x + 6} =$

(A) 0   (B) $\dfrac{1}{2}$ (C) $\dfrac{5}{6}$ (D) 1   (E) ∞

4. If $f(x) = \dfrac{x^2 - 4}{x^2 - x - 2}$, then which of the following is true?

(A) The lines $x = -1$ and $x = 2$ are vertical asymptotes

(B) The lines $x = -2$ and $x = 2$ are vertical asymptotes

(C) The line $x = 1$ is the only vertical asymptote

(D) The line $y = 1$ is the only vertical asymptote

(E) The line $x = -1$ is the only vertical asymptote

5. $\displaystyle\lim_{x\to\infty}\frac{5e^{-x}+10}{6e^{x}-1}=$

(A) $-\infty$ (B) -10 (C) 0   (D) $\dfrac{5}{6}$ (E) ∞

6. If $f(x)=\begin{cases}\dfrac{\sin x}{x}, & \text{if } x\neq 0\\ 1, & \text{if } x=0\end{cases}$, then which of the following is true?

    I. f is continuous at $x=0$.
    II.   The line $x=0$ is a vertical asymptote.
    III.   The line $y=0$ is a horizontal asymptote.

(A) None   (B) I only   (C) II only

(D) I and III only   (E) II and III only

7. $\displaystyle\lim_{x\to\frac{\pi}{2}}\frac{\sin(x)}{x}$ is

(A) 0   (B) $\dfrac{2}{\pi}$ (C) 1   (D) $\dfrac{\pi}{2}$ (E) undefined

8. If $f(x)=\begin{cases}3x+1, & \text{if } x<2\\ 9, & \text{if } x=2\\ 6x-4, & \text{if } x>2\end{cases}$, then $\displaystyle\lim_{x\to 2^{+}}f(x)$ is

(A) 6   (B) 7   (C) 8   (D) 9   (E) undefined

Chapter 1 Multiple Choice Questions

Question	Answer	AB	BC	No Calculator	Calculator Required	Neutral Calculator
1	C	x	x		x	
2	D	x	x	x		
3	B	x	x	x		
4	E	x	x	x		
5	C	x	x	x		
6	D	x	x	x		
7	B	x	x	x		
8	C	x	x	x		

AP Teacher Tips
Chapter 2: Key Concept: The Derivative

This chapter provides the theoretical underpinning for the derivative and the relationship between continuity and differentiability. All of this material is appropriate for the AB and BC examinations. The only "rule" established for computing derivatives is the power rule for positive integers. The text includes the proofs for $n = 2$ and $n = 3$. You may want to prove the general rule using the Binomial Theorem.

Section 2.1 introduces the ideas of instantaneous velocity and slope of a curve at a point, using both numeric and graphical ideas. The formal definition of derivative at a point is in Section 2.2. This section also shows how to estimate the derivative at a point using the functions $y = \sin(x)$ and $y = 2^x$. The graphical approach shows that the graph is almost linear, and sets the stage for a more formal treatment of linear approximation that comes later.

Section 2.3 expands on the idea of the "derivative at a point" to a function in its own right, defined at many points. Example 1 in this section is very important, and may give students difficulty at first. In this example, students are asked to draw the tangent line and use the slope of the line they just drew to estimate the derivative. This is using the relation between derivative and slope in just the opposite direction they have been working, and some students get confused. The time spent on this example is time well spent. This section also establishes the fact that the derivative of a linear function gives the slope of the line. It is interesting then to ask students for the equation of the line tangent to the line $y = 2x + 3$ at the point $(1, 5)$ because some students think that a tangent line can only meet the graph in one point. Section 2.4 may be one of the nicest sections in the text, and includes problems that do not commonly appear in other texts. The discussion here can help students with the meaning of the derivative without them having to worry about any computations. Mastery of this section should help with related rates and applied max/min problems later in the course. Consider treating this section as a resource section for "word problems" rather than covering it as you would more ordinary sections. Thus, you may want to assign one or two problems at a time from this section over a number of assignments in an extended period of time.

The notion of concavity is introduced in Section 2.5, and this is a <u>calculus</u> definition, as opposed to the precalculus definition of "increasing". The text points out a slight distinction between "$f'(x)$ is increasing" and "$f''(x) > 0$" (as in the handling of $y = x^4$), but because both definitions for concave up are widely used, the AP examination cannot use questions that give preference to one of these definitions. Students may tend to confuse theorems and definitions here, so be sure to make the distinction clear.

Section 2.6 deals with the relationship between continuity and differentiability, which is something that students find difficult. Many of the exercises can be approached geometrically now by using the graphing calculator, but Problem 6 shows the importance of a rigorous analysis.

Chapter 2 Multiple Choice Questions

1. The position of a particle on the x-axis, $x(t)$, is given at one second intervals by the following table for $0 \le t \le 4$.

t	0	1	2	3	4
$x(t)$	10	15	11	2	-2

    The average velocity for the particle over this time interval is

    (A) -4 (B) -3 (C) 1.6 (D) 3 (E) 4

2. If $f(x) = \cos(2x)$ means that $f'(x) = -2\sin(2x)$, then $\displaystyle\lim_{x \to \frac{\pi}{4}} \frac{\cos(2x)}{x - \frac{\pi}{4}} =$

    (A) -2 (B) -1 (C) 0 (D) 1 (E) 2

3. The power rule tells us that $\displaystyle\lim_{h \to 0} \frac{(2+h)^{17} - 2^{17}}{h} =$

    (A) 0 (B) 2^{17} (C) $2^{17}\ln(2)$ (D) 2^{16} (E) $17 \cdot 2^{16}$

4. The derivative of $f(x) = e^{k \cdot x}$ is $f'(x) = k \cdot e^{k \cdot x}$. This tells us that $\dfrac{e^{-0.999} - \dfrac{1}{e}}{0.001}$ is approximately

    (A) 0 (B) 1 (C) $\dfrac{1}{e}$ (D) $-\dfrac{1}{e}$ (E) -1

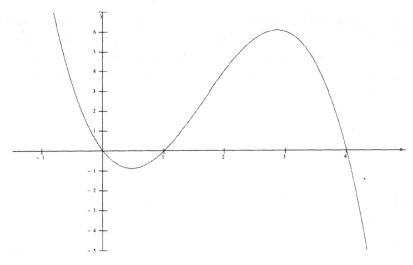

5.   The graph above is the graph of $y = f(x)$. At which of the following points is $f'(x)$ the greatest?

(A) $x = -1$ (B) $x = 0$ (C) $x = 2$ (D) $x = 3$ (E) $x = 4$

6.   If f is an increasing function whose graph lies below the x-axis and is concave up, then which of the following must be true?

   I. $f(x) < 0$
   II. $f'(x) < 0$
   III. $f''(x) < 0$

(A) I only   (B) II only   (C) III only

(D) I and II only   (E) I and III only

7.   If $f(x) = 12\sqrt{x}$, then $f'(x) = \dfrac{6}{\sqrt{x}}$. This means that an equation for the line tangent to the graph of f when $x = 9$ is

(A) $y = 36$ (B) $y = 2$ (C) $y = 36(x - 9)$

(D) $y = 2(x - 9)$ (E) $y = 2x + 18$

8. If $V(t)$ represents the number of thousands of gallons of water in a tank t hours after midnight on a fixed day, then which of the following pairs of equations can be used to express the statement, "At 3 PM there were 9000 gallons of water in the tank, and the amount of water in the tank was decreasing at the rate of 200 gallons per hour"?

(A) $V(3) = 9000$ and $V'(3) = -200$

(B) $V(3) = 9$ and $V'(3) = 200$

(C) $V(15) = 9000$ and $V'(15) = -200$

(D) $V(15) = 9$ and $V'(15) = -0.2$

(E) $V(15) = 9$ and $V'(15) = 0.2$

9. If $P(t)$ is the population, in millions, of a country t years after 1900, then what does the equation $(P^{-1})'(60) = 10$ mean?

(A) In 1960, the population was growing at rate of 10 million people per year.

(B) In 1910, the population was growing at rate of 60 million people per year.

(C) In 1960, the population was growing at the rate of $\dfrac{1}{10}$ million people per year.

(D) When the population was 60 million, it was growing at the rate of 10 million people per year.

(E) When the population was 60 million, it was growing at the rate of $\dfrac{1}{10}$ million people per year.

10. $\lim\limits_{h \to 0} \dfrac{3^2 - (3+h)^2}{h}$ is

(A) -9   (B) -6   (C) 0   (D) 6   (E) undefined

11. If $f(p) = q$ means that, at a price of p dollars, a sandwich shop can sell q thousand sandwiches per week, then the equations $f(4.5) = 1.2$, $f'(4.5) = -0.1$ mean

(A) When the price of a sandwich is $4.50, the shop can sell 1200 sandwiches per week and the profit is decreasing at $100 per week.

(B) The graph of f is a straight line going through (4.5, 1.2) with slope -1.

(C) When the price of a sandwich is $1.20, the shop can sell 4500 sandwiches per week, but the shop loses $100 per week.

(D) When the price of a sandwich is $4.50, the shop can sell 1200 sandwiches per week and the price is decreasing at 10 cents per sandwich.

(E) None of the above.

12. If $f(x) \cdot f'(x) \cdot f''(x) > 0$, then which of the following is possible?

(A) The graph is in the second quadrant and is decreasing and concave up.

(B) The graph is in the second quadrant and is decreasing and concave down.

(C) The graph is in the first quadrant and is increasing and concave down.

(D) The graph is in the third quadrant and is increasing and concave up.

(E) The graph is in the fourth quadrant and is decreasing and concave down.

13. If the graph of f goes through the points (2,5), (4,12), and (8,22), and if neither $f'(x)$ nor $f''(x)$ changes sign on the interval (2,8), then the graph must be

(A) increasing and concave up

(B) increasing and concave down

(C) decreasing and concave up

(D) decreasing and concave down

(E) none of the above.

14. If the graph of f goes through the points $(1,4)$, $(2,6)$, and $(3,10)$ then on the interval $(1,3)$ the graph of f must be

(A) increasing and concave up

(B) increasing and concave down

(C) decreasing and concave up

(D) decreasing and concave down

(E) none of the above

15. If $\lim\limits_{h \to 0} \dfrac{f(3+h)-15}{h} = 4$, then which of the following must be true?

    I. $\lim\limits_{x \to 3} f(x) = 15$

    II. $f(3) = 15$

    III. $f'(3) = 4$

(A) I only   (B) I and II only   (C) II and III only

(D) I and III only   (E) I, II, and III

16. If $\lim\limits_{h \to 0} \dfrac{f(2+h)-f(2)}{h} = 1$, then which of the following must be true?

    I. $\lim\limits_{x \to 2} f(x) = 1$

    II. f is continuous at $x = 2$

    III. $f'(2) = 1$

(A) I only   (B) II only   (C) III only

(D) II and III only   (E) I, II, and III

17. If $\lim\limits_{h \to 0} \dfrac{f(4+h)-f(4)}{h}$ does not exist, then which of the following must be true?

      I. $\lim\limits_{x \to 4} f(x)$ does not exist
      II. f is not continuous at $x = 4$
      III. f is not differentiable at $x = 4$

(A) I only   (B) II only   (C) III only

(D) II and III only   (E) I, II, and III

18. If $f(x) = \begin{cases} 2x, & \text{if } x \ge 0 \\ -x, & \text{if } x < 0 \end{cases}$, then $f'(0)$ is

(A) -1 (B) 0   (C) 1   (D) 2   (E) undefined

19. If $f'(2) = 4$, then which of the following must be true?

(A) f is continuous at $x = 2$ (B) f is continuous at $x = 4$

(C) f is differentiable at $x = 4$ (D) $(f^{-1})'(4) = \dfrac{1}{2}$ (E) $f''(1) > 0$

20. $\lim\limits_{h \to 0} \dfrac{(4+h)^2 - 16}{h}$ is

(A) -16 (B) 0   (C) 8   (D) 16   (E) undefined

21. If $f(2) = 7$, $f'(2) = 4$, and $f''(2) = 8$, which of the following must be true?

      I. $\lim\limits_{x \to 2} f(x) = 7$ II. $\lim\limits_{x \to 2} f'(x) = 4$ III. $\lim\limits_{x \to 2} f''(x) = 8$

(A) None   (B) I only   (C) II only

(D) I and II only   (E) I, II, and III

22. If $V(t)$ is the volume, in gallons, of water in a tank t hours after noon, and if $V(2) = 20$ and $V'(2) = -5$, then which of the following must be true?

    I.   At 2 p.m., the amount of water in the tank is decreasing at the rate of 5 gallons per hour.

    II.   At 3 p.m., there will be 15 gallons of water in the tank.

    III. $\dfrac{V(2) - V(0)}{2} = -5$

(A) I only   (B) II only   (C) I and II only

(D) I and III only   (E) I, II, and III

23. If f is not differentiable at $x = 0$, then which of the following must be true?
    I. f is not continuous at $x = 0$.

    II.   The graph of f does not have a tangent line when $x = 0$.

    III. $f''(0)$ does not exist.

(A) I only   (B) II only   (C) III only

(D) I and III only   (E) I, II, and III

24. If $f(x) = \begin{cases} 6x+1, & \text{if } x < 2 \\ 9, & \text{if } x = 2 \\ 6x-4, & \text{if } x > 2 \end{cases}$, then $f'(2)$ is

(A) 0   (B) 6   (C) 9   (D) 12   (E) undefined

25. If $f(x) = \begin{cases} \dfrac{x^2 - 9}{x - 3}, & \text{if } x \neq 3 \\ 6, & \text{if } x = 3 \end{cases}$, then $f'(3)$ is

(A) 0   (B) 1   (C) 3   (D) 6   (E) undefined

Chapter 2 Multiple Choice Questions

Question	Answer	AB	BC	No Calculator	Calculator Required	Neutral Calculator
1	B	x	x			x
2	A	x	x	x		
3	E	x	x	x		
4	C	x	x	x		
5	C	x	x	x		
6	A	x	x	x		
7	E	x	x	x		
8	D	x	x			x
9	E	x	x			x
10	B	x	x	x		
11	E	x	x			x
12	B	x	x			x
13	B	x	x			x
14	E	x	x			x
15	A	x	x			x
16	D	x	x			x
17	C	x	x			x
18	E	x	x	x		
19	A	x	x	x		
20	C	x	x	x		
21	D	x	x	x		
22	A	x	x	x		
23	C	x	x	x		
24	E	x	x	x		
25	B	x	x	x		

Chapter 2 Free Response Questions

1. Let $f(x) = \begin{cases} x^2 & \text{for } x \le 3 \\ Ax + B & \text{for } x > 3 \end{cases}$.

    (a) Use the definition of the derivative to find A and B so that $f'(3)$ exists. Justify your answer.

    (b) Does $f''(3)$ exist? Explain.

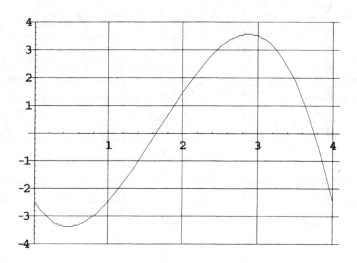

2. The graph of $y = f'(x)$, the derivative of f, is shown above. Use this graph to answer the questions that follow. Approximate answers correct to one decimal place.

    (a) For which x is $f'(x) = 0$? Explain.

    (b) For which x is $f''(x) = 0$? Explain.

    (c) On which interval or intervals is the function f increasing?

    (d) On which interval or intervals is the graph of f concave up?

    (e) Use the graph to approximate $f''(1)$.

3. Let $f(x) = \begin{cases} x+3 & \text{for } x < 0 \\ A & \text{for } x = 0 \\ \dfrac{\sin x}{x} & \text{for } x > 0 \end{cases}$.

(a) Is there a value for A that makes f continuous at $x = 0$? Justify your answer.

(b) Let $g(x) = \begin{cases} x \cdot f(x) & \text{for } x \neq 0 \\ B & \text{for } x = 0 \end{cases}$.

Is there a value of B so that g is continuous at $x = 0$? Justify your answer.

(c) Is there a value of B so that g is differentiable at $x = 0$? Justify your answer.

4. Given $f(x) = x^3$, and its inverse $f^{-1}(x) = x^{\frac{1}{3}}$. Recall that the graph of f^{-1} can be obtained from the graph of f by reflecting the graph of f across the line $y = x$. That is, the graph of f^{-1} can be obtained from the graph of f by interchanging the first and second coordinates of each point.

(a) Use the definition of the derivative to show that $f'(x) = 3x^2$.

(b) Find an equation of the line tangent to the graph of f when $x = 2$.

(c) Use the ideas presented in this problem to find the equation of the line tangent to the graph $y = x^{\frac{1}{3}}$ when $x = 8$.

(d) Using the same type of argument you used in part (c), show that if $g(x) = x^{\frac{1}{3}}$, then g is not differentiable at $x = 0$.

5. The base of a cone is a circle of radius R. The area, A, of the base is given by $A = \pi R^2$. The height of the cone is denoted by H, and the formula for the volume of the cone is given by $V = \dfrac{1}{3} AH$.

If t is the time variable, then the derivative formulas are $\dfrac{dA}{dt} = 2\pi R \dfrac{dR}{dt}$, and

$\dfrac{dV}{dt} = \dfrac{1}{3}\left(H \dfrac{dA}{dt} + A \dfrac{dH}{dt} \right)$.

The units for R and H are centimeters and, as quantities vary, the time variable t is in minutes.

(a) At the moment when $t = 7$, the height is 6 cm. and is decreasing at the rate of $\dfrac{1}{4}$ cm / min; the radius is 5 cm. and is increasing at the rate of $\dfrac{1}{2}$ cm / min.

   (i) What is the area of the base and how is it changing? (Include units of measure.)

   (ii) What is the volume of the cone, and how is it changing? (Include units of measure.)

(b) If the volume of the cone is held at a constant 50π cm^3, how is the radius changing if the height is 6 cm and increasing at a rate of $\dfrac{1}{3}$ cm/min? (Include units of measure.)

Chapter 2 Free Response Questions

Question	AB	BC	No Calculator	Calculator Required	Neutral Calculator
1	x	x			x
2	x	x			x
3	x	x	x		
4	x	x			x
5	x	x			x

Chapter 2 Solutions to Free Response Questions

1.

(a) Note that $f(3) = 9$. If f is differentiable at $x = 3$, then f must be continuous at that point. Thus $\lim\limits_{x \to 3^+} f(x) = 9$.

Also $\lim\limits_{x \to 3^+} f(x) = \lim\limits_{x \to 3^+} Ax + B = 3A + B$. So $3A + B = 9$.

Next, $f'(3) = \lim\limits_{h \to 0} \dfrac{f(3+h) - f(3)}{h}$, and to compute this limit we look at the right hand limit and the left hand limit.

For the right hand limit, we have $\lim\limits_{h \to 0^+} \dfrac{f(3+h) - f(3)}{h} = \lim\limits_{h \to 0^+} \dfrac{A(3+h) + B - (3A + B)}{h}$

$= \lim\limits_{h \to 0^+} \dfrac{Ah}{h} = A$.

For the left hand limit, $\lim\limits_{h \to 0^-} \dfrac{f(3+h) - f(3)}{h} =$

$\lim\limits_{h \to 0^-} \dfrac{(3+h)^2 - 9}{h} = \lim\limits_{h \to 0^-} \dfrac{6h + h^2}{h} = \lim\limits_{h \to 0^-} 6 + h = 6$.

Thus $A = 6$. Since $3A + B = 9$, we have $B = -9$.

(b) $f(x) = \begin{cases} x^2 & \text{for } x \le 3 \\ 6x - 9 & \text{for } x > 3 \end{cases}$. Since $f'(3) = 6$, $f'(x) = \begin{cases} 2x & \text{for } x \le 3 \\ 6 & \text{for } x > 3 \end{cases}$.

The graph of $y = f'(x)$ is the union of two lines, one with slope 2 and one with slope 0.

Where they meet at the point (3, 9), the graph has a "corner", so the graph does not have a tangent line at (3, 9), and so $f''(3)$ does not exist.

2.

(a) $f'(x) = 0$ when the given graph meets the x-axis. This occurs when $x \approx 1.6$ and $x \approx 3.8$. (These values are approximate. You just want to determine if students have the right idea or not.)

(b) $f''(x) = 0$ when the given graph has a horizontal tangent. This occurs when $x \approx 0.5$ and $x \approx 2.8$.

(c) f is increasing when $f'(x) \geq 0$, which occurs when the given graph lies above or on the x-axis. The answer is: on the interval $[1.6, 3.8]$, using the answers to (a).

(d) f is concave up when f' is increasing. Using our answer to (b), the answer here would be the interval $(0.5, 2.8)$.

(e)   To approximate $f''(1)$, we draw the line tangent to the graph of f' at the point where $x = 1$.

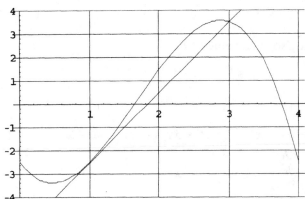

Now we compute the slope of that line. We use the points $(1, -2.5)$ and $(3, 3.5)$ on the line to get a slope of 3. Answer is $f''(1) \approx 3$.

3.
(a)   We need $\lim\limits_{x \to 0} f(x) = A$.

Now $\lim\limits_{x \to 0^+} f(x) = \lim\limits_{x \to 0^+} \dfrac{\sin(x)}{x} = 1$, while $\lim\limits_{x \to 0^-} f(x) = \lim\limits_{x \to 0^-} (x + 3) = 3$.

Thus $\lim\limits_{x \to 0} f(x)$ doesn't exist, and there is no such A.

(b)   We need $\lim\limits_{x \to 0} g(x) = B$.

Now $\lim\limits_{x \to 0^+} g(x) = \lim\limits_{x \to 0^+} \sin(x) = 0$, while $\lim\limits_{x \to 0^-} g(x) = \lim\limits_{x \to 0^-} x^2 + 3x = 0$.

Thus $\lim\limits_{x \to 0} g(x) = 0$. The value of $B = 0$ makes g continuous at $x = 0$.

(c) If g is differentiable at $x = 0$, it must also be continuous, so $B = 0$.

From part (b) we know that g is in the form $g(x) = \begin{cases} x \cdot f(x) & \text{for } x \neq 0 \\ 0 & \text{for } x = 0 \end{cases}$.

Next $g'(0) = \lim_{h \to 0} \dfrac{g(0+h) - g(0)}{h} = \lim_{h \to 0} \dfrac{hf(h) - 0}{h} = \lim_{h \to 0} f(h)$, which we know from part (a) does not exist.

The answer is "No such value of B."

4.

(a) $f'(x) = \lim_{h \to 0} \dfrac{(x+h)^3 - x^3}{h} = \lim_{h \to 0} \dfrac{x^3 + 3x^2 h + 3xh^2 + h^3 - x^3}{h} = \lim_{h \to 0} \dfrac{(3x^2 + 3xh + h^2)h}{h} = \lim_{h \to 0} 3x^2 + 3xh + h^2 = 3x^2 + 0 + 0 = 3x^2$.

(b) The slope of the line is $f'(2) = 12$ and $f(2) = 8$, so an equation for the tangent line is $y - 8 = 12(x - 2)$.

(c) The reflection changes the role of x and y, so an equation of the line tangent at the point (8, 2) must be $x - 8 = 12(y - 2)$, or $y - 2 = \dfrac{1}{12}(x - 8)$.

The slope is $\dfrac{1}{12}$, so $(f^{-1})'(8) = \dfrac{1}{12}$, the reciprocal of $f'(2)$.

(d) $g^{-1}(x) = f(x) = x^3$

The point (0, 0) is on the graph of f, and the line tangent to the graph at (0, 0) has slope $f'(0) = 0$.

An equation of the tangent line is $y = 0$. Performing the reflection sends this horizontal line into the vertical line $x = 0$.

Vertical lines have no slope, so there is no number $g'(0)$.

5.

(a) (i) Using $A = \pi R^2$ when $R = 5$, we have the area of the base is 25π cm^2.

Now, $\dfrac{dA}{dt} = 2\pi R \dfrac{dR}{dt}$ with $R = 5$ and $\dfrac{dR}{dt} = \dfrac{1}{2}$, we have $\dfrac{dA}{dt} = 5\pi$, so the area of the base is increasing at the rate of 5π cm^2/min.

(ii) Using $= \dfrac{1}{3} AH$, the volume is $\dfrac{1}{3} 25\pi \cdot 6 = 50\pi$ cm^3.

Now, $\dfrac{dV}{dt} = \dfrac{1}{3}\left(H \dfrac{dA}{dt} + A \dfrac{dH}{dt} \right)$, we have $\dfrac{dV}{dt} = \dfrac{1}{3}\left(6(5\pi) + 25\pi\left(\dfrac{-1}{4} \right) \right) = \dfrac{95\pi}{12}$, so the volume is increasing at the rate of $\dfrac{95\pi}{12} \approx 24.871$ cm^3/min.

(b) Now $\dfrac{dV}{dt} = 0 = \dfrac{1}{3}\left(H \dfrac{dA}{dt} + A \dfrac{dH}{dt} \right)$, so $H \dfrac{dA}{dt} = -A \dfrac{dH}{dt}$.

If $V = 50\pi$ cm^3, we have seen that $H = 6$ means that $A = 25\pi$, so we have $6 \dfrac{dA}{dt} = -25\pi \dfrac{1}{3}$, and $\dfrac{dA}{dt} = \dfrac{-25\pi}{18}$.

Finally, $\dfrac{dA}{dt} = 2\pi R \dfrac{dR}{dt}$ and when $A = 25\pi$, $R = 5$ so $\dfrac{-25\pi}{18} = 10\pi \dfrac{dR}{dt}$, and $\dfrac{dR}{dt} = \dfrac{-25}{180}$.

The radius is decreasing at the rate of $\dfrac{-25}{180} \approx 0.139$ cm/min.

AP Teacher Tips
Chapter 3: Shortcuts to Differentiation

This chapter is important in building analytical skills of differentiation required in both Advanced Placement Calculus AB and BC. Derivations of differentiation formulas using the limit definition of the derivative reinforce student facility in the use of the definition while also establishing the rules of differentiation. Don't neglect these explanations. Also look for the practical applications and graphical interpretations both in the section examples and in the problem sets.

All sections of Chapter 3, except for Section 3.8, Hyperbolic Functions, are required in the curriculum for both AP Calculus AB and BC. Section 3.8 motivates the differentiation of hyperbolic functions from their exponential definitions, and thus is an easily approachable topic for student enrichment/independent study.

If your students use graphing calculators that include computer algebra systems, you may want to de-emphasize or exclude their usage while learning to apply these differentiation rules. Certainly numerical explorations with the calculator can be helpful as in numerical investigations of the differentiation of exponential functions on page 118 and in Example 1, page 133, the differentiation of the sin x. Graphical investigations with a calculator enhance the analytical results as in Figure 3.11 on page 119 and in the graphs of trigonometric functions and their derivatives in Section 3.5. The concept of differentiability and local linearity is richly reinforced by error analysis performed via graphical "zoom-in" on a calculator on pages 152-153. Analytical investigation is proposed in problems 108-111, page 163, using a computer algebra system but also with encouragement of the student to develop his own algorithmic technique for differentiation. Be sure to give students the chance to do these CAS Challenge Problems and present their observations. Although no longer a required topic in AP Calculus AB or BC, Newton's Method, which is proposed as a project investigation on page 164, is a fine numerical investigation for students to get insight into an iterated algorithmic technique akin to the root finder technique employed by their calculator.

All the elementary, single-variable function differentiation necessary for the AP Calculus curriculum is included in this one chapter. However, AP teachers frequently choose to extend such rules to all six trigonometric functions, thus supplementing Section 3.5 with the differentiation of cot x, sec x and csc x. Additionally, the differentiation of $\log_a x$ could be motivated by the change of base formula $\log_a x = \dfrac{\ln x}{\ln a}$. Thus $\dfrac{d}{dx}\{\log_a x\} = \dfrac{1}{x \cdot \ln a}$.

Chapter 3 closes with theorems concerning differentiable functions. Important AP Curriculum concepts of local linearity and differentiability (Section 3.9) and the Mean Value Theorem for Derivatives and its consequences (Section 3.10) set the student up for an appropriate conceptual transition to the applications of differentiation coming in Chapter 4.

Chapter 3 Multiple Choice Questions

Questions 1-2 refer to the following graph.

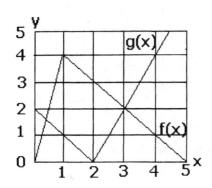

1. If $h(x) = f(x) \cdot g(x)$, then $h'(3) =$

(A) -4   (B) -2   (C) 2   (D) 4   (E) 6

2. If $m(x) = f(g(x))$, then $m'(4) =$

(A) -4   (B) -2   (C) 0   (D) 2   (E) 4

3. If $y = \dfrac{a^x}{b^x}$, when $a > 0$ and $b > 0$ then $\dfrac{dy}{dx} =$

(A) $\dfrac{a^x}{b^x}$

(B) $\dfrac{a^x \ln(a)}{b^x \ln(b)}$

(C) $\dfrac{a^x}{b^x} \ln\left(\dfrac{a}{b}\right)$

(D) $\dfrac{(ab)^x \ln(ab)}{b^{2x}}$

(E) $x\left(\dfrac{a}{b}\right)^{x-1}$

4. The line tangent to the graph of $y = (x+1)e^x$ at (0, 1) intersects the x-axis at $x =$

(A) -1   (B) $-\dfrac{1}{2}$ (C) $\dfrac{1}{2}$ (D) 1   (E) 2

Questions 5-6 refer to the table below. The function f is continuous and differentiable for $x > 0$ and $f(x)$ and $f'(x)$ have the indicated tabular values.

x	$f(x)$	$f'(x)$
1	2	1/2
2	3	1/3
3	1	-2

5. The equation of the line normal to $f(x)$ at $x = 2$ is:

(A) $y = -3x + 9$

(B) $y = -x + 4$

(C) $y = -\dfrac{1}{3}x + \dfrac{7}{3}$

(D) $y = -3x + 11$

(E) $y = -\dfrac{1}{3}x + \dfrac{11}{3}$

6. If f and f^{-1} (the inverse of f) exist, are continuous and differentiable for $x > 0$, then $\dfrac{d}{dx}\left(f^{-1}(x)\right)$ at $x = 1$ is

(A) -4   (B) -2   (C) $-\dfrac{1}{2}$ (D) $\dfrac{1}{2}$ (E) 2

7. If $3x = \sin y$, then $\dfrac{dy}{dx} =$

(A) $\dfrac{1}{\sqrt{9 - x^2}}$

(B) $\dfrac{3}{\sqrt{9 - x^2}}$

(C) $\dfrac{1}{\sqrt{1 - 9x^2}}$

(D) $\dfrac{3}{\sqrt{1 - 9x^2}}$

(E) $\dfrac{3}{\sqrt{9x^2 - 1}}$

8. If $f(x) = x^2$ and $g(x) = \sqrt{x}$ and if $h(x) = g(f(x))$, then $h'(-1) =$

(A) -2   (B) -1   (C) 0   (D) 1   (E) Does not exist

9. If $x^2 - xy + y^2 = 9$, then a vertical tangent to this curve exists at the point

(A) $\left(-2\sqrt{3}, -\sqrt{3}\right)$

(B) $\left(\sqrt{3}, 2\sqrt{3}\right)$

(C) $\left(-2\sqrt{3}, \sqrt{3}\right)$

(D) $\left(-\sqrt{3}, 2\sqrt{3}\right)$

(E) $\left(2\sqrt{3}, -\sqrt{3}\right)$

10. Using a local linearization for $f(x) = \sqrt{9 + \tan x}$ about $x = 0$, the approximate value of $f(0.3) =$

(A) 3   (B) 3.005   (C) 3.025   (D) 3.05   (E) 3.1

11. If $f(x) = \sin x + \cos x$ then the slope of a tangent line to $f(x)$ equals -1 at $x =$

(A) $-\dfrac{\pi}{2}$ (B) 0   (C) $\dfrac{\pi}{4}$ (D) $\dfrac{\pi}{2}$ (E) $\dfrac{3\pi}{4}$

12. If $y = \ln\left(\dfrac{x}{y}\right)$, then at $y = 1$, $\dfrac{dy}{dx} =$

(A) $\dfrac{1-e}{e}$ (B) $\dfrac{1}{2e}$ (C) $\dfrac{2}{e}$ (D) $2e$ (E) e^2

13. If the derivative of $y = k(x)$ equals 4 when $x = -1$, what is the derivative of $y = k(1-\sqrt{x})$ when $x = 4$?

(A) -2   (B) -1   (C) 1   (D) 2   (E) 4

14. The nth derivative of $y = 2^x$ is $\dfrac{d^n y}{dx^n} =$

(A) $n2^x \ln(2)$ (B) $2^{nx} \ln(2)$ (C) $n2^{nx} \ln(2)$ (D) $2^{nx}(\ln 2)^n$ (E) $2^x(\ln 2)^n$

15. For the differential equation $\dfrac{dy}{dt} = \sqrt{1-2y}$, if $y \neq \dfrac{1}{2}$, then $\dfrac{d^2 y}{dt^2} =$

(A) -1 (B) $-\dfrac{1}{2}$ (C) 1 (D) $2y - 1$ (E) $\dfrac{1}{2\sqrt{1-2y}}$

16. An equation of the line tangent to the graph of $xy = 1$ from the point $(3, 0)$ is

(A) $2x + 3y = 6$ (B) $2y - 3x = -9$ (C) $3y - 2x = -6$

(D) $4x + 9y = 12$ (E) $4x - 9y = 12$

17. At a time t seconds after it is thrown up in the air, a ball is at a height of $f(t) = -16t^2 + 50t + 6$ feet. The average velocity of the ball during the first two seconds, measured in ft/sec, is

(A) -18 (B) -14 (C) 14 (D) 18 (E) 36

18. If $\dfrac{dy}{dx} = \dfrac{e^{\sqrt{x}}}{\sqrt{x}}$ then one solution for y would be $y =$

(A) $\dfrac{2e^{\sqrt{x}}}{\sqrt{x}}$ (B) $\dfrac{e^{\sqrt{x}}}{\sqrt{x}}$ (C) $\dfrac{e^{\sqrt{x}}}{\sqrt{2}}$ (D) $e^{\sqrt{x}}$ (E) $2e^{\sqrt{x}}$

19. If $f(x) = x^3 + x$ and $g(x)$ is the inverse of $f(x)$, then $g'(1) =$

(A) -0.5 (B) 0.003 (C) 0.077 (D) 0.25 (E) 0.417

20. If the line $y = x + 4$ is tangent to $f(x) = ax^2 + bx$ at the point (2, 6), then $a + b =$

(A) 2   (B) 2.5   (C) 3   (D) 4   (E) 6

21. The local linearization of $y = \dfrac{1}{1-x}$ near $x = 0$ is:

(A) $y = x$ (B) $y = -x$ (C) $y = x - 1$ (D) $y = 1 - x$ (E) $y = x + 1$

22. If $f(x) = \ln\sqrt{1+x^2}$ then a horizontal tangent line to $f(x)$ exists at $x =$

(A) $-e$ (B) -1 (C) 0   (D) $\dfrac{1}{e}$ (E) $\dfrac{1}{2}$

23. The balance, B, in a savings account t years after a deposit of $10,000 is given by the formula $B = 10,000e^{0.075t}$. At what rate, measured in dollars per year, is the balance in the account changing at $t = 10$ years?

(A) 1000.91   (B) 1091.24   (C) 1587.75   (D) 8412.25   (E) 21,170.00

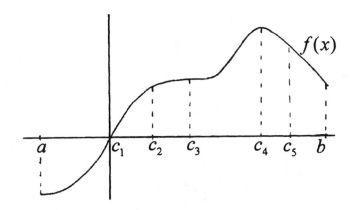

24. For the function $f(x)$ shown above, the Mean Value Theorem for Derivatives would be satisfied by which x-coordinate over the interval $a \le x \le b$?

(A) c_1 (B) c_2 (C) c_3 (D) c_4 (E) c_5

25. If f, f', and f'' are continuous on $[a, b]$, then there is a number c in (a, b) with

(A) $f(c) = 0$

(B) $f'(c) = 0$

(C) $f''(c) = 0$

(D) the instantaneous rate of change of f at $x = c$ equal to the average rate of change of f on the interval $[a, b]$

(E) $f(c)$ the maximum value of f on the interval $[a, b]$

Chapter 3 Multiple Choice Questions

Question	Answer	AB	BC	No Calculator	Calculator Required	Neutral Calculator
1	C	x	x			x
2	B	x	x			x
3	C	x	x	x		x
4	B	x	x			x
5	A	x	x			x
6	C	x	x			x
7	D	x	x	x		
8	B	x	x			x
9	A	x	x			x
10	D	x	x			x
11	D	x	x			x
12	B	x	x	x		
13	B	x	x			x
14	E	x	x	x		
15	A	x	x			x
16	D	x	x			x
17	D	x	x			x
18	E	x	x	x		
19	E	x	x		x	
20	D	x	x			x
21	E	x	x			x
22	C	x	x			x
23	C	x	x		x	
24	B	x	x			x
25	D	x	x			x

Chapter 3 Free Response Questions

1. The height of a snowdrift, measured in centimeters, is represented by

   $h(t) = 200 - \dfrac{5}{2}t^2$ where t is measured in hours since the first measurement was made at 10 am.

   (a) Evaluate and describe what the following represent in terms of the snowdrift, using units and a written description to explain.

        (i) $h(2)$
        (ii) $h'(2)$
        (iii) $h''(2)$

   (b) At what time is the snow drift 137.5 cm in height? At what rate is the height changing at this time?

   (c) The snowdrift will collapse when the rate of change in its height reaches -30 cm/hr. What time would it be expected to collapse?

2. Consider the curve $y^3 + 3x^2y - 9y = -5$

   (a) Find the slope of the curve at the point (1, 1).

   (b) A tangent line from the origin touches the curve at what y-coordinate?

   (c) Find the rate of change with respect to x of the slope of the curve at the point (1, 1)

3. If $f(x) = \sqrt{e^x}$,

   (a) Find the local linearization near $x = 0$.

   (b) Using the linearization from part (a), approximate $\dfrac{1}{e^{0.1}}$.

   (c) Is the approximation of $\dfrac{1}{e^{0.1}}$ determined in part (b) larger or smaller than the true value of $\dfrac{1}{e^{0.1}}$? Defend your answer with a geometric or a graphical argument.

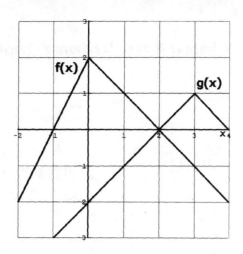

4. The graphs of functions $f(x)$ and $g(x)$ are shown above.

   (a) If $h(x) = f(g(x))$, then $h'(1) =$

   (b) If $k(x) = f(x) \cdot g(x)$, then $k'(1) =$

   (c) If $t(x) = e^{g(x)}$ then $t''(0) =$

   (d) If $q(x) = \dfrac{f(x)}{g(x)}$, then $q'(0) =$

5. Given the function $f(x) = 2^{-x}$

   (a) Find where the tangent line to $f(x)$ at $x = 0$ intersects the x-axis.

   (b) Find the x-coordinate of the point on $f(x)$ where the slope of the normal line is 1.

   (c) Find $\dfrac{d}{dx} f(|x|)$.

Chapter 3 Free Response Questions

Question	AB	BC	No Calculator	Calculator Required	Neutral Calculator
1	x	x			x
2	x	x			x
3	x	x			x
4	x	x			x
5	x	x			x

Chapter 3 Solutions to Free Response Questions

1.

(a) $h(t) = 200 - \dfrac{5}{2}t^2$

$h(2) = 200 - \dfrac{5}{2}(2^2) = 190$ cm.

At noon, the snowdrift is 190 cm high.

$h'(t) = -5t$

$h'(2) = -5(2) = -10$ cm/hr

At noon, the height of the snowdrift is decreasing at the rate of 10 cm/hr.

$h''(t) = -5$ cm/hr/hr

The rate of change with respect to time of the change in cm/hr of the drift height remains constant at -5 cm/hr/hr for all measurable times.

(b) $200 - \dfrac{5}{2}t^2 = 137.5$

$-\dfrac{5}{2}t^2 = -62.5$

$t = 25$

$t = 5$ hours after the first measurement, which is 3 pm.

$h(5) = -25$ cm/hr

(c) $h'(t) = -30$

$-5t = -30$

$t = 6$ hours after the first measurement which is 4 p.m.

2. $y^3 + 3x^2y - 9y = -5$

(a) $3y^2\dfrac{dy}{dx} + 3\left(x^2\dfrac{dy}{dx} + 2xy\right) - 9\dfrac{dy}{dx} = 0$

$(3y^2 + 3x^2 - 9)\dfrac{dy}{dx} = -6xy$

$\dfrac{dy}{dx} = \dfrac{-6xy}{3y^2 + 3x^2 - 9}$

$\dfrac{dy}{dx}_{(1,1)} = \dfrac{-6}{-3} = 2$

(b) Given the point (x, y) on the curve, and the slope from $(0, 0)$ to (x, y) is $\dfrac{y}{x}$

Tangent Slope $\dfrac{y}{x} = \dfrac{dy}{dx}$

$$\frac{dy}{dx} = \frac{-6xy}{3y^3 + 3x^2 - 9} = \frac{y}{x}$$

$-6x^2y = 3y^4 + 3x^2y - 9y$

$0 = 3y^4 + 9x^2y - 9y$

$0 = 3y\left(y^2 + 3x^2 - 3\right)$

$3y = 0$ $\qquad\qquad\qquad$ $y^2 + 3x^2 - 3 = 0$

$y = 0$ $\qquad\qquad\qquad$ $3x^2 = 3 - y^2$

Not on curve $\qquad\qquad$ $y^3 + \left(3 - y^2\right)y - 9y = -5$

$\qquad\qquad\qquad\qquad$ $3y - 9y = -5$

$\qquad\qquad\qquad\qquad$ $y = \dfrac{5}{6}$

(c) $\dfrac{d^2y}{dx^2} = \dfrac{\left(3y^3 + 3x^2 - 9\right)\left(-6\left(x\dfrac{dy}{dx} + y\right)\right) + 6xy\left(6y\dfrac{dy}{dx} + 6x\right)}{\left(3y^3 + 3x^2 - 9\right)^2}$

at $(x, y) = (1, 1)$, $\dfrac{d^2y}{dx^2} = \dfrac{-3\left(-6\left(2 + 1\right)\right) + 6\left(12 + 6\right)}{\left(-3\right)^2} = \dfrac{54 + 108}{9} = 18$

3. $f(x) = \sqrt{e^x} = e^{\frac{x}{2}}$

(a) $f'(x) = \dfrac{1}{2}e^{\frac{x}{2}}$

$f'(0) = \dfrac{1}{2}$ and $f(0) = 1$

The equation of the tangent line is $y - 1 = \dfrac{1}{2}x$

$\therefore f(x) \approx \dfrac{1}{2}x + 1$ is the local linearization

70

(b) $\dfrac{1}{e^{0.1}} = e^{-0.1} = e^{\frac{-0.2}{2}} \approx \dfrac{1}{2}(-0.2) + 1 = 0.9$

(c) $f''(x) = \dfrac{1}{4} e^{\frac{x}{2}} > 0$

The graph of $f(x)$ is concave up everywhere, and thus the tangent line (linear approximation) lies below the graph of $f(x)$. Therefore, the linear approximation is smaller than the true value of $\dfrac{1}{e^{0.1}}$.

4.
(a) $h(x) = f(g(x))$
       $h'(x) = f'(g(x)) g'(x)$
       $h'(1) = f'(g(1)) g'(1)$
       $\quad\quad = f'(-1) \cdot 1$
       $\quad\quad = 2 \cdot 1$
       $\quad\quad = 2$

(b) $h(x) = f(x) g(x)$
       $h'(x) = f(x) g'(x) + f'(x) g(x)$
       $h'(1) = f(1) g'(1) + f'(1) g(1)$
       $h'(1) = 1 \cdot 1 + (-1)(-1)$
       $h'(1) = 2$

(c) $t(x) = e^{g(x)}$
       $t'(x) = e^{g(x)} g'(x)$
       $t''(x) = e^{g(x)} g''(x) + e^{g(x)} g'(x) g'(x)$
       $t''(0) = e^{g(0)} g''(0) + e^{g(0)} g'(0) g'(0)$
       $t''(0) = e^{-2}(0) + e^{-2}(1)(1)$
       $t''(0) = e^{-2}$

(d) $q(x) = \dfrac{f(x)}{g(x)}$

Since $f'(0)$ does not exist, the quotient rule may not be applied to this problem; $q'(0)$ may or may not be defined.

Transform the equation above to:
       $f(x) = q(x) g(x)$

$$f(0) = q(0)g(0)$$

We know that $g'(0)$ exists. If $q'(0)$ exists, then $f'(0)$ must exist by the product rule. Since $f'(0)$ does not exist, $q'(0)$ cannot exist.

5.

(a) $f(x) = 2^{-x}$ $\qquad f(0) = 1$

$$f'(x) = -2^{-x}\ln(2) = -\frac{\ln(2)}{2^x}$$

$$f'(0) = -\ln(2)$$

The tangent line equation is $y - 1 = (-\ln 2)x$
$$y = (-\ln 2)x + 1$$
The tangent line intersects the x-axis when $y = 0$ or when $(-\ln 2)x + 1 = 0$

Thus, $x = \dfrac{1}{\ln 2}$

(b) The normal slope is the negative reciprocal of $\dfrac{dy}{dx} = -\dfrac{\ln 2}{2^x}$

We must find when $\dfrac{2^x}{\ln 2} = 1$

$$2^x = \ln 2$$
$$\ln(2^x) = \ln(\ln 2)$$
$$x\ln 2 = \ln(\ln(2))$$
$$x = \frac{\ln(\ln 2))}{\ln(2)}$$

(c) $f(|x|) = 2^{-|x|} = \begin{cases} 2^{-x} & \text{for } x \geq 0 \\ 2^x & \text{for } x < 0 \end{cases}$

$$\frac{d}{dx}f(|x|) = \frac{d}{dx}2^{-|x|} = \begin{cases} -2^{-x}\ln 2 & \text{for } x > 0 \\ 2^x\ln 2 & \text{for } x < 0 \end{cases}$$

At $x = 0$ the derivative of $f(|x|)$ does not exist since the left and right limits of the derivative at 0 disagree.

$$\lim_{x \to 0^+} -2^{-x}\ln 2 = -\ln 2$$
$$\lim_{x \to 0^-} 2^x\ln 2 = \ln 2$$

AP Teacher Tips
Chapter 4: Using the Derivative

All the material in Sections 4.1, 4.2, 4.3, 4.5, and 4.6 is required for both the AB and BC examinations. Section 4.4 specializes in applications to economics, and while these specific applications need not be covered, this is a nice section which shows how calculus influences disciplines other than the natural sciences. Section 4.7 covers L'Hopital's Rule, which is not required for the AB exam, but the course description does mention asymptotic behavior, as well as "comparing relative magnitudes of functions and their rates of change", with specific examples of contrasting logarithmic, polynomial, and exponential growth. Thus, AB students can also benefit from coverage of this section. The topics in Section 4.8 are strictly BC material.

Section 4.1 gives a summary of properties that have been informally talked about in the text for the previous two chapters, as well as introducing the ideas of a local extreme value, a critical point, and an inflection point. There is a wealth of topics in this section, and it needs to be covered carefully. In the problems for Section 4.1, note that the directions for sketching graphs of the functions that are given in Exercises 8-15 involve only the first derivative, and then Exercise 16 has the student return to the same functions to analyze concavity. You can either assign the problems that way, or tell students to include the instructions in Exercise 16 the first time they do a problem, or a combination of these approaches. Also note that Problems 27 and 29 give the nature of the critical point in the stem; you should insist that the students justify that the function they have found does indeed yield a local extremum of the type called for. Generally, such justification is called for on the AP examinations.

Section 4.2 provides examples for discussion that you may want to spread out over time rather than covering this section all at once. Students must learn the significance of parameters and how to deal with them. See, for example, questions 1995-BC5, 1997-AB4, and 1997-BC4. Note that although two of these questions appeared on the BC exam, all three are AB type questions.

Section 4.3 begins the discussion of applied max/min problems. In this section the functions to be optimized are given; note the frequent use of parameters in these functions. These can give students difficulty. You might suggest that if students have difficulty, they replace the parameters with numbers, do the required work, and then go back and try to replicate that work with the parameters in place. Problem 27 is the first of many problems that exploit a visual way of maximizing $\dfrac{f(x)}{x}$.

The terminology of Section 4.4 is not required for the AP examinations, but the students may enjoy seeing these examples, especially as a break from "physics".

Section 4.5 continues with applied max/min problems and in this section the student must construct the function. Students are easily overwhelmed by this material, especially if they are given a large number of these problems at once. Again, you may wish to give a few of these problems per assignment over an extended period of time so students don't get the impression it's okay not to do those problems.

Section 4.6 deals with the important topic of related rates. Students have difficulty here because they may be presented with a formula that relates two physical quantities, and this formula appears to be independent of time. Then, they are supposed to differentiate with respect to time! We hope the text's emphasis on units of measure throughout, and the verbal descriptions in Section 2.4, will help here.

Section 4.7 gives a beautiful picture of L'Hopital's Rule in Figures 4.90 and 4.91. Be sure to stress that the rule only works to measure relative magnitudes (quotients), and limits as given in Example 4 need to be rewritten before differentiating. Some students also confuse L'Hopital's Rule with the Quotient Rule.

The topic of parametric equations appears only on the Calculus BC course description. In Section 4.8, BC teachers should be careful to distinguish between velocity of a particle in the plane, and its speed. The section ends with the important connection between the slope of a curve at a point, the quotient of the y-component of velocity over the x-component, and how to compute the second derivative. This last computation can cause difficulties for students. (See Problem 44).

Chapter 4 Multiple Choice Questions

1. If $f(2) = 7$ and $f'(2) = 0$, then which of the following must be true?

        I. $f(x)$ has a local extreme value when $x = 2$
       II. $f(x) = 7$ for all x
      III. $(2, 7)$ is a point of inflection

(A) None   (B) I only   (C) II only
(D) III only   (E) I and III only

2. If f is differentiable for all x, and has a local maximum at $x = 3$, then which of the following must be true?

        I. $f'(3) = 0$
       II. $f''(3) < 0$
      III. f is continuous at $x = 3$

(A) I only   (B) II only   (C) I and II only
(D) I and III only   (E) I, II, and III

3. What are all the x-coordinates of the critical points for the graph of $f(x) = (x - 4)(x - 2)$?

(A) 2 and 4   (B) 0, 2, and 4   (C) 2, 3, and 4   (D) 0 and 3   (E) 3

4. If f is continuous on the closed interval $[1, 3]$ with $f'(x) < 0$ on the open interval $(1, 3)$, then

(A) $f(x)$ does not have a minimum on $[1, 3]$

(B) $f(x)$ does not have a maximum on $[1, 3]$

(C) $f(1)$ is the maximum value of $f(x)$ on $[1, 3]$

(D) $f(1)$ is the minimum value of $f(x)$ on $[1, 3]$

(E) $f(3)$ is the maximum value of $f(x)$ on $[1, 3]$

5. If f and f' are continuous for all x, and if f has a local maximum at $x = 4$, which of the following must be true?

  I. $f(4) > f(5)$
  II. $f'(4) = 0$
  III. $f''(4) < 0$

(A) I only   (B) II only   (C) I and II only
(D) II and III only   (E) I, II and III

6. If f, f', and f'' are continuous for all x with $f(5) = 9$, and if $f'(x)$ has a local maximum at $x = 5$, then

(A) $f'(5) = 0$

(B) the graph of f is concave up in an open interval containing $x = 5$

(C) f is increasing on an open interval containing $x = 5$

(D) the point $(5, 9)$ is a point of inflection

(E) $f''(5) < 0$

7. If $f(x) = x^2 + 2x - 8$, then $f(x)$ has a local minimum at

(A) $x = 2$ only

(B) $x = 2$ and $x = -4$

(C) $x = -4$ only

(D) $x = -1$ only

(E) $x = -1$ and $x = 2$

8. If $f(x) = xe^{-x}$, then the critical points of f are

(A) $x = -1$ only

(B) $x = 0$ only

(C) $x = 1$ only

(D) $x = 0$ and $x = -1$

(E) $x = 0$ and $x = 1$

9. The foot of a $20'$ ladder is being pulled away from a wall at the rate of 1.5 ft/sec. At the instant when the foot is 12 ft. away from the wall, the angle the ladder makes with the floor is decreasing at the rate (in radians/sec) of:

(A) $\dfrac{3}{50}$ (B) $\dfrac{1}{16}$ (C) $\dfrac{3}{40}$ (D) $\dfrac{1}{8}$ (E) $\dfrac{3}{32}$

10. If f and g are differentiable, $h(x) = f(x) - g(x)$, and $h(x)$ has a local maximum value at $x = 3$, then

(A) $f(x)$ has a local maximum value at $x = 3$

(B) $g(x)$ has a local minimum value at $x = 3$

(C) $f'(3) > g'(3)$

(D) $f'(3) = g'(3)$

(E) $f'(3) < g'(3)$

11. If $3p + 2q = 600$, the maximum value of $p \cdot q$ is

(A) 100   (B) 150   (C) 600   (D) 15,000   (E) 60,000

x	$F(x)$	$F'(x)$	$F''(x)$
2	1	3	- 4
4	3	0	- 2
6	7	5	0
8	13	6	2

12. The table above gives some information about a function F, for which F, F', and F'' are continuous for all x. Which one of the following statements must be true?

(A) $F(x)$ is not increasing on the interval [2, 8].

(B) The point (6, 7) is a point of inflection.

(C) $F(x)$ has a local minimum when $x = 4$.

(D) The line $y = 7$ is not a horizontal asymptote of $F(x)$.

(E) The line $x = 5$ could be a vertical asymptote of $F(x)$.

x	$F(x)$	$F'(x)$	$F''(x)$
2	1	3	- 4
4	3	0	- 2
6	7	5	0
8	13	6	2

13. The table above gives some information about a function F, for which F, F', and F'' are continuous for all x. Which one of the following statements must be false?

(A) The line $x = 5$ is a vertical asymptote of $F(x)$.

(B) The point (6, 7) is a point of inflection.

(C) $F(x)$ has a local maximum when $x = 4$.

(D) The line $y = 7$ is a horizontal asymptote of $F(x)$.

(E) The graph of $F(x)$ is concave down on the interval (2, 4).

78

x	$F(x)$	$F'(x)$	$F''(x)$
2	1	3	- 4
4	3	0	2
6	7	5	0
8	13	6	2

14.   The table above gives some information about a function F, for which F, F', and F'' are continuous for all x. Which of the following statements must be true?

I. $F(x)$ has a maximum value on the interval [2, 8].
II. $F(x)$ has a point of inflection for some x in the interval (2, 4).
III. $F(x)$ is increasing on [2, 8].

(A) I only   (B) I and II only   (C) I and III only

(D) II and III only   (E) I, II, and III

15.   Let $f(x) = \dfrac{\sin(x)}{e^x}$ for $x > 0$. When the minimum value of $f(x)$ occurs, then

(A) $\sin(x) = 0$ (B) $\cos(x) = 0$ (C) $\cos(x) = \sin(x)$ (D) $\cos(x) = -\sin(x)$

(E) $f(x)$ does not have any extreme values on the interval $[0, \infty)$.

16.   If $f'(x) = (x-1)^2 (x+4)$, then the function $y = f(x)$ has

(A)   one local minimum and no local maximum

(B)   no local minimum and one local maximum

(C)   one local minimum and one local maximum

(D)   one local minimum and two local maxima

(E)   two local minima and one local maximum

17. If $f''(x) = (x-1)^2(x-3)\cos(x)$, then on the interval $(0, \pi)$, how many points of inflection does the graph of $y = f(x)$ have?

(A) 1   (B) 2   (C) 3   (D) 4   (E) 5

18. If $f(x) = \dfrac{\ln(x)}{x}$, then

(A) $f(x)$ has a local maximum when $x = 1$

(B) $f(x)$ has a local minimum when $x = 1$

(C) $f(x)$ has a local maximum when $x = e$

(D) $f(x)$ has a local minimum when $x = e$

(E) $f(x)$ has no local extreme values

19. The graph of $y = x + \dfrac{1}{x}$ is both increasing and concave down on the interval

(A) $(-\infty, -1)$ (B) $(-1, 0)$ (C) $(0, 1)$ (D) $(1, \infty)$ (E) never

20. If $f'(x) = (x-1)^2(x+2)$, then f is increasing and concave down on the interval

(A) $(-\infty, -2)$ (B) $(-2, -1)$ (C) $(-2, 1)$ (D) $(-1, 1)$ (E) $(1, \infty)$

21.

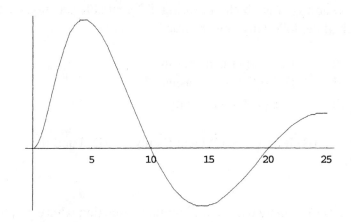

The graph of $y = f'(x)$, the derivative of f, is shown above. The function $y = f(x)$ has a local minimum on the interval $(0, 25)$ when x equals

(A) 10 only

(B) 15 only

(C) 20 only

(D) 4 and 15

(E) 10 and 20

22.

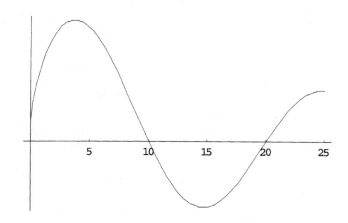

The graph of $y = f'(x)$, the derivative of f, is shown above. The function $y = f(x)$ is concave down on the interval(s)

(A) $(0, 4)$

(B) $(4, 15)$

(C) $(10, 20)$

(D) $(15, 25)$

(E) $(0, 10)$ and $(20, 25)$

23. If $f(x)$ and $g(x)$ are both increasing differentiable functions defined for all x, then which of the following must be true?

     I. $f(x)+g(x)$ is increasing
     II. $f(x) \cdot g(x)$ is increasing
     III. $f(g(x))$ is increasing

(A) I only   (B) II only   (C) I and II only   (D) I and III only   (E) I, II and III

24. If $y = f(x)$ is an increasing differentiable function whose graph lies in the first quadrant and is concave down, then $g(x) = \dfrac{1}{f(x)}$ is a function that is

(A) increasing and concave down   (B) decreasing and concave down

(C) increasing and concave up   (D) decreasing and concave up

(E) not enough information to determine

25.

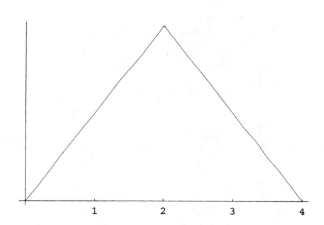

The graph of $y = f'(x)$, the derivative of f, is shown above. Which of the following is true?

     I. $y = f(x)$ has a point of inflection when $x = 2$.
     II.   The maximum value of $f(x)$ occurs when $x = 2$.
     III.   The maximum value of $f(x)$ occurs when $x = 4$.

(A) I only   (B) II only   (C) III only   (D) I and II only   (E) I and III only

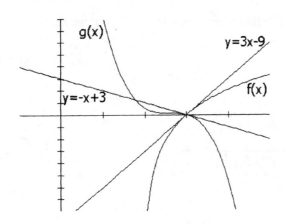

26. The functions *f* and *g* and their tangent lines at (3,0) are shown above.
$\lim\limits_{x \to 3} \dfrac{f(x)}{g(x)} =$

(A) -6
(B) -3
(C) $-\dfrac{1}{3}$
(D) $\dfrac{1}{3}$
(E) 3

27. If a particle is traveling along the parametric curve $x(t) = t^3$, $y(t) = t^2$, then the speed of the particle at $t = 2$ is

(A) 4
(B) $2\sqrt{13}$
(C) 8
(D) $2\sqrt{37}$
(E) $4\sqrt{10}$

28. If $x = 2\cos t$ and $y = \sin t$, then $\dfrac{d^2 y}{dx^2} =$

(A) $\dfrac{1}{2\sin^2 t}$
(B) $-\dfrac{1}{2\sin^2 t}$
(C) $\dfrac{1}{\sin^2 t}$
(D) $\dfrac{1}{\sin^3 t}$
(E) $-\dfrac{1}{4\sin^3 t}$

29. If a curve is traced out by the parametric equations $x(t) = t^2 - 4$ and $y(t) = 3 + \sin(t)$, then the curve has a horizontal tangent when $t =$

(A) 0
(B) $\dfrac{\pi}{2}$
(C) 2
(D) π
(E) no such value

30. The graphs of the two functions $f(t)$ and $g(t)$ are shown:

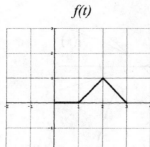

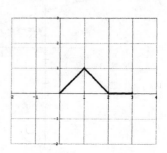

The motion of the particle whose coordinates at time t are $x = f(t)$ and $y = g(t)$ is:

(A)

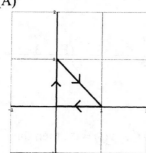

(B)

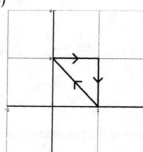

(C)

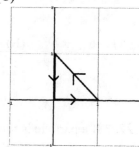

(D)

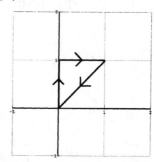

(E)

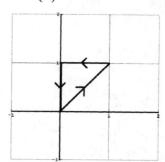

Chapter 4 Multiple Choice Questions

Question	Answer	AB	BC	No Calculator	Calculator Required	Neutral Calculator
1	A	x	x			x
2	D	x	x			x
3	E	x	x	x		
4	C	x	x			x
5	B	x	x			x
6	D	x	x			x
7	D	x	x	x		
8	C	x	x	x		
9	E	x	x			x
10	D	x	x			x
11	D	x	x	x		
12	A	x	x			x
13	A	x	x			x
14	B	x	x			x
15	C	x	x	x		
16	A	x	x	x		
17	B	x	x	x		
18	C	x	x	x		
19	A	x	x	x		
20	D	x	x	x		
21	C	x	x			x
22	B	x	x			x
23	D	x	x			x
24	D	x	x	x		
25	E	x	x			x
26	B	x	x			x
27	E		x	x		
28	E		x	x		
29	B		x	x		
30	A		x			x

Chapter 4 Free Response Questions

1. Alice Gardener wants to build a rectangular enclosure with a dividing fence in the middle of the rectangle. On one side, she plans to put some goats; on the other side she wants to raise some vegetables.

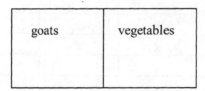

The fence along the outside of the rectangle costs $3 per foot, but the dividing fence costs $12 per foot.

(a) Alice decides to spend $240 on the fencing, what is the maximum area she can enclose? Justify your answer.

(b) If Alice decides that she wants to enclose 300 square feet, what is the minimum cost?

2. Let $f(x) = Ax^3 + Bx^2 + 40$.

(a) Find A and B so that $f(4) = 8$ and $f'(4) = 0$.

(b) For the A and B that you found in part (a), does f have a local extreme value when $x = 4$? If so, is it a local maximum or minimum? Justify your answer.

(c) Can you find constants P and Q so that $g(x) = Px^3 + 6x^2 + Q$ has a local maximum at $x = 4$ when $g(4) = 8$? Justify your answer.

3. Let $f(x) = \dfrac{\ln(x)}{x}$

(a) Find the value of x that maximizes $f(x)$. Justify your answer.

(b) Let $h(x) = \dfrac{k \ln(x)}{x}$. Is there a value of k so that $x = 1$ gives the maximum value of $h(x)$? If so, find this value.

(c) Let $g(x) = \dfrac{C + \ln(x)}{x}$. Is there a value of C so that $x = 1$ gives the maximum value of $g(x)$? If so, find this value.

4. Consider the portion of the parabola $y = 12 - x^2$ for $0 \le x \le \sqrt{12}$.

(a) For each x, $0 < x \le \sqrt{12}$, let $R(x)$ be area of the rectangle with sides parallel to the axes and with one vertex at $(0, 0)$ and the opposite vertex on the graph. What is the maximum value of $R(x)$? Justify your answer.

(b) For each x, $0 < x \le \sqrt{12}$, let $T(x)$ be the area of the triangle bounded by the coordinate axes and the line tangent to the graph at the point $(x, 12 - x^2)$. What is the minimum value of $T(x)$? Justify your answer.

5. Let f be a twice-differentiable function such that $f(x) > 0$ for all x, and let $g(x) = \left(f(x)\right)^2$.

(a) Use the second derivative test to show that if g has a local minimum value at $x = a$, then so does f.

(b) Use the result of part (a) to find the point on the parabola $y = x^2$ closest to the point (9, 8).

6. (a) Graph the following parametric curves indicating direction along each curve for $t \in \mathbb{R}$.

I

$x(t) = t^2$

$y(t) = t^4$

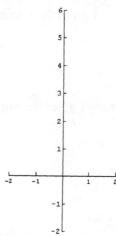

II

$x(t) = t^2$

$y(t) = t$

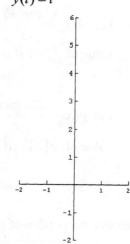

III

$x(t) = \sin(t)$

$y(t) = \sin^2(t)$

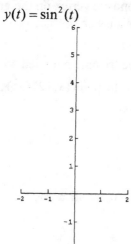

IV

$x(t) = e^t$

$y(t) = e^{2t}$

(b) For which of the above curve(s) is

   (i)   the first derivative nonexistent at $x = 0$?

   (ii)   the second derivative nonexistent at $x = 0$?

(c) If the above cases represent particle motion, at what time(s) in each case is the speed equal to zero?

Chapter 4 Free Response Questions

Question	AB	BC	No Calculator	Calculator Required	Neutral Calculator
1	x	x	x		
2	x	x	x		
3	x	x	x		
4	x	x	x		
5	x	x		x	
6		x	x		

Chapter 4 Solutions to Free Response Questions

1.

(a) Let x be length of the base of the rectangle and y be the length of the height. We need to maximize $A = xy$.

The cost of the fencing is $3x + 3x = 6x$ for the top and bottom, and $3y + 12y + 3y = 18y$ for the sides and middle.

The total cost is $6x + 18y$, which we set equal to 240.

Next solve for y in terms of x, getting $y = \dfrac{1}{18}(240 - 6x)$.

The area is now given by $A = x \cdot \dfrac{1}{18}(240 - 6x)$.

$\dfrac{dA}{dx} = \dfrac{1}{18}[(240 - 6x) + x \cdot -6] = \dfrac{240 - 12x}{18}$, which is 0 when $x = 20$.

Thus $y = \dfrac{120}{18} = \dfrac{20}{3}$ and the area is $20 \cdot \dfrac{20}{3} = \dfrac{400}{3}$ square feet.

Note that $\dfrac{d^2 A}{dx^2} = \dfrac{-12}{18} < 0$, and there is only one critical point, so this is a maximum.

(b) Now we set $xy = 300$, and minimize $C = 6x + 18y$. Solving for y, we have $y = \dfrac{300}{x}$,

so $C = 6x + 18\dfrac{300}{x} = 6x + \dfrac{5400}{x}$. $\dfrac{dC}{dx} = 6 - \dfrac{5400}{x^2}$, which is 0 when $x = 30$.

Thus $y = 10$, and the total cost is \$360. Note that $\dfrac{d^2 C}{dx^2} = \dfrac{2 \cdot 5400}{x^3}$ which is positive

when $x = 30$, and 30 is the only critical number so the cost of \$360 is a minimum.

2.

(a) $f'(x) = 3Ax^2 + 2Bx$, so set $A \cdot 64 + B \cdot 16 + 40 = 8$ and $3A \cdot 16 + 2B \cdot 4 = 0$, getting $A = 1$ and $B = -6$.

(b) $f''(x) = 6Ax + 2B$, so with $A = 1$, $B = -6$, and $x = 4$, $f''(4) = 12 > 0$, so f has a local minimum when $x = 4$.

(c)   Note that $6 = -B$, which suggests that we look at $h(x) = -f(x)$. If $h(x) = -f(x)$, then the graph of h is a reflection across the x-axis of the graph of f, and so $h(x)$ has a local maximum at $x = 4$. But since the value of $h(4)$ is -8, we need to translate the graph up 16 units. Let $g(x) = h(x) + 16$. Thus $Q = -40 + 16 = -24$, and $P = -1$.

Note: these values of P and Q can also be found directly using the methods of parts (a) and (b) with the proper justification.

3.

(a) $f'(x) = \dfrac{1 - \ln(x)}{x^2}$, so $f'(x) = 0$ when $x = e$. If $x < e$, then $\ln(x) < 1$, so $f'(x) > 0$, and f is increasing. If $x > e$, then $\ln(x) > 1$, so $f'(x) < 0$ and f is decreasing. Thus $x = e$ gives the maximum value of $f(x)$.

(b)   No. $h(x) = kf(x)$, and multiplying by a constant changes the value of the maximum, but not where it occurs.

(c) $g'(x) = \dfrac{1 - C - \ln(x)}{x^2}$, which is 0 when $x = e^{C-1}$. Thus $C = 1$ is the desired number.

4.

(a) $R(x) = x \cdot y = x(12 - x^2) = 12x - x^3$, so $R'(x) = 12 - 3x^2$.
Setting $R'(x) = 0$, we have $x = 2$ as the only critical point. $R''(2) = -12 < 0$, which means a local maximum. Since there is only one critical point, $x = 2$ is a global maximum.

The maximum area is $R(2) = 16$.

(b)   Let us call a point on the graph $(A, 12 - A^2)$, so the slope of the tangent line at this point is $-2A$.

Thus the equation of the tangent line is $y - (12 - A^2) = -2A(x - A)$. To find the y-intercept, set $x = 0$, getting $y = 12 + A^2$.
To find the x-intercept, set $y = 0$, getting $x = \dfrac{12 + A^2}{2A}$.

Thus the area of the triangle is $\dfrac{1}{2}\left(\dfrac{12+A^2}{2A}\right)\left(12+A^2\right)$.

Using x in place of A, we have $T(x) = \dfrac{1}{4}\dfrac{\left(12+x^2\right)^2}{x}$

$= \dfrac{1}{4}\dfrac{\left(x^4 + 24x^2 + 144\right)}{x} = \dfrac{1}{4}\left(x^3 + 24x + \dfrac{144}{x}\right)$.

Thus $T'(x) = \dfrac{1}{4}\left(3x^2 + 24 - \dfrac{144}{x^2}\right)$.

Setting $T'(x) = 0$, and multiplying through by $4x^2$, and then dividing by 3, we have $x^4 + 8x^2 - 48 = 0$, or $\left(x^2 + 12\right)\left(x^2 - 4\right) = 0$. The only solutions to this equation are $x = \pm 2$. Because of domain restrictions, we chose $x = 2$, as we did in part (a).

Finally, $T''(x) = \dfrac{1}{4}\left(6x + \dfrac{288}{x^3}\right)$, so $T''(2) > 0$, and the local minimum becomes a global minimum because there is only one critical point and the function is concave up. The minimum value of $T(x)$ is $T(2) = 32$.

5.

(a) Since f is twice differentiable, so is $g(x) = (f(x))^2$ and $g'(x) = 2f(x)f'(x)$.

If g has a local extreme value at $x = a$, then $g'(a) = 0 = 2f(a)f'(a)$. Since $f(a) > 0$, it follows that $f'(a) = 0$. Thus we can use the second derivative test at $x = a$.

Now $g''(x) = 2(f'(x)f'(x) + f(x)f''(x))$, so
$g''(a) = 2(f'(a)f'(a) + f(a)f''(a)) = 2(0 + f(a)f''(a)) = 2f(a)f''(a)$.

Finally, since $f(a) > 0$, the sign of $g''(a)$ is the same as the sign of $f''(a)$.

(b) If we let $f(x)$ be the distance from $(9, 8)$ to a point on $y = x^2$, we have

$$f(x) = \sqrt{(x-9)^2 + (y-8)^2} = \sqrt{(x-9)^2 + (x^2-8)^2}\,.$$

We let $g(x) = (f(x))^2 = (x-9)^2 + (x^2-8)^2 =$
$x^2 - 18x + 81 + x^4 - 16x^2 + 64 = x^4 - 15x^2 - 18x + 145$.

Thus $g'(x) = 4x^3 - 30x - 18$. We set $4x^3 - 30x - 18 = 0$ and get three solutions: $x = 3, x = -0.634,$ and $x = -2.366$.

Evaluating, we have $g(3) = 37$, $g(-0.634) = 158.544$, and $g(-2.366) = 134.956$

Finally, since $\lim_{x \to \infty} f(x) = \infty$ and $\lim_{x \to -\infty} f(x) = \infty$, we know f must have a minimum, and that this must therefore also be a local minimum.

Thus the minimum of f occurs when $x = 3$, and the distance is $\sqrt{37}$.

6. (a)   I   II

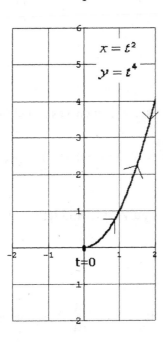

III	IV

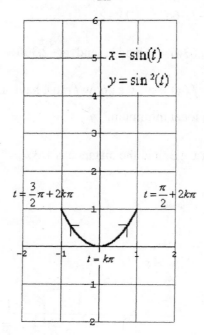 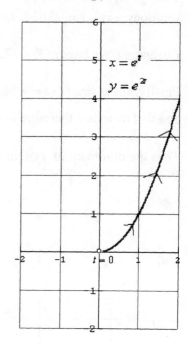

(b)   (i)   The 1st derivative is nonexistent at $x = 0$ in curves II and IV.

I)   We know that $\dfrac{\frac{dy}{dt}}{\frac{dx}{dt}} = \dfrac{4t^3}{2t}$. When $x = 0$, $t = 0$. This produces the

indeterminate form $\dfrac{0}{0}$. Applying L'Hôpital's Rule, we

get $\left.\dfrac{dy}{dx}\right|_{x=0} = 0$.

II)   Since $\dfrac{dy}{dx} = \dfrac{1}{2t}$ when $x = 0$, $t = 0$. $\therefore \dfrac{dy}{dx}$ does not exist

III)   Since $\dfrac{dy}{dx} = \dfrac{2\sin t\cos t}{\cos t} = 2\sin t$ when $x = 0$, $t = k\pi$, where k is any

integer. $\therefore \dfrac{dy}{dx} = 0$

IV) Since $\dfrac{dy}{dx} = \dfrac{2e^{2t}}{e^t} = 2e^t$ and when $x = 0$ this curve does not exist.

$\therefore \dfrac{dy}{dx}$ does not exist.

(ii) The 2nd derivative is nonexistent at $x = 0$ in curves II and IV.

I) $\dfrac{d^2 y}{dx^2} = \dfrac{\dfrac{d}{dt}\left(\dfrac{dy}{dx}\right)}{\dfrac{dx}{dt}} = \dfrac{4t}{2t}$. When $x = 0$, $t = 0$ and we get the

indeterminate form $\dfrac{0}{0}$. Applying L'Hôpital's Rule, we get

$\dfrac{d^2 y}{dx^2} = 2 \quad \therefore$ at $x = 0, \dfrac{d^2 y}{dx^2}$ exists

II) Since $\dfrac{dy}{dx}$ does not exist at $x = 0$ then $\dfrac{d^2 y}{dx^2}$ does not exist

III) $\dfrac{d^2 y}{dx^2} = \dfrac{\dfrac{d}{dt}(2\sin t)}{\cos t} = \dfrac{2\cos t}{\cos t} = 2$

$\therefore$ at $t = k\pi$, where k is any integer, $\dfrac{d^2 y}{dx^2}$ exists

IV) $\dfrac{d^2 y}{dx^2}$ cannot exist at $x = 0$ since $\dfrac{dy}{dx}$ does not exist at $x = 0$

(b) The speed is zero when $\sqrt{\left(\dfrac{dx}{dt}\right)^2 + \left(\dfrac{dy}{dt}\right)^2} = 0$

I) $\sqrt{(2t)^2 + (4t^3)^2} = 0$ When $t = 0$ the speed is 0.

II) $\sqrt{(2t)^2 + 1} = 0$ The speed is never 0.

III) $\sqrt{(\cos t)^2 + (2\sin t \cos t)^2} = 0$

$|\cos t| \sqrt{1 + 4\sin^2 t} = 0$ when $|\cos t| = 0$

The speed is zero when $t = \dfrac{\pi}{2} + k\pi$, where k is any integer.

IV) $\sqrt{(e^t)^2 + (2e^{2t})^2} = 0$

Since $\sqrt{(e^t)^2 + (2e^{2t})^2}$ is never 0, the speed is never 0.

AP Teacher Tips
Chapter 5: Key Concept: The Definite Integral

The concepts covered in chapter 5 are crucial for both AB and BC calculus students. Upper and lower (and left and right) Riemann sums are introduced in section 5.1, and revisited in section 7.5. Exercises 6 and 7 on page 246 foreshadow the trapezoid rule (covered in section 7.5).

The use of calculator programs that perform Riemann Sums is helpful, especially when large partitions are used. However, teachers should take care that students are able to perform such calculations "by hand" or by using only the scientific calculator capability of the calculator. Problems like numbers 15 and 16 on page 247 for tabular presentation of a function, and numbers 25 and 26 on page 248 for graphical presentation of a function are an excellent foundation for students' understanding of the rich array of applications of the definite integral as well as calculations of Riemann Sums.

Section 5.2 covers the definition of the definite integral as the limit of a Riemann Sum. Finding areas is also covered here. Exercises 12 – 18 on page 253 ask students to calculate the area between a curve and the horizontal axis. Since calculation of area is a common application of the integral tested on the AP exams, AP teachers may wish to supplement the problem set with a few more area problems from old AP exams.

The Fundamental Theorem is introduced in Section 5.3. (The second part of the Fundamental Theorem is covered in section 6.4.) The box on page 256 is a must-study item for students. A thorough understanding of the result that says, "The integral of the rate of change (derivative) of a function tells you net change in the function" is essential for students in the realm of application of the integral. Such problems have become a fixture on AP exams. The problems on pages 261 - 264 are a rich source of applications of the definite integral. Assign a sample that covers various function representations. For instance, numbers 17 (tabular), 31 (symbolic), and 33 (graphical) cover the gamut. Don't neglect the more tradition applications, like average value (Problem 29) and velocity and distance (Problem 34). Volume is covered in Chapter 8.

Section 5.4 covers a host of results that are necessary for both AP calculus courses. This section includes properties of limits of integration (Theorem 5.2), the linearity properties of integrals (Theorem 5.3), and comparison properties (Theorem 5.4). Coverage of these is required of all AP Calculus students. Exercises 2 and 3 on page 270 have appeared on past AP exams. Problems 36 - 39 on page 272 provide a nice conceptual review of a variety of concepts.

The review exercises and problems at the end of Chapter 5 are extensive and on-target as far as agreement with the direction of the AP exams. A representative sample from these includes numbers 6, 7, 14, 15, 17, 26, 29, 36, and 40.

Students who have calculators that include a computer algebra system could be challenged with problems 49 - 55 on page 278. Some of these involve setting up and evaluating the limit of Riemann Sums for power functions.

Chapter 5 Multiple Choice Questions

1. The function f has the values given in the table on the closed interval [3, 5]. What is the value of a left-hand Riemann sum for f over the closed interval [3, 5] using four subintervals of equal length?

x	3	3.5	4	4.5	5
$f(x)$	12	13	16	15	10

(A) 27   (B) 28   (C) 33   (D) 56   (E) 66

2. The total area of the region bounded by the graph of $y = x(1-x)(x-2)$ and the x-axis is

(A) $-\dfrac{1}{4}$ (B) 0   (C) $\dfrac{1}{4}$ (D) $\dfrac{1}{2}$ (E) $\dfrac{3}{4}$

3. The functions f and g are both continuous for all x. If f is an even function and g is an odd function, then $\int_{-5}^{5}\left(f(x)+g(x)\right)dx =$

(A) $\int_{0}^{5}\left(f(x)+g(x)\right)dx$ (B) $2\int_{0}^{5}\left(f(x)+g(x)\right)dx$ (C) $2\int_{0}^{5}f(x)\,dx$

(D) $\int_{0}^{5}f(x)\,dx$ (E) $2\int_{0}^{5}g(x)\,dx$

4. The noontime temperature of water at the surface of a lake over a year is given by $T(x) = 9\sin\left(\dfrac{2\pi}{365}(x-11)\right)+70$, where x is the number of days since January 1 and $T(x)$ is measured in degrees Fahrenheit. To the nearest degree, what is the average noontime temperature of water at the surface of the lake over the first 90 days of the year?

(A) 0   (B) 70   (C) 74   (D) 79   (E) 6704

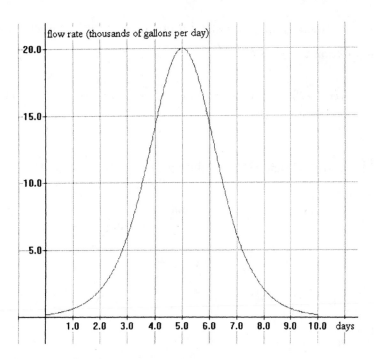

flow rate (thousands of gallons per day)

5. The rate of flow of water, in thousands of gallons per day, into a mountain lake over the course of a 10 day time period is given by the graph above. Which of these is closest to the amount of water, in thousands of gallons, that flowed into the lake over the 10 days?

(A) 0   (B) 10   (C) 25   (D) 40   (E) 65

6. The temperature of a cup of hot chocolate changes at the rate of $r(t) = -6e^{-0.12t}$ °C per minute, with t measured in minutes. Which of the following choices most accurately describes the change in temperature between $t = 0$ and $t = 5$?

(A) increases by 2.707   (B) decreases 0.325   (C) decreases by 22.559
(D) increases by 0.039   (E) decreases by 3.293

7. If $\dfrac{d}{dt} G(t) = F''(t)$, then $\displaystyle\int_0^3 F''(t)\, dt =$

(A) $G(3)$ (B) $G(3) - G(0)$ (C) $F''(3) - F''(0)$
(D) $F''(3)$ (E) $F(3) - F(0)$

8. If $\displaystyle\int_a^4 f(x)\, dx = 4$ and $\displaystyle\int_a^3 f(x)\, dx = 6$, then $\displaystyle\int_4^3 f(x)\, dx =$

(A) -10   (B) -2   (C) 2   (D) 10   (E) 34

9. If $g(t) = 2t - t^2$, then using a right-hand Riemann sum with four subintervals of equal length, approximate $\int_{-3}^{5} g(t)\, dt$.

(A) -16 (B) -20 (C) -35 (D) -40 (E) -70

10. If $g(t) = \int e^t \cos(e^t)\, dt$ and $g(0) = 1$, then $g(2)=$

(A) $\sin(e^2)$
(D) $\cos(e^2) - 1$
(B) $e^2\sin(e^2) - 1$
(E) $\sin(e^2) + 1 - \sin(1)$
(C) $e^2\cos(e^2) - 1$

11. $\lim_{n \to \infty}\left(\dfrac{1^3}{n} + \dfrac{\left(1+\dfrac{1}{n}\right)^3}{n} + \dfrac{\left(1+\dfrac{2}{n}\right)^3}{n} + ... + \dfrac{2^3}{n} \right) =$

(A) $\dfrac{15}{4}$ (B) e^3 (C) $\dfrac{e^4}{4}$ (D) 4 (E) $\dfrac{17}{4}$

12. If $\int_{1}^{5} 2 - 3f(t)\, dt = 20$, then $\int_{1}^{5} f(t)\, dt =$

(A) $\dfrac{-22}{3}$ (B) $\dfrac{-20}{3}$ (C) -6 (D) -4 (E) 24

13. If f is continuous and $0 \le f(x) \le \sqrt{3}$ for all x in the closed interval [0, 2], then which of the following must be true?

I. $\int_{0}^{2} f(x)\, dx \le 2\sqrt{3}$ II. $\int_{0}^{2} f(x)\, dx \ge 0$ III. $f(c) = \dfrac{\sqrt{3}}{2}$ for some c in [0, 2]

(A) I only (B) II only (C) I and II only

(D) I and III only (E) I, II, and III

14. The function f is continuous for all real numbers and $f(x) > 0$ for all x in the closed interval [4, 7]. The average value of $f(x)$ on [4, 7] is 5. What is the area of the region bounded by the graph of $y = f(x)$, the x-axis, and the lines $x = 4$ and $x = 7$?

(A) 5   (B) 15   (C) 20   (D) 35   (E) 55

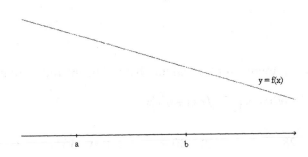

15. The function f is decreasing and linear on the closed interval [a, b], as shown in the figure above. Which of the following inequalities is true?

(A) $\int_a^b f''(x)\,dx < \int_a^b f'(x)\,dx < \int_a^b f(x)\,dx$ (B) $\int_a^b f'(x)\,dx < \int_a^b f''(x)\,dx < \int_a^b f(x)\,dx$

(C) $\int_a^b f(x)\,dx < \int_a^b f'(x)\,dx < \int_a^b f''(x)\,dx$ (D) $\int_a^b f(x)\,dx < \int_a^b f''(x)\,dx < \int_a^b f'(x)\,dx$

(E) $\int_a^b f''(x)\,dx < \int_a^b f(x)\,dx < \int_a^b f'(x)\,dx$

16. The velocity of a particle moving along a line is given by $v(t) = 2 + 4t^2$. Using a left-hand Riemann sum with $\Delta t = 1/2$, what is an estimate for the distance traveled by the particle from $t = 0$ to $t = 2$?

(A) 11   (B) $\dfrac{44}{3}$ (C) 20   (D) 22   (E) 40

17. If f is an even function and $\int_1^2 f(t)\,dt = 4$ and $\int_1^5 f(t)\,dt = 6$, then $\int_{-5}^{-2} f(t)\,dt =$

(A) -10   (B) -6   (C) -2   (D) 2   (E) 10

18. If f is a continuous function for all real numbers, which of the following must be true?

I. If $a = b$, then $\int_a^b f(t)\, dt = 0$ II. $\int_3^{10} f(x)\, dx = \int_3^{10} f(t)\, dt$ III. $\int_2^8 f(x)\, dx > \int_2^3 f(x)\, dx$

(A) I only   (B) II only   (C) I and II only

(D) I and III only   (E) I, II, and III

19. The function f is continuous for all real numbers. The average value of $f(x)$ on the closed interval $[4, 7]$ is 5. What is $\int_4^7 2 \cdot f(x) + 6 \; dx$?

(A) 6   (B) 28   (C) 30   (D) 36   (E) 48

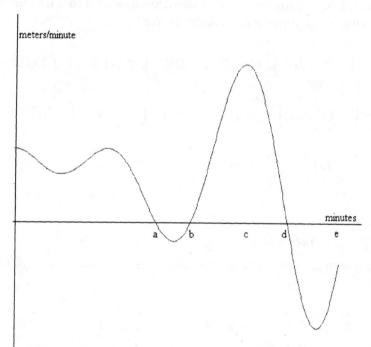

20. The rate of change $R(t)$, in meters per minute, of the altitude of an airplane over a portion of its flight is given in the graph above. At what time during the portion of the flight shown in the graph is the airplane at its highest altitude?

(A) a   (B) b   (C) c   (D) d   (E) e

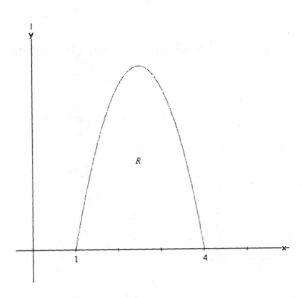

21. The area of the region R bounded by the graph of $y = f(x)$ and the x-axis in the figure above is 7. What is $\int_1^4 (2f(x) + 5) \, dx$?

(A) 14   (B) 19   (C) 29   (D) 42   (E) 57

22. If $\dfrac{d}{dx}(f(x) \cdot \ln(2)) = G(x)$, then $\int_3^4 G(x) \, dx =$

(A) $f(4) \cdot \ln(2) - f(3) \cdot \ln(2)$

(B) $f'(4) \cdot \ln(2) - f'(3) \cdot \ln(2)$

(C) $\dfrac{f(4)}{2} - \dfrac{f(3)}{2}$

(D) $G(4) - G(3)$

(E) $G'(4) - G'(3)$

Chapter 5 Multiple Choice Questions

Question	Answer	AB	BC	No Calculator	Calculator Required	Neutral Calculator
1	B	x	x	x		
2	D	x	x	x		
3	C	x	x	x		
4	C	x	x		x	
5	E	x	x			x
6	C	x	x		x	
7	B	x	x	x		
8	C	x	x			x
9	D	x	x	x		
10	E	x	x	x		
11	A	x	x			x
12	D	x	x			x
13	C	x	x			x
14	B	x	x			x
15	B	x	x	x		
16	A	x	x	x		
17	D	x	x			x
18	C	x	x			x
19	E	x	x			x
20	D	x	x			x
21	C	x	x			x
22	A	x	x			x

Chapter 5 Free Response Questions

1. The temperature, $H(t)$, of a cup of hot chocolate is changing at the rate of
    $R(t) = -18.9e^{-0.27t}$ °C/minute for all $t \geq 0$.

    (a) Find all values of $t \geq 0$ for which $R(t)$ is decreasing. Interpret your answer in terms of
         the graph of $y = H(t)$.

    (b) What is the net change in the temperature of the hot chocolate between $t = 0$ and
         $t = 10$?

    (c) What is the average rate of change of the temperature of the hot chocolate between
         $t = 0$ and $t = 10$?

    (d) The temperature of the chocolate was $H = 90°C$ at $t = 0$. Explain the meaning of
         $90 + \int_0^t R(u)\,du$

2. The charge C on an electric capacitor changes at the rate $D(t) = -0.36 \cdot e^{-0.0513t}$ volts/sec,
    where $t \geq 0$ is measured in seconds. At time $t = 0$, the charge on the capacitor is 7 volts.

    (a) Write an equation for the line tangent to the graph of $y = C(t)$ at $t = 0$, and find the
         t-intercept of this line.

    (b) What is the charge on the capacitor at $t = 15$ seconds?

    (c) If the charge on the capacitor decreased at the same rate it was decreasing at $t = 0$,
         would its charge at $t = 15$ have been greater or less than your answer to part (b)? Use
         $D'(t)$ to justify your answer.

    (d) Write an equation that could be used to find the time when the charge on the capacitor
         is equal to half its initial charge of 7 volts. Do not solve the equation.

3. During a rainstorm, which begins at midnight, water flows into a pond at the rate of $F(t) = 200\left(1 + \sin\left(\dfrac{t^2}{12}\right)\right)$ liters/hour, where t is measured in hours since midnight. During the same storm, water flows out of the pond through a drain at the rate of $D(t) = 100\left(1 + \sin\left(\dfrac{(t-1)^2}{15}\right)\right)$ liters/hour, where t is measured in hours since midnight. The storm ends at 11:30 am, when $t = 11.5$. Let $A(t)$ be the amount of water in the pond at time t between 0 and 11.5.

(a) Sketch a graph of $F(t) - D(t)$ on the axes provided. Explain the meaning of $F(t) - D(t)$ in terms of water in the pond.

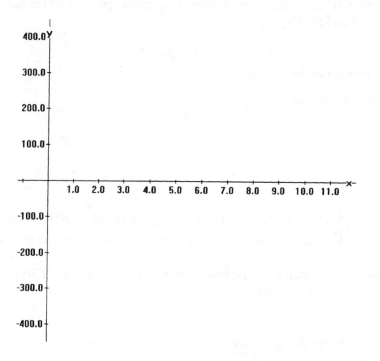

(b) Find the value of t when $A(t)$ is a minimum. Give a reason for your answer.

(c) When is $A(t)$ increasing at its fastest rate?

(d) What is the net change in $A(t)$ during the rainstorm?

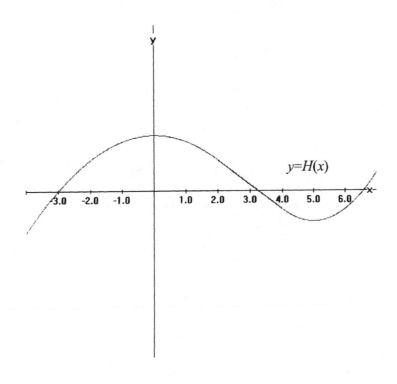

y=H(x)

4. Part of the graph of $H(x)$ is shown above. H is differentiable for all real numbers, and its graph consists of a parabolic piece for $x < 2$, a linear piece for $2 \le x \le 4$, and another parabolic piece for $x > 4$. The function $f = H'$, the derivative of H, is continuous for all real numbers.

(a) Is $f(1)$ positive, negative, or 0? Justify your answer.

(b) Find all values of x where f is increasing. Justify your answer.

(c) Find all values of x where $f'(x) = 0$. Justify your answer.

(d) On the axes provided, sketch a possible graph of $y = f(x)$.

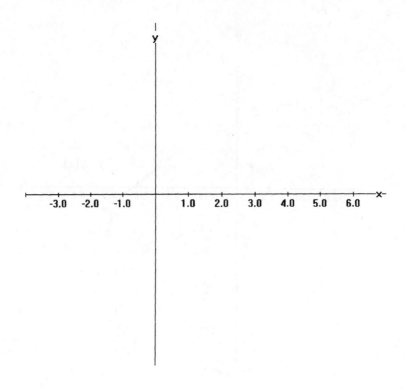

Year	1960	1965	1970	1975	1980	1985	1990
Rate	10.82	13.06	14.61	14.99	18.60	19.33	22.46

5. Annual coal production on the United States (in quadrillion BTU per year) is given in the table above. Let $f(t)$ be the rate of coal production t years since 1960.

(a) Estimate $f'(15)$, and explain its meaning in terms of coal production.

(b) Use a right-hand Riemann sum with three subintervals of equal length to approximate $\int_0^{30} f(t)\, dt$. Explain the meaning of this integral in terms of coal production.

(c) If $f'(t) > 0$ for all t in the closed interval [0,30], will the approximation you made in part (b) overestimate or underestimate the exact value of $\int_0^{30} f(t)\, dt$? Give a reason for your answer.

Chapter 5 Free Response Questions

Question	AB	BC	No Calculator	Calculator Required	Neutral Calculator
1	x	x		x	
2	x	x		x	
3	x	x		x	
4	x	x			x
5	x	x		x	

Chapter 5 Solutions to Free Response Questions

1.

(a) $R(t)$ is decreasing when $R'(t) = 5.103e^{-0.27t} < 0$. This is never true, so $R(t)$ is never decreasing.

$H'(t) = R(t)$ and $H''(t) = R'(t)$.

Since $R'(t) > 0$ for all t, the graph of $y = H(t)$ is always concave up.

(b) Net change in temperature $= H(10) - H(0) = \int_0^{10} R(t)\, dt = -65.296 \ °C$

(c) Average rate of change of the temperature $= \dfrac{1}{10-0} \int_0^{10} R(t)\, dt = -6.5296 \ °C/\text{minute}$.

(d) $\int_0^t R(u)\, du = H(t) - H(0)$, so $90 + \int_0^t R(u)\, du = 90 + H(t) - 90 = H(t)$. This is the temperature of the hot chocolate at time t minutes.

2.

(a) $C(0) = 7$, $C'(0) = D(0) = -0.36 \text{ volts/sec}$. $y - 7 = -0.36(t - 0)$. At the t- intercept, $y = 0$ so $t = \dfrac{-7}{-0.36} = 19.444$ seconds.

(b) $C(15) - C(0) = \int_0^{15} D(t)\, dt = -3.767$ volts. So, $C(15) = 7 + (-3.767) = 3.233$ volts.

(c) If the charge decreased at the constant rate of -0.36 volts/sec, the charge after 15 seconds would have been less than 3.233 volts.

$C''(t) = D'(t) = (-0.36) \cdot (-0.0513) \cdot e^{-0.0513t} > 0$ for all t.

The graph of $y = C(t)$ is always concave up, so a tangent line is always below the graph of $y = C(t)$. (On the tangent line, at $t = 15$, $y = 1.6$ volts)

(d) Solve $C(t) - C(0) = \int_0^t D(t)\, dt = -3.5$

110

3.

(a)

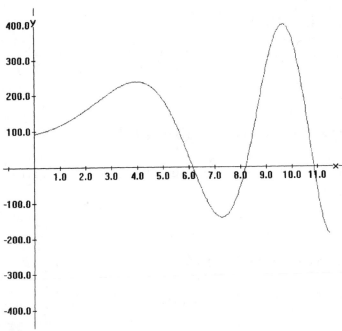

$F(t) - D(t)$ is the rate of change of $A(t)$. It measures the rate at which the amount of water in the pond is changing at time t.

(b) $t = 0$.

At $t = 8.183$, $A'(t) = F(t) - D(t)$ changes from negative to positive so $A(t)$ has a local minimum at this time. $A(0)$ and $A(11.5)$ are endpoint minima.

However, $A(8.183) > A(0)$, since $A(8.183) - A(0) = \int_{0}^{8.183} A'(t)\, dt > 0$. (Between $x = 0$ and $x = 8.183$ the area above the x-axis is greater than the area below the x-axis).

Similarly, $A(11.5) > A(0)$ since there is more positive area than negative from $t = 0$ to $t = 11.5$.

(c) $A(t)$ increases at its fastest rate where $A'(t)$ is a maximum.

Solving $A''(t) = 0$ gives $t = 3.979, 7.273, 9.648$.

Checking the values of $A'(t)$ at these three values and the end points of the interval gives $A'(0) = 93.338$, $A'(3.979) = 237.940$, $A'(7.273) = -140.343$, $A'(9.648) = 395.344$, and $A'(11.5) = = -187.503$.

So, at $t = 9.648$, $A'(t)$ is a maximum and $A(t)$ is increasing at its fastest rate.

(d) $A(11.5) - A(0) = \int_0^{11.5} A'(t)\, dt = 1379.305$ liters.

4.

(a) $f(1)$ is negative. $H'(x) = f(x)$, so $H'(1) = f(1)$.

From the graph of $y = H(x)$, H is decreasing at $x = 1$, so $H'(1) = f(1) < 0$.

(b) $x > 4$.

f is increasing where $f'(x) = H''(x) > 0$.

From the graph of $y = H(x)$, $f'(x) = H''(x) > 0$ for all $x > 4$.

(c) $2 \le x \le 4$.

$f'(x) = H''(x) = 0$ where the graph of $y = H(x)$ is linear. The second derivative of any linear function is 0.

(d)

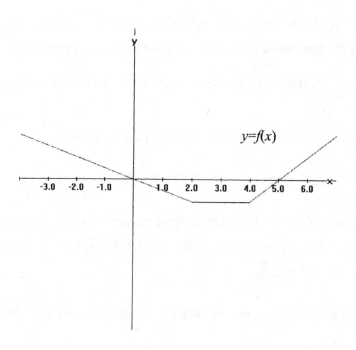

5.

(a) $f'(15) \approx \dfrac{18.60 - 14.61}{10} = 0.399$ quadrillion BTU/year^2.

This means that in 1975, the amount of coal produced in a year is increasing at the rate of approximately 0.399 quadrillion BTU per year.

(b) $\int_0^{30} f(t)dt \approx 10 \cdot (14.61 + 18.60 + 22.46) = 556.7$ quadrillion BTU.

This approximates the total amount of coal produced in the United States between 1960 and 1990.

(c) Since $f'(t) > 0$, $f(t)$ is increasing on $[0,30]$.

Therefore, a right-hand sum will over-estimate $\int_0^{30} f(t)\, dt$.

On each sub-interval, the right-hand rectangle will include a piece of area not under the graph of $y = f(t)$.

AP Teacher Tips
Chapter 6: Constructing Antiderivatives

The material in Sections 6.1 - 6.4 is required for both the AB and BC Examinations. Section 6.5 is interesting from both a physical and an historical point of view. Be sure, however, that your students see lots of problems with non-constant acceleration, and that they don't use "Physics formulas" on the AP Examinations.

Chapter 6 is to Chapter 5 as Chapter 3 is to Chapter 2; that is to say, Chapter 6 develops computational skills for evaluating definite integrals, which were introduced conceptually in Chapter 5. Many of the exercises in Section 6.1 are, in a sense, familiar to the students; for example, compare Problem 23 with Problem 21 of Section 2.5. The added attraction is that students are now able to compute:
net change of the antiderivative = (the area above the axis) minus (the area below the axis).

Be careful with the language here; area is always positive whether the region under discussion is above or below the *x*-axis (the area of a circle centered at the origin is not zero). Whether the integrand is positive or negative determines whether the antiderivative increases or decreases, and the area gives the absolute value of the amount of increase or decrease. It is important that students not identify the definite integral with area, but realize that area is one application when the integrand is non-negative.

The Fundamental Theorem of Calculus, as presented in Theorem 5.1, establishes the importance of recognizing a given function as the derivative of some other function. That is, the FTC establishes the importance of finding antiderivates in the computation of definite integrals. Section 6.1 and Section 6.2 tackle the problem of finding antiderivatives from a multi-representational viewpoint, as is called for in the AP Calculus Course Description.

Section 6.3 gives another reason for finding antidervatives, i.e., solving differential equations. One must stress the additive constant when finding antiderivative analytically, starting in Section 6.2, or else satisfying initial conditions in Section 6.3 is impossible.

Section 6.4 deals with the other version of the FTC: every continuous function has an antiderivative, which can be realized as a function defined by an integral. Students have trouble with this version of the theorem, due at least in part to their difficulty in recognizing that one can define a specific function using a definite integral with a variable upper limit of integration. You may want to review material such as Exercises 2 and 3 in Section 5.4 and Exercises 5 and 6 in Section 6.1, which provide numerical question stems. In a similar vein, Problems 8, 9, 16, 17, and 18 in Section 6.1 provide graphical question stems. Finally, be sure to cover Exercises 8 - 10, which show how important this version of the FTC is in solving a differential equation with a given initial condition. One can always write a solution in this form. Usually, a "simpler" antiderivative can then be found. As in these three problems, if a "simpler" antiderivative cannot be found, one must be satisfied with this form. One can use the calculator to graph the solution, and if the value of the solution at a point other than the one specifying the initial condition is needed, then one must resort to numerical techniques to evaluate the definite integral.

Chapter 6 Multiple Choice Questions

1. An antiderivative of $\cos(3x)$ is

(A) $\dfrac{1}{2}(\cos(3x))^2$

(B) $\dfrac{-1}{2}(\cos(3x))^2$

(C) $-3\sin(3x)$

(D) $\dfrac{1}{3}\sin(3x)$

(E) $\dfrac{-1}{3}\sin(3x)$

2. Given the following table of values for $f'(x)$, and the fact that $f(2) = 10$, which of the choices best approximates $f(8)$?

x	2	4	6	8
$f'(x)$	7	13	20	22

(A) $10 + 13 \cdot 2 + 20 \cdot 2 + 22 \cdot 2$

(B) $7 \cdot 2 + 13 \cdot 2 + 20 \cdot 2 + 22 \cdot 2$

(C) $10 + 7 \cdot 2 + 13 \cdot 4 + 20 \cdot 6$

(D) $10 + 7 \cdot 2 + 13 \cdot 4 + 20 \cdot 6 + 22 \cdot 8$

(E) $10 + 7 \cdot 2 + 13 \cdot 2 + 20 \cdot 2 + 22 \cdot 2$

3. $\displaystyle\int \frac{4x^3 + 2x + 1}{x^2}\,dx =$

(A) $\dfrac{x^4 + x^2 + x}{\frac{1}{3}x^3} + C$

(B) $\dfrac{x^4 + x^2 + x + C}{\frac{1}{3}x^3 + C}$

(C) $2x^2 + \ln|x| - \dfrac{1}{x} + C$

(D) $2x^2 + 2\ln|x| - \dfrac{1}{x} + C$

(E) $2x^2 + 2\ln|x| + \dfrac{1}{x} + C$

4. $\int \dfrac{1}{e^{2x}} dx =$

(A) $\dfrac{1}{e^{2x}} + C$ (B) $\dfrac{1}{2e^{2x}} + C$ (C) $\dfrac{-1}{2e^{2x}} + C$

(D) $\dfrac{-2}{e^{2x}} + C$ (E) $\dfrac{2}{e^{2x}} + C$

5. The average value of $y = \sqrt{x}$ on the interval $[1, 16]$ is

(A) 2.500   (B) 0.333   (C) 42   (D) $\dfrac{42}{15}$ (E) $\dfrac{63}{15}$

6. $\int (x^2 + 3)^2 dx =$

(A) $\dfrac{1}{3}(x^2 + 3)^3 + C$ (B) $\dfrac{1}{6x}(x^2 + 3)^3 + C$

(C) $\dfrac{1}{5}x^5 + 2x^3 + 9x + C$ (D) $\dfrac{1}{5}x^5 + 9x + C$

(E) $4x(x^2 + 3) + C$

7. If $\dfrac{dV}{dt} = \sin(t)$ and $V(0) = 5$, then $V(t) =$

(A) $\cos(t) + 5$ (B) $-\cos(t) + 5$ (C) $-\cos(t) + 6$

(D) $\cos(t) + 4$ (E) $\dfrac{1}{2}(\sin(t))^2 + 5$

8. If $V'(t) = 3\sqrt{t}$ and $V(1) = 7$, then $V(4) =$

(A) 23   (B) 21   (C) 13   (D) 10   (E) 6.25

9. If a yam is thrown up into the air from an initial height of 9 feet with an initial velocity of 80 feet per second, then what is its maximum height, in feet?
    (Assume $a(t) = -32 \text{ ft}/\text{sec}^2$ is the acceleration.)

(A) 234   (B) 184   (C) 175   (D) 109   (E) 80

10. If $f(x) = \int_1^x \cos(t^2)dt$, then $f'(x) =$

(A) $\cos(x^2)$ (B) $\sin(x^2)$ (C) $-2x\sin(x^2)$ (D) $2x\sin(x^2)$ (E) $2x\cos(x^2)$

11. If $g(x) = \int_x^4 e^{\sqrt{t}}dt$, then $g'(x) =$

(A) $e^2 - e^{\sqrt{x}}$ (B) $e^{\sqrt{x}}$ (C) $-e^{\sqrt{x}}$ (D) $e^{\sqrt{x}} - e^2$ (E) $\dfrac{e^{\sqrt{x}}}{2\sqrt{x}}$

12. The solution to $y' = \dfrac{1}{\sqrt{x+1}}$ with $y(0) = 4$, is $y =$

(A) $2\sqrt{x+1}+4$ (B) $2\sqrt{x+1}+2$ (C) $\sqrt{x+1}+4$

(D) $\sqrt{x+1}+3$ (E) $\dfrac{\sqrt{x+1}}{2}+\dfrac{7}{2}$

13. If $g(x) = \int_0^{x^2} \dfrac{1}{3t^2+1}dt$, then $g'(x) =$

(A) $\dfrac{1}{3x^2+1}$ (B) $\dfrac{2x}{3x^2+1}$ (C) $\dfrac{1}{3x^4+1}$ (D) $\dfrac{2x}{3x^4+1}$ (E) $\dfrac{12x^3}{3x^4+1}$

117

14. If $f(x) = \int_1^x \dfrac{1}{t^2 - 4} \, dt$, then the domain of f is

(A) $(-\infty, -2) \cup (-2, 2) \cup (2, \infty)$

(B) $(0, 2) \cup (2, \infty)$

(C) $[1, 2) \cup (2, \infty)$

(D) $(-2, 2)$

(E) $[1, 2)$

15. If $f(x) = \int_A^{x^2 - 9} \cos(\sqrt{t}) \, dt$, then the least value of A for which $f(x)$ can be defined is

(A) $-\infty$ (B) -3 (C) 0 (D) 3 (E) 9

16. $\displaystyle\int \dfrac{6x^2 + 1}{x} \, dx =$

(A) $(2x^3 + x)\ln|x| + C$

(B) $3x^2 \ln|x| + C$

(C) $3x^2 + \ln|x| + C$

(D) $3x^2 + x + C$

(E) $2x^3 + x + C$

17. $\displaystyle\int \dfrac{1}{\cos^2(3t)} \, dt =$

(A) $\ln\left|\cos^2(3t)\right| + C$

(B) $\dfrac{1}{3}\ln\left|\cos^2(3t)\right| + C$

(C) $\dfrac{-1}{3\cos(3t)} + C$

(D) $\tan(3t) + C$

(E) $\dfrac{1}{3}\tan(3t) + C$

18. If $y' = \cos(x^2)$ and $y(0) = 3$, then $y(2) =$

(A) -2.614 (B) -0.653 (C) 2.346 (D) 3.461 (E) 4.999

19. The function $f(x) = 3 + \int_5^x \sqrt{t^2 + 1}\, dt$ is a solution to which of the following situations?

(A) $f'(x) = \sqrt{x^2 + 1} - \sqrt{26}$, with $f(3) = 5$

(B) $f'(x) = \sqrt{x^2 + 1} - \sqrt{26}$, with $f(5) = 3$

(C) $f'(x) = \sqrt{x^2 + 1}$, with $f(5) = 3$

(D) $f'(x) = \sqrt{x^2 + 1}$, with $f(3) = 5$

(E) $f'(x) = \dfrac{x}{\sqrt{x^2 + 1}}$, with $f(5) = 3$

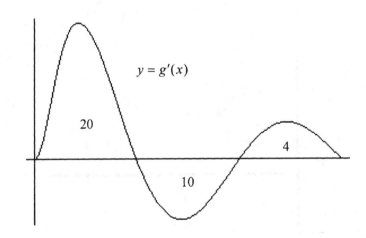

20. The graph of $y = g'(x)$ on the interval $0 \le x \le 15$ is shown above. The numbers in the regions give the area of the region. If $g(0) = 8$, what is $g(15)$?

(A) 14   (B) 16   (C) 22   (D) 34   (E) 42

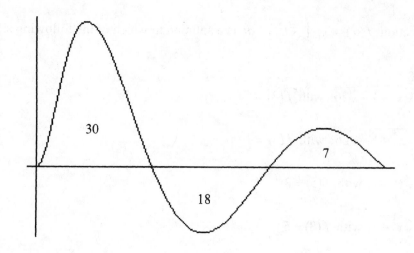

21. The graph of $y = g'(x)$ on the interval $0 \le x \le 15$ is shown above. The numbers in the regions give the area of the region. If $g(0) = 14$, then the maximum value of $g(x)$ on the interval $[0, 15]$ is

(A) 19   (B) 30   (C) 33   (D) 44   (E) 69

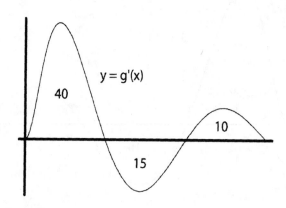

22. The graph of the derivative of g on the interval $0 \le x \le 20$ is shown above.

If $g(0) = 60$, the minimum value of $g(x)$ on the interval $0 \le x \le 20$ is

(A) 0   (B) 10   (C) 15   (D) 60   (E) 85

120

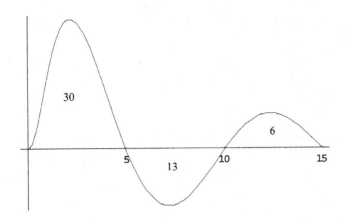

23. The graph of $y = f'(x)$ is shown above. If $f(5) = 20$, then the minimum value of $f(x)$ on the interval $0 \le x \le 15$ is

(A) -30   (B) -13   (C) -10   (D) 7   (E) 20

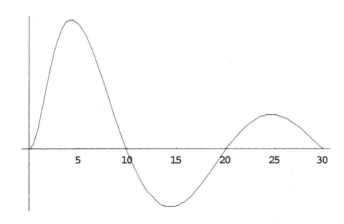

24. The graph of $y = f'(x)$ is shown above. On the open interval (0, 30), the graph of f has

(A) exactly two local maxima.

(B) exactly two local minima.

(C) exactly one local maximum and one point of inflection.

(D) exactly one local minimum and two points of inflection.

(E) exactly three points of inflection.

121

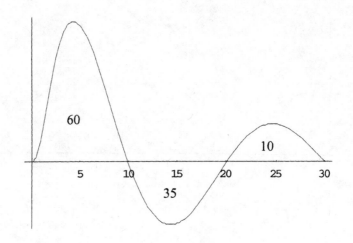

25. The graph of $y = f(t)$ is given above. If $g(x) = 100 + \int_{20}^{x} f(t)dt$, and the numbers between the graph and the x-axis give the area of the region, then the maximum value of $g(x)$ on the interval $[0, 30]$ is

(A) 100   (B) 110   (C) 125   (D) 135   (E) 95

Chapter 6 Multiple Choice Questions

Question	Answer	AB	BC	No Calculator	Calculator Required	Neutral Calculator
1	D	x	x	x		
2	A	x	x			x
3	D	x	x	x		
4	C	x	x	x		
5	D	x	x	x		
6	C	x	x	x		
7	C	x	x	x		
8	B	x	x	x		
9	D	x	x	x		
10	A	x	x	x		
11	C	x	x	x		
12	B	x	x	x		
13	D	x	x	x		
14	D	x	x	x		
15	C	x	x	x		
16	C	x	x	x		
17	E	x	x	x		
18	D	x	x		x	
19	C	x	x			x
20	C	x	x			x
21	D	x	x			x
22	D	x	x			x
23	C	x	x			x
24	E	x	x			x
25	D	x	x			x

Chapter 6 Free Response Questions

1. A particle travels along the *x*-axis so that its velocity is given by $v(t) = \cos(3t)$ for $0 \leq t \leq 2$. When $t = 0$, the particle is at $x = 5$.

    (a) For what values of *t* is the particle moving to the right?

    (b) What is the smallest *x*-coordinate of the particle?

    (c) What is the total distance the particle travels?

2. Let $g(x) = \int_{4}^{x} \frac{1}{(t^2 - 81)^2} dt$.

    (a) What is the domain of *g*?

    (b) What is $g(4)$?

    (c) What is $g'(4)$?

    (d) Find any relative extreme values of *g*. Justify your answer.

3. Let $g(x) = \int_{4}^{x^2} \sqrt{t^2 - 9} dt$.

    (a) What is the domain of *g*?

    (b) What is $g(2)$?

    (c) What is $g'(2)$?

    (d) Find any local extreme values of *g*. Justify your answer.

4. A body moves so that its acceleration at time t is given by $A(t) = -32 + 2v(t)$, where $v(t)$ is the velocity at time t. Time is in seconds, and the velocity is in feet per second.

   (a) Show that $v(t) = 16 + Ce^{2t}$ is a possible velocity function.

   (b) If v is in the form indicated in part (a), and $v(0) = 0$, what is C?

   (c) Is there a time, t, for which $A(t) = 0$? Explain.

   (d) If the body starts at an initial height of 100 feet, find the height as a function of t.

5. Let $g(x) = \int_2^x |t| \ dt$.

   (a) What is $g(4)$?

   (b) What is $g(-4)$?

   (c) Does g have any critical points? If so, identify each one. Justify your answer.

   (d) Does the graph of g have any points of inflection? If so, identify each one. Justify your answer.

Chapter 6 Free Response Questions

Question	AB	BC	No Calculator	Calculator Required	Neutral Calculator
1	x	x		x	
2	x	x	x		
3	x	x	x		
4	x	x			x
5	x	x	x		

Chapter 6 Solutions to Free Response Questions

1.

(a) The particle moves to the right when $v(t) > 0$; thus for t in the intervals $\left(0, \dfrac{\pi}{6}\right)$ and $\left(\dfrac{\pi}{2}, 2\right)$.

(b) The minimum value of x occurs when $t = \dfrac{\pi}{2}$, when $x = 5 + \displaystyle\int_0^{\frac{\pi}{2}} \cos(3t)\,dt = 4.666$

(c) The total distance is $\displaystyle\int_0^{\frac{\pi}{6}} \cos(3t)\,dt - \int_{\frac{\pi}{6}}^{\frac{\pi}{2}} \cos(3t)\,dt + \int_{\frac{\pi}{2}}^2 \cos(3t)\,dt = 1.240$.

2.

(a) The domain of the integrand, $f(t) = \dfrac{1}{(t^2 - 81)^2}$, consists of three intervals:

$(-\infty, -9)$, $(-9, 9)$, and $(9, \infty)$.

Because 4 is in the domain of g, and because the integral is not defined over an interval containing one of the vertical asymptotes, $t = -9$ and $t = 9$, the domain of g is the interval (-9, 9).

(b) $g(4) = \displaystyle\int_4^4 \dfrac{1}{(t^2 - 81)^2}\,dt = 0$

(c) $g'(4) = \dfrac{1}{(4^2 - 81)^2} = \dfrac{1}{4225}$

(d) Since $g'(x) = \dfrac{1}{(x^2 - 81)^2} > 0$ for all x in (-9, 9), g is an increasing function and so does not have any relative extreme values.

3.

(a)   The domain of the integrand, $\sqrt{t^2-9}$, is $(-\infty,-3]\cup[3,\infty)$.

Since the interval of integration must include 4, the interval with end points 4 and x^2 must be in the interval $[3,\infty)$.

Since 4 is in the interval, we must require that x^2 also be in the interval. Thus we need $x^2 \geq 3$. The domain of g is $(-\infty,-\sqrt{3}]\cup[\sqrt{3},\infty)$

(b) $g(2)=\int_4^4 \sqrt{t^2-9}\ dt = 0$

(c) $g'(x)=\sqrt{(x^2)^2-9}\cdot 2x = 2x\sqrt{x^4-9}$, so $g'(2)=4\sqrt{7}$

(d)   The numbers $x=0$, $x=9^{\frac{1}{4}}$, and $x=-9^{\frac{1}{4}}$ are not in the domain of g', so $g'(x)$ is never 0, and there is no local extreme value.

4.

(a) $A(t)=v'(t)=2Ce^{2t}$.

Also $A(t)=-32+2v(t)=-32+2(16+Ce^{2t})=2Ce^{2t}$.

Thus $v(t)=16+Ce^{2t}$ satisfies the equation.

(b) $v(0)=16+C = 0$, so $C=$ -16.

(c)   Using $A(t)=v'(t)=-32e^{2t}$, we see that $A(t)\neq 0$, since e^{2t} is never 0.

(d) $h(t)=\int v(t)dt = \int 16-16e^{2t}dt = 16t-8e^{2t}+k$.

Setting $h(0)=100$, we have $-8+k=100$, so $k=108$, and $h(t)=16t-8e^{2t}+108$.

5.

(a) $g(4) = \int_2^4 |t|\, dt = \int_2^4 t\, dt$ (since $t \geq 0$ on the interval [2, 4]) $= \frac{1}{2}t^2\Big|_2^4 = 8 - 2 = 6$.

(b) $g(-4) = \int_2^{-4} |t|\, dt = -\int_{-4}^2 |t|\, dt = -\left(\int_{-4}^0 -t\, dt + \int_0^2 t\, dt\right) = -\left(\frac{-t^2}{2}\Big|_{-4}^0 + \frac{t^2}{2}\Big|_0^2\right) = -10$.

(c) Since the integrand is continuous for all t, g is differentiable for all x and $g'(x) = |x|$.

Thus the only critical point is where $g'(x) = 0$, which is $x = 0$.

(d) $g''(x) = \begin{cases} -1 & \text{for } x < 0 \\ 1 & \text{for } x > 0 \end{cases}$ and is undefined for $x = 0$.

Now the graph of g has a tangent line at $(0, g(0))$, is concave down to the left of $(0, g(0))$ and is concave up to the right of $(0, g(0))$. Thus this point is a point of inflection.

Finally, $g(0) = \int_2^0 |t|\, dt = -\int_0^2 t\, dt = -2$, so the point of inflection is (0, -2).

AP Teacher Tips
Chapter 7: Integration

For Calculus AB sections 7.1: Integration by Substitution and 7.5: Approximating Definite Integrals (using Left, Right, and Midpoint Riemann Sums and the Trapezoidal Rule) are required. Additionally for Calculus BC sections 7.2: Integration by Parts, 7.4: Algebraic Identities (method of partial fractions with non-repeated linear factors in the denominator), 7.7: Improper Integrals, and 7.8: Comparison of Improper Integrals are required.

Section 7.1 is a good section to spend a few days with students practicing finding antiderivatives and then move on. You might want to include five antidifferentiation problems on each homework assignment for the next several weeks. Take the problems from the ones at the end of Section 7.1 that have not already been assigned as well as the problems from the review exercises at the end of Chapter 7 that are appropriate.

In Section 7.5 emphasize the geometrical nature of the approximation techniques. Students do not need to memorize a formula for any of the rules if they understand the geometry and how to find the area of a rectangle and the area of a trapezoid. It is helpful for the students to have programs in their calculators for each of the approximation techniques. These should be used to confirm answers and to generate answers when many subdivisions are used. On the AP Examination students must show their work and not calculator results when answering questions that ask for an approximation to a definite integral using one of these techniques.

For Calculus BC the additional sections mentioned above are very important. Integration by Parts appears on every AP Exam in one form or another. Students should experience problems in which several applications of Parts is needed and well as examples in which reduction formulas are generated. Trigonometric Substitution which appears in Section 7.4 is not necessary for Calculus BC but Partial Fractions which is also in the section is required. However, it is only necessary to discuss the case in which the denominators have non-repeated linear factors. The reason for this is to enable students to solve the differential equation for the Logistic Growth Model. The other place that Calculus BC students will encounter Partial Fractions is in their study of Telescoping Series. When selecting examples for Partial Fractions consider the following examples:

(a) Solve $\dfrac{dy}{dt} = y(1-y)$, $y(0) = 0.1$ (b) Solve $\dfrac{dx}{dt} = x(L-x)$, $y(0) = 0.2L$

(c) Find the sum: $\displaystyle\sum_{n=3}^{\infty} \frac{1}{n^2 - 1}$ (d) Find the sum: $\displaystyle\sum_{k=4}^{\infty} \frac{1}{k^2 - 4}$

Each of these use Partial Fractions and are the basis for problems the students should work.

(a) $\displaystyle \int \frac{dy}{y(1-y)} =$

(b) $\displaystyle \int \frac{dx}{x(L-x)} =$

(c) $\displaystyle \int \frac{dy}{x^2-1} =$

(d) $\displaystyle \int \frac{dy}{x^2-4} =$

Sections 7.7 and 7.8 have a nice tie in with series that the students will study in Chapters 9 and 10. Be sure to spend time with Example 3 on page 350. Ask your students to determine the values of p for which $\displaystyle \int_{}^{\infty} \frac{dx}{x^p}$ is convergent and the values of p for which the improper integral is divergent. Section 7.8 gets the students ready for the comparison tests.

Don't forget to look at the projects at the end of the chapter. Students can certainly benefit from spending some time working on them.

Chapter 7 Multiple Choice Questions

1. $\displaystyle\int_2^\infty \frac{dx}{x^3}$ is

(A) $\dfrac{1}{8}$ (B) $\dfrac{1}{4}$ (C) $\ln 8$ (D) 2   (E) divergent

2. $\displaystyle\int_1^2 \frac{3}{x(x+3)}\,dx =$

(A) $-\dfrac{3}{20}$ (B) $-\dfrac{9}{20}$ (C) $\ln\left(\dfrac{2}{5}\right)$ (D) $\ln\left(\dfrac{8}{5}\right)$ (E) $\ln\left(\dfrac{5}{3}\right)$

3. $I = \displaystyle\int_0^\infty e^{-2x}\,dx$

(A) $0 < I \le \dfrac{1}{2}$ (B) $\dfrac{1}{2} < I \le 1$ (C) $1 < I \le 5$

(D) $5 < I \le 10$ (E) $I > 10$

4. A particle moves along the x-axis with its velocity given by $v(t) = \dfrac{1}{1+t^2}$, $t \ge 1$. The total distance traveled by the particle is

(A) $\dfrac{\pi}{4}$ (B) $\dfrac{\pi}{2}$ (C) π (D) 2π (E) infinite

5. The unbounded region below the graph of $y = \dfrac{1}{x}$, above the x-axis, and to the right of the line $x = 1$ has an area that is

(A) $\dfrac{1}{2}$ (B) 1   (C) $\dfrac{\pi}{2}$ (D) π (E) infinite

132

6. The unbounded region below the graph of $y = \dfrac{1}{x}$, above the x-axis, and to the right of the line $x = 1$ is revolved about the x-axis to produce a solid. The volume of this solid is given by $\pi \displaystyle\int_1^\infty \dfrac{1}{x^2}\,dx$. This volume is

(A) $\dfrac{1}{2}$ (B) 1 (C) $\dfrac{\pi}{2}$ (D) π (E) infinite

7. The substitution $\sqrt{x} = \cos y$ in the integral $\displaystyle\int_{\frac{1}{2}}^1 \dfrac{\sqrt{1-x}}{\sqrt{x}}\,dx$ results in the integral

(A) $\displaystyle\int_0^{\frac{1}{2}} \sin^2 y\,dy$ (B) $2\displaystyle\int_0^{\frac{1}{2}} \dfrac{\sin^2 y}{\cos y}\,dy$ (C) $2\displaystyle\int_0^{\frac{\pi}{4}} \dfrac{\sin^2 y}{\cos y}\,dy$

(D) $2\displaystyle\int_0^{\frac{\pi}{4}} \sin^2 y\,dy$ (E) $2\displaystyle\int_0^{\frac{\pi}{6}} \sin^2 y\,dy$

8. $\displaystyle\int_0^4 \dfrac{dy}{(y-2)^2}$ is

(A) -1 (B) 1 (C) 0 (D) $-\dfrac{1}{12}$ (E) infinite

9. Use a midpoint Riemann sum with four subdivisions of equal length to approximate the value of $\displaystyle\int_0^8 \dfrac{dx}{1+x^2}$.

(A) $2\left[\dfrac{1}{2} + \dfrac{1}{10} + \dfrac{1}{26} + \dfrac{1}{50}\right]$ (B) $\left[\dfrac{1}{2} + \dfrac{1}{10} + \dfrac{1}{26} + \dfrac{1}{50}\right]$ (C) $2\left[\dfrac{1}{5} + \dfrac{1}{17} + \dfrac{1}{37} + \dfrac{1}{65}\right]$

(D) $2\left[1 + \dfrac{1}{5} + \dfrac{1}{17} + \dfrac{1}{37}\right]$ (E) $\left[\dfrac{1}{5} + \dfrac{1}{17} + \dfrac{1}{37} + \dfrac{1}{65}\right]$

10. When you use the trapezoidal rule with four equal subintervals to approximate $\int_0^2 e^{x^2}\,dx$, this approximation is larger than the value given by your calculator's built-in integrator by approximately

(A) 4.0   (B) 4.1   (C) 4.2   (D) 4.3   (E) 4.4

11. Let f be a differentiable function for all real numbers. $\int f(x)\cos x\,dx =$

(A) $-f(x)\sin x + \int \sin(x)f'(x)\,dx$

(B) $f(x)\sin x - \int \sin(x)f'(x)\,dx$

(C) $f(x)\sin x + \int \sin(x)f'(x)\,dx$

(D) $f(x)\cos x + \int \cos(x)f'(x)\,dx$

(E) $f'(x)\sin x + \int \sin(x)f(x)\,dx$

12. $\int \dfrac{dx}{x^2 - 5x + 4} =$

(A) $\dfrac{1}{3}\ln\left|(x-1)(x-4)\right| + C$

(B) $\ln\left|\dfrac{x-1}{x-4}\right| + C$

(C) $\ln\left|(x-1)(x-4)\right| + C$

(D) $\dfrac{1}{3}\ln\left|\dfrac{x-4}{x-1}\right| + C$

(E) $\dfrac{1}{3}\ln\left|\dfrac{x-1}{x-4}\right| + C$

13. $\int x^3 \sin x\,dx =$

(A) $3x^2\cos x + C$

(B) $-x^3\cos x + 3x^2\sin x + 6x\cos x - 6\sin x + C$

(C) $-\dfrac{1}{4}x^4\cos x + C$

(D) $-x^3\cos x - 3x^2\sin x + 6x\cos x + 6\sin x + C$

(E) $x^3\cos x - 3x^2\sin x - 6x\cos x + 6\sin x + C$

14. Let S be the region in the first quadrant that is bounded by the graphs of
$y = e^{-x} \sin x$ and $x = k$ for $0 \le k \le \dfrac{\pi}{2}$. The area of S is

(A) $\dfrac{1}{2} e^{-k} (\cos k + \sin k) + \dfrac{1}{2}$ (B) $\dfrac{1}{2} e^{-k} (\cos k + \sin k) - \dfrac{1}{2}$ (C) $\dfrac{1}{2} e^{-k} (\cos k - \sin k) + \dfrac{1}{2}$

(D) $-\dfrac{1}{2} e^{-k} (\cos k + \sin k) + \dfrac{1}{2}$ (E) $-\dfrac{1}{2} e^{-k} (\cos k + \sin k) - \dfrac{1}{2}$

15. Which of the following improper integrals are convergent?

I. $\displaystyle\int_0^2 \dfrac{1}{\sqrt{x}}\, dx$ II. $\displaystyle\int_0^2 \dfrac{1}{x}\, dx$ III. $\displaystyle\int_0^2 \dfrac{1}{x^2}\, dx$

(A) I only   (B)   II only   (C)   III only
(D) I and II only   (E)   II and III only

16. $\displaystyle\int \sin^3 x \cos x \, dx =$

(A) $\sin^4 x + C$ (B) $-\dfrac{1}{4}\sin^4 x + C$ (C) $-\cos^3 x \sin x + C$

(D) $\dfrac{1}{4}\sin^4 x + C$ (E) $-\sin^4 x + 3\sin^2 x \cos^2 x + C$

17. $\displaystyle\int_0^1 x e^{-x^2}\, dx =$

(A) $\dfrac{1}{2e}(e-1)$ (B) $\dfrac{2}{e}(e-1)$ (C) $\dfrac{1}{2e}$ (D) $\dfrac{1}{e}$ (E) $\dfrac{2}{e}$

18. If the substitution $y = x^2$ is used in $\displaystyle\int_4^9 \dfrac{4x}{1+x^4}\, dx$, the resulting definite integral is

(A) $4\displaystyle\int_{16}^{81} \dfrac{1}{1+y^2}\, dy$ (B) $2\displaystyle\int_2^3 \dfrac{1}{1+y^2}\, dy$ (C) $2\displaystyle\int_{16}^{81} \dfrac{y}{1+y^2}\, dy$

(D) $2\displaystyle\int_2^3 \dfrac{y}{1+y^2}\, dy$ (E) $2\displaystyle\int_{16}^{81} \dfrac{1}{1+y^2}\, dy$

19. An antiderivative of $x\sqrt{x+1}$ is

(A) $\dfrac{1}{3}x^2(x+1)^{\frac{3}{2}}$

(B) $\dfrac{2}{3}\left(x^3+x^2\right)^{\frac{3}{2}}$

(C) $\dfrac{2}{5}(x+1)^{\frac{5}{2}}-\dfrac{2}{3}(x+1)^{\frac{3}{2}}$

(D) $\dfrac{2}{5}(x+1)^{\frac{5}{2}}+\dfrac{2}{3}(x+1)^{\frac{3}{2}}$

(E) $\dfrac{2}{5}(x+1)^{\frac{3}{2}}+\dfrac{2}{3}(x+1)^{\frac{1}{2}}$

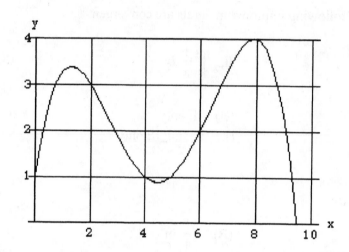

20. The graph of the function f is shown above. Use the trapezoidal rule with four equal subdivisions to approximate the area below the graph of f and above the x-axis for $0 \le x \le 8$.

(A) 15   (B) 16   (C) 17   (D) 18   (E) 19

21. An antiderivative of $\dfrac{x^2}{\sqrt[3]{1-x^3}}$ is

(A) $\ln\sqrt{1-x^3}$

(B) $\dfrac{1}{2}\left(1-x^3\right)^{\frac{2}{3}}$

(C) $-\dfrac{1}{2}\left(1-x^3\right)^{\frac{2}{3}}$

(D) $-\left(1-x^3\right)^{\frac{1}{3}}$

(E) $\dfrac{3}{2}\left(1-x^3\right)^{\frac{1}{3}}$

136

22. $\int_0^4 \dfrac{e^{\sqrt{x}}}{\sqrt{x}}\, dx$ is closest to

(A) 4   (B) 7   (C) 10   (D) 13   (E) 16

23. Use the substitution $x = 2\sin w$ and the identity $\cos^2 y = \dfrac{1}{2}\left(1 + \cos 2y\right)$ to evaluate $\int_0^1 \sqrt{4 - x^2}\, dx$. The value of this definite integral is

(A) $\dfrac{\pi}{2} + \dfrac{1}{\sqrt{3}}$
(B) $\pi - \sqrt{3}$
(C) $\dfrac{\pi\sqrt{3}}{2}$
(D) $\dfrac{\pi}{3} + \dfrac{\sqrt{3}}{2}$
(E) $2 - \sqrt{3}$

24. $\int_0^1 \dfrac{1}{1 + e^{-x}}\, dx =$

(A) $\dfrac{1}{1 + e}$
(B) $\ln 2$
(C) $\dfrac{1}{2}$
(D) $\ln\left(\dfrac{1 + e}{2}\right)$
(E) $\ln(1 + e)$

25. $\int \tan^2 x\, dx =$

(A) $\dfrac{1}{3}\tan^3 x + C$
(B) $2\ln|\cos x| + C$
(C) $\tan x + C$

(D) $\tan x - 1 + C$
(E) $\tan x - x + C$

Chapter 7 Multiple Choice Questions

Question	Answer	AB	BC	No Calculator	Calculator Required	Neutral Calculator
1	A		x	x		
2	D		x	x		
3	A		x	x		
4	A		x	x		
5	E		x	x		
6	D		x	x		
7	D	x	x	x		
8	E		x	x		
9	A	x	x			x
10	C	x	x		x	
11	B		x			x
12	D		x	x		
13	B		x	x		
14	D		x	x		
15	A		x	x		
16	D	x	x	x		
17	A	x	x	x		
18	E	x	x	x		
19	C	x	x	x		
20	C	x	x			x
21	C	x	x	x		
22	D	x	x	x		
23	D	x	x	x		
24	D	x	x	x		
25	E	x	x	x		

Chapter 7 Free Response Questions

1. Let S be the region in the first quadrant above the line $y = 1$ and below the graph of $y = 1 + e^{-x}$.

   (a) Show that the area of region S is finite and determine its value. Justify your answer.

   (b) Find the value of k, so that the line $x = k$ divides the region S into two pieces of equal area.

   (c) The volume of the region produced when region S is revolved about the line $y = 2$ is given by $\pi \int_0^\infty \left(1 - \left(1 - e^{-x} \right)^2 \right) dx$. Determine if this volume is finite or infinite. Justify your answer.

2. Let f be the function defined by $f(x) = e^{\sqrt{x}}$ for $0 \le x \le 4$.

   (a) What is the average rate of change of f on this interval?

   (b) Determine the area in the first quadrant below the secant line from $\left(0, f(0) \right)$ to $\left(4, f(4) \right)$.

   (c) Determine the area in the first quadrant below the graph of $y = f(x)$ for $0 \le x \le 4$.

   (d) What relationship exists between the two areas that you determined? A similar relationship does not exist for the function $g(x) = e^x$. Use $g''(x)$ to explain why.

3. Let f be a function that has continuous first and second derivatives. Some values of f and f' are shown in the table below.

x	0	1	2	3	4	5	6	7	8	9
$f(x)$	4	10	8	6	13	14	20	21	18	16
$f'(x)$	6	−1	−2	−3	2	1	3	1	−1	−1

   (a) $\displaystyle \int_1^3 x f'\left(x^2 \right) dx =$

(b) $\int_0^2 2f''(3x)dx =$

(c) Use the trapezoidal rule with three equal subdivisions to approximate $\int_3^9 f(x)dx$.

4. Let f be the function defined by $f(x)=\sqrt{64x-x^3}$ for $0\le x\le 8$ where both x and $f(x)$ are measured in feet. Let S be the region in the first quadrant bounded by the graph of $y=f(x)$.

(a) Use a midpoint Riemann sum with two subdivisions of equal length to approximate the area of region S. Include units of measure.

(b) Let g be the function defined by $g(x)=\int_0^x f(w)dw$ for $0\le x\le 8$. When $x=4$, x is increasing at the rate of $\frac{1}{4}$ ft/min. At what rate is g changing when $x=4$? Include units of measure.

(c) In terms of region S, explain the meaning of your answer to part (b).

5. Let h be the function defined by $h(x)=\dfrac{1}{x^2+2x+2}$.

(a) Evaluate $\int_1^5 (x+1)\cdot h(x)dx$.

(b) Use the trapezoidal rule with four equal subdivisions to approximate $\int_1^5 (x+1)\cdot h(x)dx$.

(c) What is the percent error of your approximation in part (b)?

(d) Write x^2+2x+2 in the form $(x+a)^2+b$ and use this new form to evaluate $\int_1^5 h(x)dx$.

Chapter 7 Free Response Questions

Question	AB	BC	No Calculator	Calculator Required	Neutral Calculator
1		x	x		
2		x	x		
3	x	x	x		
4	x	x			x
5	x	x		x	

Chapter 7 Solutions to Free Response Questions

1.

(a) $Area = \int_0^\infty \left(\left(1 + e^{-x} \right) - 1 \right) dx = \lim_{L \to \infty} \int_0^L e^{-x} \, dx = \lim_{L \to \infty} \left(-e^{-x} \right) \Big|_0^L = \lim_{L \to \infty} \left(1 - e^{-L} \right) = 1$

$Area = 1$

(b) $\frac{1}{2} = \int_0^k e^{-x} \, dx = \left(-e^{-x} \right) \Big|_0^k = 1 - e^{-k} \Rightarrow e^{-k} = \frac{1}{2}$

$k = \ln 2$

(c) $\pi \int_0^\infty \left(1 - \left(1 - e^{-x} \right)^2 \right) dx = \lim_{L \to \infty} \pi \int_0^\infty \left(2e^{-x} - e^{-2x} \right) dx = \pi \lim_{L \to \infty} \left(-2e^{-x} + \frac{1}{2} e^{-2x} \right) \Big|_0^L =$

$\pi \lim_{L \to \infty} \left(\left(-2e^{-L} + \frac{1}{2} e^{-2L} \right) - \left(-2 + \frac{1}{2} \right) \right) = \frac{3\pi}{2}$.

The volume is finite.

2.

(a) Average Rate $= \dfrac{f(4) - f(0)}{4 - 0} = \dfrac{e^2 - 1}{4}$

(b) The area of the trapezoid formed $= \dfrac{1}{2}(4) \left[f(0) + f(4) \right] = 2 \left(1 + e^2 \right) = 2e^2 + 2$.

(c) Let $y = \sqrt{x} \Rightarrow y^2 = x$ and $2y \, dy = dx$. Substitute into $\int_0^4 e^{\sqrt{x}} \, dx$ and the result is $\int_0^2 2y e^y \, dy$.

Use Parts: $u = 2y$ and $dv = e^y \, dy$
$\quad\quad\quad\quad du = 2 \, dy$ and $v = e^y$

$\int_0^2 2y e^y \, dy = \left(2y e^y - 2e^y \right) \Big|_0^2 = \left(4e^2 - 2e^2 \right) - (-2) = 2e^2 + 2$

(d) They are equal. Since $g''(x) = e^x > 0$ for all x, the graph of g is always concave upward. This means that the area below the secant line from $\left(a, g(a) \right)$ to $\left(b, g(b) \right)$ will be larger than the area below the graph of $y = g(x)$ on $[a,b]$.

3.

(a) $\int_1^3 xf'(x^2)\,dx = \frac{1}{2}f(x^2)\Big|_1^3 = \frac{1}{2}\big(f(9)-f(1)\big) = \frac{1}{2}(16-10) = 3$

(b) $\int_0^2 2f''(3x)\,dx = \frac{2}{3}f'(3x)\Big|_0^2 = \frac{2}{3}\big(f'(6)-f'0\big) = \frac{2}{3}(3-6) = -2$

(c) $\int_3^9 f(x)\,dx \approx \frac{1}{2}(2)\big(f(3)+2f(5)+2f(7)+f(9)\big) = (6+2\cdot14+2\cdot21+16) = 92$

4.

(a) $\int_0^8 f(x)\,dx \approx 4\big(f(2)+f(6)\big) = 4\big(\sqrt{120}+\sqrt{168}\big) = 95.664 \text{ ft}^2$

(b) $g(x) = \int_0^x f(w)\,dw = \int_0^x \sqrt{64w-w^3}\,dw$

$\dfrac{dg}{dt} = f(x)\cdot\dfrac{dx}{dt} = \sqrt{64x-x^3}\cdot\dfrac{dx}{dt}\,;\qquad \dfrac{dg}{dt}\Big|_{x=4} = \sqrt{256-64}\cdot\dfrac{1}{4} = \sqrt{12}\,\dfrac{\text{ft}^2}{\text{min}}\,.$

(c) The area of region S is increasing at the rate of $\sqrt{12}\,\dfrac{\text{ft}^2}{\text{min}}$ when $x=4$ feet.

5.

(a) $\int_1^5 (x+1)\cdot h(x)\,dx = \int_1^5 \dfrac{x+1}{x^2+2x+2}\,dx = \dfrac{1}{2}\ln\big|x^2+2x+2\big|\,\Big|_1^5 = \dfrac{1}{2}(\ln 37 - \ln 5) = \dfrac{1}{2}\ln\left(\dfrac{37}{5}\right) = 1.00074$

(b) $\int_1^5 (x+1)\cdot h(x)\,dx = \int_1^5 \dfrac{x+1}{x^2+2x+2}\,dx \approx \dfrac{1}{2}(1)\left(\dfrac{2}{5}+2\left(\dfrac{3}{10}\right)+2\left(\dfrac{4}{17}\right)+2\left(\dfrac{5}{26}\right)+\dfrac{6}{37}\right) = 1.009$

(c) $\dfrac{\left|\dfrac{1}{2}\ln\left(\dfrac{37}{5}\right)-1.008682891\right|}{\dfrac{1}{2}\ln\left(\dfrac{37}{5}\right)} = 0.0079\,.$ The percent error is 0.79%.

(d) $\int_1^5 h(x)\,dx = \int_1^5 \dfrac{1}{x^2+2x+2}\,dx = \int_1^5 \dfrac{1}{(x^2+2x+1)+1}\,dx = \int_1^5 \dfrac{1}{(x+1)^2+1}\,dx = \tan^{-1}(x+1)\Big|_1^5$

$= \tan^{-1}(6)-\tan^{-1}(2)$

AP Teacher Tips
Chapter 8: Using the Definite Integral

AP teachers should be judicious in their coverage of Chapter 8. In particular, although area and volume questions still appear regularly on AP exams and are a must-emphasize item, some of the applications of the definite integral later in the chapter could safely be de-emphasized or skipped altogether if there are time constraints.

Example 1 on page 368 is an unusual calculation of the area of an isosceles triangle using slicing. It is well placed, and provides a gentle introduction to finding volumes using the same slicing method. This method also serves to reinforce the definition of definite integral covered in Chapter 5. Traditional "area under a curve" problems appear like clockwork on AP exams, often in the free response section of the exam in tandem with a volume question. Area problems were covered in Chapter 5.

The geometric applications in Section 8.2 involving volumes of solids of revolution are important to both AB and BC students. Note that solids of revolution are an example of solids of known cross sectional area, and students should be taught to think of them that way. Every single Calculus AB and nearly every BC exam since 1969 has had a free response question involving area and volume! Also note that the only volume problems that will appear on AP exams involve known cross sections, and that these include problems where the cross sections are either disks or washers (when a region is revolved around a horizontal or vertical line), and problems where the cross sections are other familiar shapes from geometry, such as triangles and rectangles. Older AP exams may include problems that were solved more easily using the method of cylindrical shells, but that topic is no longer required for AP exams.

A nice project for students is having them construct a physical model of a solid of revolution or a solid with a known cross section. These models could then be displayed in the classroom as visualization aids.

Arc length is also covered in section 8.2 but is a required topic only for BC students.

Problems 9, 10, 22-25, 30, and 32 on page 380 give good coverage for AB students. BC students should additionally solve exercises 11 and 14 for arc length.

Section 8.3 can be skipped by Calculus AB students, but the calculus of polar curves is a required topic for Calculus BC. In particular, students should be able to calculate the area of a region enclosed by a polar curve, as well as its arc length and slope at a point. In addition, students should be familiar with the most common polar curves. These are covered sufficiently by the examples in the text. Problems 20, 24, 26, 30, 31, 32, and 34 provide students with a variety of practice problems. Problem 38 involves a "short cut" formula for the arc length of a polar curve. Though it is not necessary for students to memorize that formula (since they can use the parametric formula on page 388), it's a nice exercise to derive it.

From section 8.4 on, teachers have the option of picking and choosing the application they wish to cover. However, none of them appears explicitly in the topic outline of the courses. Some of the applications, however, are accessible as AP questions with little or no explanation on the exam, and as such, probably should be coved in the course. In particular, applications that involve calculating the total mass of a quantity from its density follow directly from the idea of integrating a rate of change to calculate net change. Here, density can be likened to rate. It is not essential to cover center of mass problems.

Problems 5, 10, 11, and 14 on pages 397-398 would give nice coverage for AP exam preparation.

Work problems are a traditional application of the integral. Though not specifically an AP topic, work affords an interesting physical context to discuss applications of the integral. On page 406, problems 3, 6, and 12 cover the material sufficiently. Sections 8.6 through 8.8, involving application to economics, statistics, and probability could be safely skipped, or touched on lightly if time becomes short.

In summary, both AB and BC students should be able to use the integral to calculate areas and volumes, find distance traveled from velocity, calculate the average value of a quantity, and solve problems by integrating a rate function to find net change. BC students should further be able to find the length of a curve, including curves defined parametrically and polar curves. Both AB and BC students should cover problems involving density.

The review exercises and problems at the end of Chapter 8 are a rich source. A representative sample includes numbers 7, 10, 31, 45 (work), 48 (work), 52 (volume of Mt. Shasta), 57, and 58. In addition, problem 8 on page 433 is a nice population density problem.

Chapter 8 Multiple Choice Questions

1. Which of the following integrals gives the area of the region bounded by the graphs of $y = 2^{\sqrt{x}} - 1$, $y = 7$, and the y-axis?

   (A) $\int_0^9 7 - \left(2^{\sqrt{x}} - 1\right) dx$

   (B) $\int_0^{16} 7 - \left(2^{\sqrt{x}} - 1\right) dx$

   (C) $\int_0^3 7 - \left(2^{\sqrt{x}} - 1\right) dx$

   (D) $\int_0^9 \left(2^{\sqrt{x}} - 1\right) - 7 \, dx$

   (E) $\int_0^7 2^{\sqrt{x}} - 1 \, dx$

2. What is the volume of the solid generated by revolving the region bounded by the axes, the line $x = 1$, and the graph of $y = e^{2x}$ about the x-axis?

   (A) $\dfrac{e^2}{2}$

   (B) $\dfrac{\pi}{2}\left(e^2 - 1\right)$

   (C) $\dfrac{e^4}{4}$

   (D) $\dfrac{\pi}{4}\left(e^4 - 1\right)$

   (E) $\pi\left(\dfrac{3e^4 - 1}{8}\right)$

3. The base of a solid is the region in the first quadrant bounded by the axes and the graph of $y = 3 - x$. Cross sections of the solid perpendicular to the x-axis are isosceles right triangles with the hypotenuse in the xy-plane. Which integral gives the volume of the solid?

   (A) $\int_0^3 \dfrac{(3-x)^2}{2} \, dx$

   (B) $\int_0^3 \dfrac{(3-x)^2}{4} \, dx$

   (C) $\pi\int_0^3 (3-x)^2 \, dx$

   (D) $\int_0^3 \dfrac{3-x}{4} \, dx$

   (E) $\int_0^3 \dfrac{(3-x)^2}{2\sqrt{2}} \, dx$

4. The derivative of a continuous function is given by $f'(x) = \ln x$. Which integral gives the length of the curve $y = f(x)$ from $x = 1$ to $x = 2$?

   (A) $\int_1^2 \ln(x) \, dx$

   (B) $\int_1^2 \sqrt{1 + \ln(x)} \, dx$

   (C) $\int_1^2 \sqrt{1 + (\ln(x))^2} \, dx$

   (D) $\int_1^2 \sqrt{1 + \dfrac{1}{x^2}} \, dx$

   (E) $\int_1^2 \sqrt{1 + (x\ln(x) - x)^2} \, dx$

5. Which integral gives the length of the parametric curve defined by $x(t) = ae^{2t}$, $y(t) = b\sin(3t)$ from $t = 0$ to $t = 1$?

(A) $\int_0^1 \sqrt{\left(2ae^{2t}\right)^2 + \left(3b\cos(3t)\right)^2}\, dt$

(B) $\int_0^1 \sqrt{2a\left(e^{2t}\right)^2 + 3b\left(\cos(3t)\right)^2}\, dt$

(C) $\int_0^1 \left(\left(2ae^{2t}\right)^2 + \left(3b\cos(3t)\right)^2\right) dt$

(D) $\int_0^1 \sqrt{2ae^{2t} + 3b\cos(3t)}\, dt$

(E) $\int_0^1 \sqrt{\left(ae^{2t}\right)^2 + \left(b\cos(3t)\right)^2}\, dt$

6. If the area under the graph of $y = e^{kx}$ from $x = 0$ to $x = 1$ is 2, then $k =$

(A) 0.853　　(B) 1.060　　(C) 1.099　　(D) 1.256　　(E) 1.718

7. Water leaks out of a tank through a circular hole with radius 3 cm. At time t (in seconds), the velocity of water flowing through the hole is $v = f(t)$ cm/sec. Which integral represents the total volume of water lost in the first minute?

(A) $9\pi \int_0^{60} \left(f(t)\right)^2 dt$

(B) $9\pi \int_0^1 f(t)\, dt$

(C) $6\pi \int_0^{60} f(t)\, dt$

(D) $\int_0^{60} f(t)\, dt$

(E) $9\pi \int_0^{60} f(t)\, dt$

8. If $-\sqrt{8} \le f'(x) \le \sqrt{8}$ for all x in the closed interval $[1, 3]$, then which inequality describes all possible lengths, s, of the graph of $y = f(x)$ from $x = 1$ to $x = 3$?

(A) $0 \le s \le 2\sqrt{8}$

(B) $0 \le s \le 3\sqrt{8}$

(C) $2 \le s \le 6$

(D) $3 \le s \le 18$

(E) $2 \le s \le 2\sqrt{8}$

9. What is the volume of the solid generated by revolving the region bounded by the x-axis, the line $x = 4$, and the graph of $y = \sqrt{x}$ about the x-axis?

(A) $\dfrac{16}{3}$　　(B) 8　　(C) $\dfrac{16\pi}{3}$　　(D) 8π　　(E) $\dfrac{128\pi}{5}$

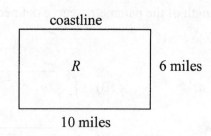

coastline

R 6 miles

10 miles

10. The population density along a 10-mile long stretch of a straight seacoast is given by the formula $500 + 1000e^{\frac{-x^2}{6}}$ people per square mile, where x is the distance in miles from the coast. Approximately how many people live within the 6 miles by 10 miles rectangular region R with one side on the 10-mile long coast, as shown in the figure above?

(A) 5170   (B) 7171   (C) 9993   (D) 43025   (E) 51696

Distance from end (ft)	0	3	6	9	12	15
Radius of cross section (ft)	1.4	1.4	1.2	1.0	0.9	0.8

11. Circular cross sections of a 15-foot log have the radii given in the table above at the specified distances from one end of the log. If a right-hand Riemann sum is used to approximate the volume of the log, the approximation is

(A) 18.378 ft^3 (B) 22.525 ft^3 (C) 55.135 ft^3 (D) 67.576 ft^3 (E) 73.608 ft^3

12. The altitude of a square pyramid, measured from the base up, is 21m. Each side of the square base is 4 m. If square cross sections parallel to the base are used to calculate the volume of the pyramid with an integral, the integral is

(A) $\int_0^{21} \left[\left(\frac{4}{21} \right)(21 - h) \right]^2 dh$

(B) $\int_0^{21} \left[\left(\frac{21}{4} \right)(21 - h) \right]^2 dh$

(C) $\int_0^{21} \left[\left(\frac{21}{4} \right)(4 - h) \right]^2 dh$

(D) $\int_0^4 \left[\left(\frac{4}{21} \right)(21 - h) \right]^2 dh$

(E) $\int_0^4 \left[\left(\frac{21}{4} \right)(4 - h) \right]^2 dh$

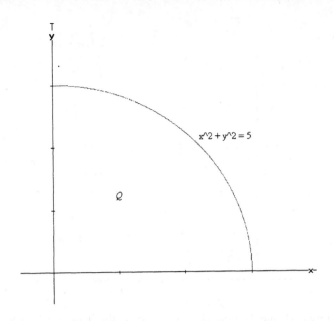

x^2 + y^2 = 5

13. The figure above shows the quarter circle Q in the first quadrant bounded by the axes and the graph of $x^2 + y^2 = 5$. Which of the following is a Riemann Sum that approximates the area of Q using horizontal strips of uniform width Δy ?

(A) $\displaystyle\sum_{k=1}^{n}\left(5 - y_k^2\right)\Delta y$

(B) $\displaystyle\sum_{k=1}^{n}\sqrt{\left(5 - y_k^2\right)}\,\Delta y$

(C) $\displaystyle\sum_{k=1}^{n}\left(5 - \Delta y^2\right) y_k$

(D) $\displaystyle\sum_{k=1}^{n}\frac{\pi}{4}\left(5 - y_k^2\right)\Delta y$

(E) $\displaystyle\sum_{k=1}^{n}\frac{1}{4}\sqrt{\left(5 - y_k^2\right)}\,\Delta y$

14. The base of a solid is the region in the first quadrant bounded by the x-axis, the lines $x = 1$ and $x = 3$, and the graph of $y = \dfrac{2}{x^3}$. Cross sections of the solid perpendicular to the x-axis are squares. Which integral gives the volume of the solid?

(A) $\displaystyle\int_{1}^{3}\frac{8}{x^9}\,dx$

(B) $\displaystyle\int_{1}^{3}\frac{2}{x^6}\,dx$

(C) $\displaystyle\pi\int_{1}^{3}\frac{4}{x^6}\,dx$

(D) $\displaystyle\int_{1}^{3}\frac{2}{x^3}\,dx$

(E) $\displaystyle\int_{1}^{3}\frac{4}{x^6}\,dx$

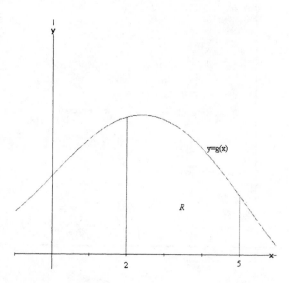

15. The region R shown above, bounded by the x-axis, the lines $x = 2$ and $x = 5$, and the graph of $y = g(x)$, is the base of a solid with square cross sections perpendicular to the x-axis. The volume of this solid is 64. What is the volume of the solid generated by revolving R about the x-axis?

(A) 64π (B) $\dfrac{64}{\pi}$ (C) 192   (D) $192\,\pi$ (E) $16\,\pi$

16. The density of an air pollutant at height h meters above the surface of a city is given by $p(h)$ grams/m^3. Which expression gives the total mass in grams of the air pollutant inside a cylindrical column of air with radius 50 m and height 200 m and with base on the surface of the earth?

(A) $\displaystyle\int_0^{200} p(h)\,dh$ (B) $\displaystyle\int_0^{200} 2500\,p(h)\,dh$ (C) $\displaystyle\int_0^{200} 2500\pi\,p(h)\,dh$

(D) $\displaystyle\int_0^{50} 40000\,p(h)\,dh$ (E) $\displaystyle\int_0^{50} 40000\pi\,p(h)\,dh$

17. The speed of a particle moving in the plane is given by $s(t) = \sqrt{t^2 + \cos^2(2t)}$ for any time t. Approximately how far did the particle travel from $t = 0$ to $t = \pi$?

(A) 4.391   (B) 5.587   (C) 6.540   (D) 7.216   (E) 11.906

Depth (m)	0	10	20	30	40	50
Density of gas (g/m^3)	6	12	14	18	22	24

18. A vertical mine shaft with square cross sections measuring 2 m on each side is filled with a poisonous gas. The density of the gas at various depths in the shaft appears in the table above. Using five subintervals of equal depth, what is the trapezoidal estimate of the total amount of gas in the shaft between a depth of 0 meters and 50 meters?

(A) 81 g   (B) 810 g   (C) 1620 g   (D) 2880 g   (E) 3240 g

19. The cross sectional area of a solid at a distance x cm from one end of the solid is given by $A(x) = 2x + e^{3x}$. If the solid extends from $x = 0$ to $x = 3$, what is its volume?

(A) $\dfrac{26+e^9}{3}$ (B) $5 + e^9$ (C) $3e^9 - 1$ (D) $8 + e^9$ (E) $9 + \dfrac{e^9}{3}$

20. The equation $L = \int_1^2 \sqrt{4t^2 + 9}\, dt$ represents the length L of a parametrically defined curve from $t = 1$ to $t = 2$. Which pair of equations could define the curve with length L?

(A) $x(t) = 8t$

$y(t) = 0$

(B) $x(t) = \dfrac{4}{3}t^3$

$y(t) = 9t$

(C) $x(t) = t^2$

$y(t) = 3t$

(D) $x(t) = 2t$

$y(t) = 3$

(E) $x(t) = \dfrac{2}{\sqrt{3}}t^{\frac{3}{2}}$

$y(t) = 3\sqrt{t}$

21. At $t = 0$, a particle is at the point $(0, 3)$. The particle moves along the y-axis so that its velocity at any time $t \geq 0$ is given by $v(t) = 2t + \sin(t)$. Where is the particle at time $t = \pi$?

(A) $(0, \pi^2 - 1)$ (B) $(0, \pi^2 + 1)$ (C) $(0, \pi^2 + 3)$ (D) $(0, 1)$ (E) $(0, \pi^2 + 5)$

22. For any time $t \geq 0$, the acceleration of a particle moving along a line is given by $a(t) = 4 + 8t^3$. At $t = 0$, the velocity of the particle is 3. What is the velocity of the particle at $t = 2$?

(A) 35   (B) 40   (C) 43   (D) 96   (E) 99

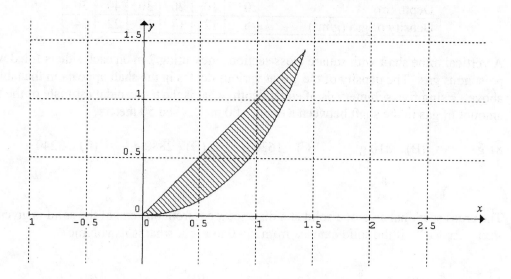

23. What is the area of the shaded region in the first quadrant enclosed by the polar graphs of $r(\theta) = 2\tan\theta$ and $\theta = \dfrac{\pi}{4}$, as shown in the figure above?

(A) $4 - \pi$ 　　 (B) $2 - \dfrac{\pi}{2}$ 　　 (C) $1 - \dfrac{\pi}{4}$ 　　 (D) $\dfrac{1}{2}$ 　　 (E) $\dfrac{1}{4}$

24. Which of the following expressions gives the length of the polar curve defined by $r = \theta^2$ from $\theta = 0$ to $\theta = \dfrac{\pi}{2}$?

(A) $\displaystyle\int_0^{\pi/2} \sqrt{\left(2\theta\cos\theta - \theta^2\sin\theta\right)^2 + \left(2\theta\sin\theta + \theta^2\cos\theta\right)^2}\, d\theta$

(B) $\displaystyle\int_0^{\pi/2} \left(2\theta\cos\theta - \theta^2\sin\theta\right)^2 + \left(2\theta\sin\theta + \theta^2\cos\theta\right)^2\, d\theta$

(C) $\displaystyle\int_0^{\pi/2} \sqrt{\left(-2\theta\sin\theta\right)^2 + \left(2\theta\cos\theta\right)^2}\, d\theta$

(D) $\displaystyle\int_0^{\pi/2} \sqrt{\left(2\theta\cos\theta - \theta^2\sin\theta\right) + \left(2\theta\sin\theta + \theta^2\cos\theta\right)}\, d\theta$

(E) $\dfrac{\pi^2}{4}$

Chapter 8 Multiple Choice Questions

Question	Answer	AB	BC	No Calculator	Calculator Required	Neutral Calculator
1	A	x	x	x		
2	D	x	x	x		
3	B	x	x			x
4	C		x			x
5	A		x	x		
6	D	x	x		x	
7	E	x	x			x
8	C		x			x
9	D	x	x	x		
10	E	x	x		x	
11	C	x	x		x	
12	A	x	x			x
13	B	x	x			x
14	E	x	x			x
15	A	x	x			x
16	C	x	x			x
17	B	x	x		x	
18	E	x	x		x	
19	A	x	x	x		
20	C	x	x	x		
21	E	x	x	x		
22	C	x	x	x		
23	B		x	x		
24	A		x			x

Chapter 8 Free Response Questions

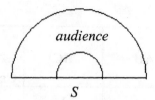

S

1.   The audience at an outdoor show fills a semicircular strip composed of two concentric circles with the stage S at the center, as shown in the figure above. A semicircular barricade with the stage at the center keeps the audience at least 3 meters from the stage. The density of people at a distance of x meters from the stage is $3 - \dfrac{x}{8}$ people per square meter, for $3 \leq x \leq 24$.

(a)   How fast is the density of people changing at a distance of 12 meters from the stage? Using appropriate units, interpret your answer.

(b)   How many people are in the audience between 3 and 24 meters of the stage?

(c)   Write an equation that could be solved to determine the radius within which half the audience is contained. Do not solve.

(d)   If the density of people in the audience was uniform, and the number of people in the audience was the same as your answer to part (b), what would the density be?

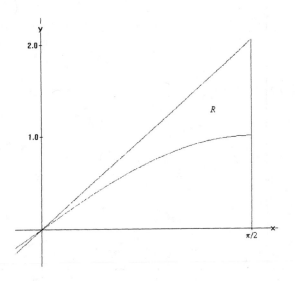

2. The region R in the figure above is bounded by the graphs of $y = kx$ (where $k \geq 1$), $y = \sin(x)$, and the line $x = \pi/2$.

(a) If $k = 2$, find the area of R.

(b) Find the value of k so that the area of R is 2.

(c) If $k = 2$, write an integral expression for the volume of the solid generated by revolving R about the x-axis. Do not evaluate.

(d) Write an equation that could be used to find the value of k so that the perimeter of region R is 2. Do not solve the equation.

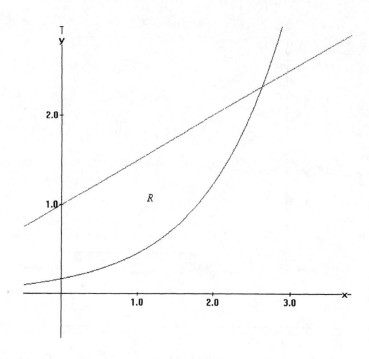

3.   The region R shown above is bounded by the graphs of $y = \dfrac{x}{2} + 1$, $y = \dfrac{e^x}{6}$ and the y-axis.

(a)   Find the area of R.

(b)   The area of R is divided in half by the vertical line $x = k$. Find the value of k, for $0 < k < 3$.

(c)   Find the volume of the solid whose base is the region R and whose cross sections cut by planes perpendicular to the x-axis are squares.

(d)   The volume of the solid described in part (c) is divided in half by a plane perpendicular to the x-axis containing the line $x = j$. Write an equation that could be used to find the value of j. Do not solve.

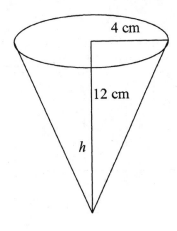

4. A conical cup with radius 4 cm and depth 12 cm is used to serve a snow cone. Snow falls into the cup at the constant rate of 16 cm³/sec until the snow fills the conical cup exactly to the top. Flavored syrup is then poured on the snow, and the density of syrup at a height of h cm from the bottom of the cone is given by $d(h) = \dfrac{10}{12+h}$ grams/cm³.

The volume of a cone with radius r and height h is $V = \dfrac{1}{3}\pi r^2 h$.

(a) How long does it take to fill the cone with snow? Round your answer to the nearest second.

(b) How fast is the depth of the snow changing when the depth is 6 cm?

(c) Write an integral expression in terms of a single variable for the total number of grams of flavored syrup in the cone. Do not evaluate.

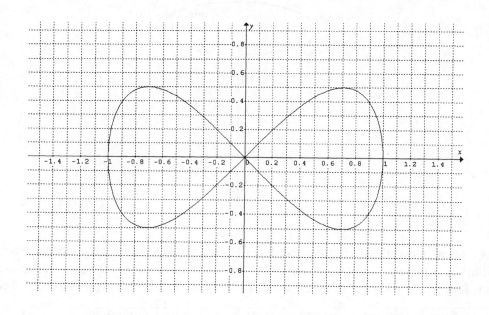

5. The graph of the curve defined by the Cartesian equation $x^4 - x^2 + y^2 = 0$ is shown in the figure above.

(a) Show that, if $y \neq 0$, then $\dfrac{dy}{dx} = \dfrac{x - 2x^3}{y}$.

(b) Find the x-coordinates of the point in the first quadrant where the tangent line to the graph is horizontal. Justify that the value of y at this point is a local maximum.

(c) The same curve is defined by the polar equation $r^2(\theta) = \sec^2 \theta - \tan^2 \theta \sec^2 \theta$, the left loop for $\dfrac{3\pi}{4} \leq \theta \leq \dfrac{5\pi}{4}$ and the right loop for $-\dfrac{\pi}{4} \leq \theta \leq \dfrac{\pi}{4}$. Use this polar form to find the area of the region in the first quadrant bounded by the graph and the x-axis.

(d) Use the Cartesian equation to find the area of the region described in part (c).

Chapter 8 Free Response Questions

Question	AB	BC	No Calculator	Calculator Required	Neutral Calculator
1	x	x		x	
2		x	x		
3	x	x		x	
4	x	x	x		
5		x	x		

Chapter 8 Solutions to Free Response Questions

1.

(a) $\sigma(x) = 3 - \dfrac{x}{8}$, so $\sigma'(x) = -\dfrac{1}{8}$ and $\sigma'(12) = -\dfrac{1}{8} \dfrac{\text{person per square meter}}{\text{meter}}$.

This means that at $x = 12$ meters (and indeed for all x), the density of people is decreasing at the rate of 1/8 person per square meter every meter you move away from the stage.

(b) $\sum \left(3 - \dfrac{x}{8}\right) \dfrac{\text{people}}{\text{meter}^2} \cdot \left(\dfrac{2\pi x}{2} \Delta x\right) \text{meter}^2$; $\displaystyle\int_3^{24}\left(3 - \dfrac{x}{8}\right)(\pi x)\, dx \approx 866$ people.

(c) $\displaystyle\int_3^r \left(3 - \dfrac{x}{8}\right)(\pi x)\, dx = 433$

(d) $\dfrac{866}{\dfrac{\pi\left(24^2 - 3^2\right)}{2}} \approx 0.972 \dfrac{\text{people}}{\text{meter}^2}$ or $\displaystyle\int_3^{24} c(\pi x)\, dx = 866$, $c = 0.972$.

2.

(a) $A = \displaystyle\int_0^{\frac{\pi}{2}} (2x - \sin x)\, dx$

$= x^2 + \cos x \Big|_0^{\frac{\pi}{2}}$

$= \dfrac{\pi^2}{4} - 1$

(b) $\displaystyle\int_0^{\frac{\pi}{2}} (kx - \sin x)\, dx = 2$

$k\dfrac{x^2}{2} + \cos x \Big|_0^{\frac{\pi}{2}} = 2$

$k\dfrac{\pi^2}{8} - 1 = 2$

$k = \dfrac{24}{\pi^2}$

As long as k > 1, the integral represents the area of the region. We can confirm that $k = \dfrac{24}{\pi^2} > 1$.

(c) $V = \pi \int_0^{\frac{\pi}{2}} (2x)^2 - (\sin x)^2 \, dx$

(d) $\int_0^{\frac{\pi}{2}} \sqrt{1 + \cos^2 x} \, dx + \int_0^{\frac{\pi}{2}} \sqrt{1 + k^2} \, dx + \left(k\dfrac{\pi}{2} - 1 \right) = 2$

3. The curves intersect where $\dfrac{a}{2} + 1 = \dfrac{e^a}{6}$; $a \approx 2.63149$

(a) $A = \int_0^a \left(\dfrac{x}{2} + 1 \right) - \left(\dfrac{e^x}{6} \right) dx \approx 2.214$

(b) $\int_0^k \left(\dfrac{x}{2} + 1 \right) - \left(\dfrac{e^x}{6} \right) dx = \dfrac{2.214}{2}$; $k = 1.137$

(c) $V = \int_0^a \left(\dfrac{x}{2} + 1 - \dfrac{e^x}{6} \right)^2 dx \approx 2.0369$

(d) $\int_0^j \left(\dfrac{x}{2} + 1 - \dfrac{e^x}{6} \right)^2 dx = \dfrac{2.0369}{2}$

4.

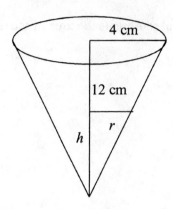

(a) $V = \dfrac{1}{3}\pi 4^2 \cdot 12 = 64\pi \ \text{cm}^3$; $t = \dfrac{64\pi \ \text{cm}^3}{\dfrac{16 \ \text{cm}^3}{\text{sec}}} = 4\pi \ \text{sec} \ \approx 13 \ \text{sec}$

(b) From similar triangles, $\dfrac{r}{h} = \dfrac{4}{12}$ or $r = \dfrac{1}{3}h$ and $\dfrac{dr}{dt} = \dfrac{1}{3}\dfrac{dh}{dt}$.

$$V = \dfrac{1}{3}\pi \dfrac{h^2}{9}h = \dfrac{1}{27}\pi h^3$$

$$\dfrac{dV}{dt} = \dfrac{1}{9}\pi h^2 \dfrac{dh}{dt}$$

$$16 = \dfrac{1}{9}\pi 6^2 \dfrac{dh}{dt}$$

$$\dfrac{4}{\pi} \ \text{cm/sec} = \dfrac{dh}{dt}$$

(c) $\displaystyle\int_0^{12}\left(\dfrac{10}{12+h}\right)\cdot\left(\pi r^2\right)dh = \int_0^{12}\left(\dfrac{10}{12+h}\right)\cdot\left(\pi\left(\dfrac{h}{3}\right)^2\right)dh$

162

5.

(a) Differentiate implicitly and solve for $\dfrac{dy}{dx}$:

$$4x^3 - 2x + 2y\frac{dy}{dx} = 0$$

$$2y\frac{dy}{dx} = 2x - 4x^3$$

$$\frac{dy}{dx} = \frac{2x - 4x^3}{2y}$$

$$\frac{dy}{dx} = \frac{x - 2x^3}{y}.$$

(b) The tangent line is horizontal where $\dfrac{dy}{dx} = 0$. So $x - 2x^3 = 0$, and $x(1 - 2x^2) = 0$. The only solution to this that is in the first quadrant is $x = \sqrt{\dfrac{1}{2}}$. In the first quadrant, we have $x > 0$ and $y > 0$, while $\dfrac{dy}{dx} = \dfrac{x(1 - 2x^2)}{y}$ is positive for $0 < x < \sqrt{\dfrac{1}{2}}$ and negative for $\sqrt{\dfrac{1}{2}} < x < 1$. Therefore, y is a maximum at $x = \sqrt{\dfrac{1}{2}}$.

(c) The portion of the curve in the first quadrant extends from $\theta = 0$ (where $r = 1$) to $\theta = \dfrac{\pi}{4}$ (where $r = 0$). Thus,

$$A = \frac{1}{2}\int_0^{\pi/4} \sec^2\theta - \tan^2\theta \sec^2\theta \, d\theta$$

$$= \frac{1}{2}\left(\tan\theta - \frac{1}{3}\tan^3\theta\Big|_0^{\pi/4}\right)$$

$$= \frac{1}{3}.$$

(d) Isolating y in the Cartesian equation gives $y = \sqrt{x^2 - x^4} = x\sqrt{1 - x^2}$ for $x > 0$ and $y > 0$, in the first quadrant. Thus,

$$A = \int_0^1 x\sqrt{1 - x^2}\, dx$$

$$= -\frac{1}{2}\int_1^0 u^{1/2}\, du$$

$$= -\frac{1}{2}\cdot\frac{2}{3}u^{3/2}\Big|_1^0$$

$$= \frac{1}{3}.$$

AP Teacher Tips
Chapter 9: Sequences and Series

This chapter is for Calculus BC only. All of the sections need to be covered.

Section 9.1 deals with infinite sequences. It is important that students understand the distinction between a sequence and a series. A sequence is a list of terms and a series is a sum of terms. Frequently these terms are used interchangeably in English – not so in Mathematics. Students should be able to work with sequences that are defined by a general term as well as sequences that are defined recursively.

Section 9.2 deals with Geometric Series, a very important type of series. Students will use it in comparisons and to write certain power series more easily than by using Taylor's theorem. It is essential that students can work in both directions, that is: (1) given a series that is geometric with an appropriately-sized ratio, write an expression for the sum of the series and give the interval of convergence where appropriate, and (2) recognize a fraction as the sum of an infinite geometric series.

Example 1:   Consider the series $2 + 6x + 18x^2 + 54x^3 + \cdots$. Express the series in closed form. For what values of x do the closed form and the series give the same value? Note this will lead to an interval of convergence.

Solution: $2 + 6x + 18x^2 + 54x^3 + \ldots = \dfrac{\text{first term}}{1 - \text{ratio}} = \dfrac{2}{1 - 3x}, |x| < \dfrac{1}{3}$.

Example 2: What geometric series has a sum of $\dfrac{1}{1 + x^2}$? For what values of x are this geometric series and $\dfrac{1}{1 + x^2}$ the same?

Solution: $\dfrac{1}{1 + x^2} = \dfrac{\text{first term}}{1 - \text{ratio}} = 1 - x^2 + x^4 - x^6 + \ldots, |x| < 1$.

Note that this will be useful in Chapter 10 when determining the Maclaurin Series for $f(x) = \tan^{-1} x$.

$f'(x) = \dfrac{1}{1 + x^2} = 1 - x^2 + x^4 - x^6 + \ldots, -1 < x < 1$

$f(x) = C - \dfrac{1}{3}x^3 + \dfrac{1}{5}x^5 - \dfrac{1}{7}x^7 + \ldots$, with center $x = 0$ and radius 1.

We need to determine C and if there is convergence at either endpoint.

$f(0) = C$ and $f(0) = \tan^{-1}(0) = 0 \Rightarrow C = 0$.

At $x = -1$ the series is $-\left(1 - \dfrac{1}{3} + \dfrac{1}{5} - \dfrac{1}{7} + \ldots\right)$ which is the opposite of the alternating harmonic series and converges to $-\ln 2$.

At $x = 1$ the series is $1 - \dfrac{1}{3} + \dfrac{1}{5} - \dfrac{1}{7} + \ldots$ which is the alternating harmonic series and converges to $\ln 2$.

Thus, $\tan^{-1}(x) = x - \dfrac{1}{3}x^3 + \dfrac{1}{5}x^5 - \dfrac{1}{7}x^7 + \ldots, \quad -1 \le x \le 1$.

In Section 9.3 the sequence of Partial Sums and Integral Test are discussed. Both of these are important for the students to understand. The definition of the sum of a series as the limit of the sequence of partial sums is something that needs to be revisited as the students work through both this chapter and Chapter 10.

As the students work further with series and use a variety of convergence tests and determine series expansions for functions as well as intervals of convergence, they frequently forget what it means to write that a series is convergent. You should include problems in this section that deal with

Telescoping Series. For example, $\displaystyle\sum_{n=2}^{\infty} \dfrac{1}{n^2 - n} = \sum_{n=2}^{\infty} \dfrac{1}{n-1} - \dfrac{1}{n}$.

$S_2 = 1 - \dfrac{1}{2}$, $S_3 = 1 - \dfrac{1}{2} + \dfrac{1}{2} - \dfrac{1}{3} = 1 - \dfrac{1}{3}$, $S_4 = 1 - \dfrac{1}{3} + \dfrac{1}{3} - \dfrac{1}{4} = 1 - \dfrac{1}{4}$, $S_n = 1 - \dfrac{1}{n}$.

$\displaystyle\lim_{n \to \infty} S_n = 1$, so $\displaystyle\sum_{n=2}^{\infty} \dfrac{1}{n^2 - n} = 1$.

When students use the Integral Test on the AP Examination they must indicate that the series they are testing satisfies the hypotheses of the Integral Test. Otherwise, there will be a deduction.

Students should be made aware that the biggest use they will make of Integral Test is in proving the conditions for convergence of a p-series. This very important class of series is presented in this section; however, the groundwork for the conclusion that a p-series is convergent for $p > 1$ and divergent otherwise is completed in Chapter 7. This presents an opportunity for the students to revisit the work done in Chapter 7.

Theorem 9.2 needs to be emphasized. It is important to note that part 3 of this theorem is generally referred to as the nth Term Test or in some texts as the Fundamental Divergence Test. Students frequently incorrectly use the converse of this Test as a reason for convergence. Be on the look out for this error. This is a test for divergence, not convergence.

In Section 9.4 the students are introduced to a variety of tests for convergence of series of non-negative constants. There is a stronger form of the Limit Comparison Test than the one in the text, however, the form given in the text is the one that is most frequently on AP Examinations.

Limit Comparison Test – stronger form
Suppose that $a_n > 0$ and $b_n > 0$ for all $n \geq N$ (N a positive integer).

1. If $\lim\limits_{x \to \infty} \dfrac{a_n}{b_n} = c$, $0 < c < \infty$, then $\sum a_n$ and $\sum b_n$ both converge or both diverge.

2. If $\lim\limits_{x \to \infty} \dfrac{a_n}{b_n} = 0$ and $\sum b_n$ converges, then $\sum a_n$ converges.

3. If $\lim\limits_{x \to \infty} \dfrac{a_n}{b_n} = \infty$ and $\sum b_n$ diverges, then $\sum a_n$ diverges.

Alternating Series are in this section along with the Alternating Series Test and an Error Bound for Alternating Series which converge by this test. This error bound frequently appears on AP Examinations.

Students need time to work a variety of problems so that they can become familiar with the conditions under which particular tests work best. For example, the Ratio Test generally works well if the general term has exponentials or factorials and generally does not work well if neither appears. A major place that students use these tests is in checking for convergence at endpoints of intervals of convergence for power series.

The terms Absolute Convergence and Conditional Convergence are defined. By testing for absolute convergence all the tests for series of non-negative terms become applicable for series that contain some terms that are negative.

Power Series are introduced in Section 9.5 and time should be spent on the highlighted material on page 465. This tells us that the convergence is orderly. Teachers should assign problems 30-33 on page 470 and if needed make up or find more problems like these. Students need to be able to look at the terms of a series and write a general term for the series. This should begin with Geometric Series, the first type of series studied.

Chapter 9 Multiple Choice Questions

1. Which of the following series are convergent?

   I. $\displaystyle\sum_{n=1}^{\infty}(-1)^{n+1}\frac{1}{3n+1}$
   II. $\displaystyle\sum_{n=1}^{\infty}\frac{1}{n}\left(\frac{4}{3}\right)^{n}$
   III. $\displaystyle\sum_{n=4}^{\infty}\frac{1}{n\ln n}$

   (A) I only
   (B) II only
   (C) III only
   (D) I and III only
   (E) I, II and III

2. Which of the following series are convergent?

   I. $\displaystyle\sum_{n=1}^{\infty}\frac{1}{n^{2}}$
   II. $\displaystyle\sum_{n=1}^{\infty}\frac{(-1)^{n+1}}{n}$
   III. $\displaystyle\sum_{n=1}^{\infty}\frac{1}{\sqrt{n}}$

   (A) I only
   (B) III only
   (C) I and II only

   (D) I and III only
   (E) II and III only

3. $\displaystyle\sum_{n=1}^{\infty}a_{n}(x-3)^{n}$ converges at $x=-6$ and diverges at $x=-9$. At $x=9$ the series is

   (A) conditionally convergent
   (B) absolutely convergent
   (C) alternating

   (D) divergent
   (E) cannot be determined

4. $\displaystyle\sum_{n=1}^{\infty}a_{n}(x-3)^{n}$ converges at $x=-6$ and diverges at $x=-9$. At $x=13$ the series is

   (A) conditionally convergent
   (B) absolutely convergent
   (C) alternating

   (D) divergent
   (E) cannot be determined

5. $\sum_{n=1}^{\infty} a_n (x-3)^n$ converges at $x = -6$ and diverges at $x = -9$. At $x = 16$ the series is

(A) conditionally convergent (B) absolutely convergent (C) alternating

(D) divergent (E) cannot be determined

6. If $f(x) = \sum_{k=1}^{\infty} \left(\cos^2 x\right)^k$, then $f(1) =$

(A) 0.292 (B) 0.412 (C) 0.417 (D) 1.175 (E) 2.710

7. For the series $\sum_{k=1}^{\infty} a_k$ the nth partial sum $S_n = \sum_{k=1}^{n} a_k = \dfrac{2n+1}{n}$. The 3rd term of the series is

(A) $-\dfrac{1}{6}$ (B) $-\dfrac{1}{2}$ (C) $\dfrac{1}{6}$ (D) $\dfrac{1}{2}$ (E) $\dfrac{7}{3}$

8. Which of the following series converge?

I. $\sum_{n=1}^{\infty} \dfrac{n}{n+1}$ II. $\sum_{n=1}^{\infty} \dfrac{\sin n}{n^2}$ III. $\sum_{n=1}^{\infty} \dfrac{\cos n\pi}{n}$

(A) I only (B) II only (C) I and II only
(D) II and III only (E) I, II, and III

9. Which of the following infinite sequences converge?

I. $\left\{\dfrac{2n-3}{4n+1}\right\}$ II. $\{\sin n\pi\}$ III. $\left\{\dfrac{n}{e^n}\right\}$

(A) I only (B) III only (C) I and III only
(D) I, II, and III (E) none

168

10. The radius of convergence for the power series $\displaystyle\sum_{n=1}^{\infty} \frac{x^n n^n}{n!\,2^n}$ is

(A) $\dfrac{1}{2}$ (B) $\dfrac{2}{e}$ (C) 1 (D) $\dfrac{e}{2}$ (E) 2

11. What is the sum of the infinite geometric series $\dfrac{2}{3} + \dfrac{4}{27} + \dfrac{8}{243} + \cdots$?

(A) $\dfrac{6}{11}$ (B) $\dfrac{9}{11}$ (C) $\dfrac{6}{7}$ (D) $\dfrac{9}{7}$ (E) 2

12. $\displaystyle\sum_{n=0}^{\infty} \frac{4^n + 2\left(3^n\right)}{8^n} =$

(A) 2.2 (B) 3.6 (C) 4.0 (D) 5.2 (E) 6.0

13. The value of the series $5 - \dfrac{5^2}{2!} + \dfrac{5^3}{3!} - \dfrac{5^4}{4!} + \cdots$ is

(A) e^{-5} (B) $1 - e^{-5}$ (C) $\sin(-5) + \cos(-5)$
(D) $1 + e^{-5}$ (E) $\sin(-5) - \cos(-5)$

14. The sequence $\{a_n\}$ is defined so that $a_1 = \dfrac{1}{2}$, $a_2 = \dfrac{3}{2}$, and $a_n = \dfrac{a_{n-1}}{a_{n-2}}$. a_4 is

(A) $\dfrac{1}{2}$ (B) $\dfrac{2}{3}$ (C) $\dfrac{3}{2}$ (D) 2 (E) 3

15. If $a_n = \left(\dfrac{(4+n)^{50}}{4^{n+1}}\right)\left(\dfrac{4^n}{(3+n)^{50}}\right)$ then the infinite sequence $\{a_n\}$ converges to

(A) $\dfrac{1}{4}$ (B) $\dfrac{3}{4}$ (C) 1   (D) $\dfrac{4}{3}$ (E) $\left(\dfrac{4}{3}\right)^{50}$

16. For what integer q, $q > 0$, will both $\displaystyle\sum_{n=1}^{\infty} \dfrac{1}{n^q}$ and $\displaystyle\sum_{n=1}^{\infty}\left(\dfrac{q}{3}\right)^n$ converge?

(A) 1   (B) 2   (C) 3   (D) 4   (E) 5

17. For what values of x is the series $\displaystyle\sum_{n=1}^{\infty} \dfrac{(x+1)^n}{\sqrt{n}}$ a convergent alternating series?

(A) $-\infty < x < -1$ (B) $-2 \leq x < -1$ (C) $-2 \leq x < 0$
(D) $-1 < x < 0$ (E) No values of x

18. Which of the following series converge?

I. $\displaystyle\sum_{n=1}^{\infty} \dfrac{\sqrt{n+1}}{n^3 + 6n + 1}$ II. $\displaystyle\sum_{n=4}^{\infty} \dfrac{1}{n\ln n}$ III. $\displaystyle\sum_{n=1}^{\infty}\left[\left(\dfrac{2}{3}\right)^n + \dfrac{1}{n}\right]$

(A) I only   (B) II only   (C) III only
(D) I and II only   (E) I and III only

19. $\displaystyle\sum_{n=1}^{\infty} \dfrac{1}{n^2 + n} =$

(A) $\dfrac{1}{2}$ (B) $\dfrac{3}{4}$ (C) 1   (D) $\dfrac{5}{4}$ (E) $\dfrac{3}{2}$

20. For what value of x, if any, is -0.4 the sum of the infinite series $\dfrac{2}{3}x + \dfrac{4}{3}x^2 + \dfrac{8}{3}x^3 + \cdots$?

(A) -3 (B) $-\dfrac{1}{3}$ (C) $\dfrac{1}{3}$ (D) 3 (E) no such value

21. The infinite series $\displaystyle\sum_{n=1}^{\infty} (-1)^{n+1}\left(1+\dfrac{1}{n}\right)^n$ is

(A) absolutely convergent   (B) conditionally convergent   (C) divergent

(D) convergent to e (E) convergent to a number less than 2

22. The interval of convergence for the power series $\displaystyle\sum_{n=1}^{\infty} \dfrac{(x-1)^n}{2^n n^2}$ is

(A) $-1 \le x \le 1$ (B) $0 \le x \le 2$ (C) $-1 \le x \le 3$ (D) $-1 \le x < 3$ (E) $-1 < x < 3$

23. The radius of convergence for the power series $\displaystyle\sum_{n=0}^{\infty} \dfrac{n+2}{4n-3}\cdot\dfrac{(x+2)^n}{2^n}$ is

(A) 0 (B) 1 (C) 2 (D) 4 (E) 8

24. The Maclaurin series for the function f is $\displaystyle\sum_{n=0}^{\infty} a_n x^n$ where $a_0 = 1$ and $a_n = \dfrac{a_{n-1}}{n+1}$ for $n \ge 1$. The value of a_4 is

(A) $\dfrac{1}{720}$ (B) $\dfrac{1}{120}$ (C) $\dfrac{1}{24}$ (D) 120 (E) 720

25. When the terms of the series $1 - \dfrac{1}{2^2} + \dfrac{1}{3^2} - \dfrac{1}{4^2} + \cdots$ are rearranged there is no change in the sum of the series. The reason this is true is that the series $1 - \dfrac{1}{2^2} + \dfrac{1}{3^2} - \dfrac{1}{4^2} + \cdots$ is

(A) convergent

(B) conditionally convergent

(C) divergent

(D) absolutely convergent

(E) convergent to a number less than one

Chapter 9 Multiple Choice Questions

Question	Answer	AB	BC	No Calculator	Calculator Required	Neutral Calculator
1	A		x			x
2	C		x			x
3	B		x			x
4	E		x			x
5	D		x			x
6	B		x		x	
7	A		x			x
8	D		x	x		
9	D		x	x		
10	B		x	x		
11	C		x	x		
12	D		x	x		
13	B		x	x		
14	D		x	x		
15	A		x	x		
16	B		x			x
17	B		x			x
18	A		x			x
19	C		x	x		
20	E		x	x		
21	C		x	x		
22	C		x			x
23	C		x			x
24	B		x	x		
25	D		x			x

Chapter 9 Free Response Questions

1. Let W be the series $W = \sum_{n=1}^{\infty} \left(\frac{t-1}{t+2} \right)^{n-1}$, $t \neq 1$.

   (a) Find the value of W when $t = 0$.

   (b) For what values of t does W converge? Show the analysis that leads to your conclusion.

   (c) Find all the values of t for which the sum of the series W is greater than $\frac{3}{4}$.

2. Consider the series $S = \sum_{k=1}^{\infty} \frac{1}{k^4}$ and the function $E(n) = \int_{n}^{\infty} \frac{1}{x^4} \, dx$, $n \geq 1$.

   (a) Use the Integral Test to show that $\sum_{k=1}^{\infty} \frac{1}{k^4}$ is convergent.

   (b) Showing your use of limits, express $E(n)$ without an integral.

   (c) It is true that S has the property that $S < S_n + E(n)$, where S_n is the nth partial sum of the series. It is known that $S_{100} = \sum_{k=1}^{100} \frac{1}{k^4} = 1.082322905\ldots$. Use the value of S_{100} and the property $S < S_n + E(n)$ to approximate $\sum_{k=1}^{\infty} \frac{1}{k^4}$.

   (d) Use a diagram that involves the graph of $y = \frac{1}{x^4}$ to show why $S < S_n + E(n)$.

3. Let f be the function defined by $f(x) = \sum_{n=1}^{\infty} \frac{x^n n^n}{6^n n!}$.

   (a) Find the radius of convergence for this series.

   (b) Use the first two terms of this series to approximate the value of $f(-2)$.

   (c) Estimate the amount of error in your approximation in part (b). Justify your answer.

4. Consider the series $\sum\limits_{n=0}^{\infty} \dfrac{(-1)^n}{2n+1}(x-2)^n$.

   (a) Find the interval of convergence for this series. Justify your answer.

   (b) For what values of x is the series absolutely convergent and for what values of x is the series conditionally convergent?

   (c) For what values of x is the series a convergent alternating series?

   (d) Let $f(x) = \sum\limits_{n=0}^{\infty} \dfrac{(-1)^n}{2n+1}(x-2)^n$. Use the first 3 terms of this series to approximate $f(2.5)$. Give an estimate of the error in your approximation of $f(2.5)$. Justify this error estimate.

5. Let $a = \sum\limits_{n=0}^{\infty}(-1)^n x^n$ and $b = \sum\limits_{n=0}^{\infty} 2^n x^n$ for all x in their intervals of convergence.

   (a) Write the functions to which each of these series converge and include their respective intervals of convergence.

   (b) Let $P = \left(\sum\limits_{n=0}^{\infty}(-1)^n x^n \right)\left(\sum\limits_{n=0}^{\infty} 2^n x^n \right)$. Thus, P is the series that results when a and b are multiplied. What is the interval of convergence for the series P? Give an explanation of your reasoning.

   (c) P can be written as a linear combination of a and b, that is, $P = c_1 a + c_2 b$ or $P = c_1 \sum\limits_{n=0}^{\infty}(-1)^n x^n + c_2 \sum\limits_{n=0}^{\infty} 2^n x^n$. Use partial fractions to find the values of c_1 and c_2.

   (d) Explain which representation of P is easier to use to write out the first 4 terms of the series for P. $P = c_1 \sum\limits_{n=0}^{\infty}(-1)^n x^n + c_2 \sum\limits_{n=0}^{\infty} 2^n x^n$ or $P = \left(\sum\limits_{n=0}^{\infty}(-1)^n x^n \right)\left(\sum\limits_{n=0}^{\infty} 2^n x^n \right)$.

Chapter 9 Free Response Questions

Question	AB	BC	No Calculator	Calculator Required	Neutral Calculator
1		x	x		
2		x			x
3		x			x
4		x			x
5		x	x		

Chapter 9 Solutions to Free Response Questions

1.

(a) When $t = 0$, $W = \sum_{n=1}^{\infty} \left(-\frac{1}{2} \right)^{n-1}$. This is a convergent geometric series, since $|r| = \frac{1}{2} < 1$.

$$W = \frac{\text{first term}}{1\text{-ratio}} = \frac{1}{1 - \left(-\frac{1}{2} \right)} = \frac{1}{\frac{3}{2}} = \frac{2}{3}.$$

(b) W is a geometric series with $r = \frac{t-1}{t+2}$. The series will converge when $|r| = \left| \frac{t-1}{t+2} \right| < 1$.

W is convergent for $t > -\frac{1}{2}$ and $t \neq 1$.

(c) $W = \frac{1}{1 - \frac{t-1}{t+2}} = \frac{t+2}{3}$. $W > \frac{3}{4}$ when $\left(\frac{t+2}{3} > \frac{3}{4} \right)$ and $\left(t > -\frac{1}{2} \text{ and } t \neq 1 \right)$.

$W > \frac{3}{4}$ when $t > \frac{1}{4}$ and $t \neq 1$.

2.

(a) Since $\frac{1}{x^4} > 0$ for all $x > 1$ and is monotonically decreasing to zero, the Integral Test applies.

$\int_1^{\infty} \frac{1}{x^4} \, dx = \lim_{L \to \infty} \int_1^L \frac{1}{x^4} \, dx = \lim_{L \to \infty} \left. \frac{-1}{3x^3} \right|_1^L = \lim_{L \to \infty} \left(\frac{1}{3} - \frac{1}{3L^3} \right) = \frac{1}{3}$. Since the improper integral

converges, the series $\sum_{k=1}^{\infty} \frac{1}{k^4}$ must also converge.

(b) $E(n) = \lim_{L \to \infty} \int_n^L \frac{1}{x^4} \, dx = \lim_{L \to \infty} \left. \frac{-1}{3x^3} \right|_n^L = \lim_{L \to \infty} \left(\frac{1}{3n^3} - \frac{1}{3L^3} \right) = \frac{1}{3n^3}$.

(c) $\sum_{k=1}^{\infty} \frac{1}{k^4} = \sum_{k=1}^{100} \frac{1}{k^4} + \sum_{k=101}^{\infty} \frac{1}{k^4} < S_{100} + E(100) = 1.082322905 + \frac{1}{3(100)^2} = 1.082356238$

$\sum_{k=1}^{\infty} \frac{1}{k^4} \approx 1.082356238$

177

(d) $\displaystyle\sum_{k=1}^{\infty}\frac{1}{k^4}=\sum_{k=1}^{n}\frac{1}{k^4}+\sum_{k=n+1}^{\infty}\frac{1}{k^4}<S_n+E(n)=S_n+$ Area under curve from $x=n$ to ∞.

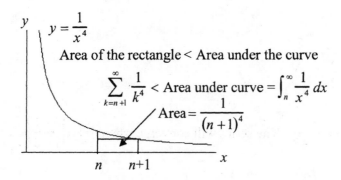

$y=\dfrac{1}{x^4}$

Area of the rectangle < Area under the curve

$$\sum_{k=n+1}^{\infty}\frac{1}{k^4}<\text{Area under curve}=\int_{n}^{\infty}\frac{1}{x^4}\,dx$$

$$\text{Area}=\frac{1}{(n+1)^4}$$

3.

(a) Ratio Test: $L=\displaystyle\lim_{n\to\infty}\left|\frac{a_{n+1}}{a_n}\right|=\lim_{n\to\infty}|x|\cdot\frac{(n+1)^{n+1}}{6^{n+1}(n+1)!}\cdot\frac{6^n\cdot n!}{n^n}=|x|\lim_{n\to\infty}\left(\frac{n+1}{n}\right)^n\cdot\frac{1}{6}=\frac{e}{6}|x|$

$L<1$ when $|x|<\dfrac{6}{e}$. The radius of convergence is $\dfrac{6}{e}$.

(b) $f(x)=\dfrac{1}{6}x+\dfrac{1}{18}x^2+\dfrac{1}{48}x^3+\cdots$

$f(-2)\approx\dfrac{1}{6}(-2)+\dfrac{1}{18}(-2)^2=-\dfrac{1}{9}$

(c) When $x=-2$ the series is a convergent and alternating. If the alternating series converges by the alternating series test, an error bound is the magnitude of first omitted term. That is, the error is less than $\left|\dfrac{1}{48}(-2)^3\right|=\dfrac{1}{6}$.

4.

(a) Ratio Test: $L = \lim_{n \to \infty} \left| \dfrac{a_{n+1}}{a_n} \right| = \lim_{n \to \infty} |x - 2| \cdot \dfrac{2n+1}{2n+3} = |x-2|$; $\quad L < 1$ for $1 < x < 3$

At $x = 1$ the series is $\displaystyle\sum_{n=0}^{\infty} \dfrac{1}{2n+1}$, which diverges by limit comparison with the harmonic series because the harmonic series is divergent and $\displaystyle\lim_{n \to \infty} \dfrac{\frac{1}{2n+1}}{\frac{1}{n}} = \dfrac{1}{2} \neq 0.$

At $x = 3$ the series is $\displaystyle\sum_{n=0}^{\infty} \dfrac{(-1)^n}{2n+1}$. This series converges by the Alternating Series Test because it is an alternating series in which the magnitude of the terms is monotonically decreasing to zero.

The interval of convergence is $1 < x \leq 3$.

(b) The series is absolutely convergent for $1 < x < 3$, the interior of the interval, and conditionally convergent at the endpoint $x = 3$.

(c) This is a convergent alternating series for $2 < x \leq 3$.

(d) At $x = 2.5$ the series is an alternating series in which the magnitude of the terms are monotonically decreasing to zero. The error in using the first 3 terms is smaller than the magnitude of the 4th term.

$$f(x) = 1 - \dfrac{(x-2)}{3} + \dfrac{(x-2)^2}{5} - \dfrac{(x-2)^3}{7} + \cdots; \quad f(2.5) \approx 1 - \dfrac{(0.5)}{3} + \dfrac{(0.5)^2}{5} = \dfrac{53}{60} = 0.883\overline{3}$$

$$\text{Error} < \dfrac{(0.5)^3}{7} = \dfrac{1}{56} = 0.018$$

5.

(a) Both series are geometric. $a = \dfrac{1}{1+x}, -1 < x < 1$ and $b = \dfrac{1}{1-2x}, -\dfrac{1}{2} < x < \dfrac{1}{2}$.

(b) The interval would need to meet the conditions for both a and b.
The interval of convergence is $-\dfrac{1}{2} < x < \dfrac{1}{2}$.

(c) $P = \left(\displaystyle\sum_{n=0}^{\infty} (-1)^n x^n \right)\left(\displaystyle\sum_{n=0}^{\infty} 2^n x^n \right) = \dfrac{1}{1+x} \cdot \dfrac{1}{1-2x} = \dfrac{1}{(1+x)(1-2x)}$

$\dfrac{1}{(1+x)(1-2x)} = \dfrac{c_1}{1+x} + \dfrac{c_2}{1-2x} \quad\Rightarrow\quad 1 = c_1(1-2x) + c_2(1+x)$

Let $x = -1$: $1 = c_1(3) + 0 \Rightarrow c_1 = \dfrac{1}{3}$; Let $x = \dfrac{1}{2}$: $1 = 0 + c_2\left(\dfrac{3}{2}\right) \Rightarrow c_2 = \dfrac{2}{3}$

$P = \dfrac{\frac{1}{3}}{1+x} + \dfrac{\frac{2}{3}}{1-2x} = \dfrac{1}{3}\displaystyle\sum_{n=0}^{\infty}(-1)^n x^n + \dfrac{2}{3}\displaystyle\sum_{n=0}^{\infty} 2^n x^n$

(d) To list the terms using $P = \dfrac{1}{3}\left(1 - x + x^2 - x^3 + \ldots\right) + \dfrac{2}{3}\left(1 + 2x + 4x^2 + 8x^3 + \ldots\right)$ it is necessary to distribute the constants and combine like terms.

To list the terms using $P = \left(1 - x + x^2 - x^3 + \ldots\right)\left(1 + 2x + 4x^2 + 8x^3 + \ldots\right)$ it is necessary to distribute $\left(1 - x + x^2 - x^3 + \ldots\right)$ over $\left(1 + 2x + 4x^2 + 8x^3 + \ldots\right)$.

The first process is relatively easy and the second process is not.

AP Teacher Tips
Chapter 10: Approximating Functions Using Series

This chapter is for Calculus BC only. Sections 10.1 - 10.4 need to be covered. You should have the students work many of the questions from past AP Examinations that deal with the topic of series.

Section 10.1 deals with Taylor Polynomials as approximations for functions. Students need to know what a Taylor Polynomial approximation for a function f is and how it is determined. Graphing calculators give students an opportunity to see how well a Taylor Polynomial approximates a given function. AP questions on this topic frequently ask a student to write a Taylor Polynomial of a certain degree or order from given data.

Section 10.2 extends the idea of Taylor Polynomials to Taylor Series by thinking of the polynomial as going on forever. Students should memorize the Maclaurin expansions for $\sin x$, $\cos x$, e^x, $\ln(1 + x)$, and $\tan^{-1} x$, along with their intervals of convergence. These are extremely useful when writing series expansions for more complicated functions that contain these functions. Again students should use their calculators to look at the graph of a function and its Taylor Series. Students should observe that, as more terms from the series are used, the quality of the approximation expands further from the center of the interval of convergence to the ends of the interval of convergence. Students should observe that for cases where the interval of convergence is not all real numbers, for example $-1 \le x < 1$, that using more terms from the series does not improve the agreement between the approximation and the function outside the interval of convergence.

This section fills out the types of series of constants for which students should be able to determine sums. Previously, they should have worked with geometric series and telescoping series. These are examples of series for which an expression for the nth partial sum may be written in closed form and the limit taken to determine the sum of the series. In the case of geometric series, there is a formula. In the case of telescoping series, partial fractions are used to decompose the general term into simple fractions so S_n may be determined explicitly. In this section known Maclaurin Series are evaluated at a fixed point and the resulting series of constants is presented for the student to determine the sum. Students must recognize the series being evaluated and at which point.

Binomial Series are discussed in this section. This type of series is not mentioned in the AP Course Description; however, it is worth covering if time allows. This presents the opportunity to link to the Binomial Theorem which was studied in Algebra 2 or Pre-calculus.

Section 10.3 deals with manipulation of series. If a power series is differentiated or antidifferentiated the resulting series has the same center and radius of convergence. Endpoints need to be tested individually to determine convergence or divergence at these points. Additionally, students use known series to write series for other functions. For example, it would require a lot of work to use Taylor's Theorem to write the Maclaurin series for $f(x) = xe^{-x^2}$.

However, using the series for e^t makes this task relatively simple.

$$e^t = 1 + t + \frac{t^2}{2!} + \frac{t^3}{3!} + \cdots + \frac{t^n}{n!} + \cdots, \text{ so } e^{-x^2} = 1 + \left(-x^2\right) + \frac{\left(-x^2\right)^2}{2!} + \frac{\left(-x^2\right)^3}{3!} + \cdots + \frac{\left(-x^2\right)^n}{n!} + \cdots;$$

$$f(x) = xe^{-x^2} = x - x^3 + \frac{x^5}{2!} - \frac{x^7}{3!} + \cdots + (-1)^n \frac{x^{2n+1}}{n!} + \cdots$$

Section 10.4 deals with the error in using the nth Taylor Polynomial to approximate the function. The error bound that is given is the Lagrange Remainder that is mentioned in the AP Course Description for Calculus BC. Generally, students find this very difficult and need a number of examples before it becomes understandable. There have been two AP questions since 1999 that required the use of this error bound. In all other cases the series in question was alternating and the error bound for a convergent alternating series in which all the terms have magnitudes that are monotonically decreasing to zero was able to be used.

Chapter 10 Multiple Choice Questions

1. A series expansion for xe^{-x} is

(A) $1+x+\dfrac{1}{2!}x^2+\dfrac{1}{3!}x^3+...$

(B) $1-x+\dfrac{1}{2!}x^2-\dfrac{1}{3!}x^3+...$

(C) $1+\dfrac{1}{2!}x+\dfrac{1}{3!}x^2+\dfrac{1}{4!}x^3+...$

(D) $x+x^2+\dfrac{1}{3!}x^3+\dfrac{1}{4!}x^4+...$

(E) $x-x^2+\dfrac{1}{2!}x^3-\dfrac{1}{3!}x^4+...$

2. A series expansion for $\dfrac{\sin x}{x}$ is

(A) $1-\dfrac{1}{3!}x^2+\dfrac{1}{5!}x^4-\dfrac{1}{7!}x^6+...$

(B) $1+\dfrac{1}{3!}x^2+\dfrac{1}{5!}x^4+\dfrac{1}{7!}x^6+...$

(C) $x-\dfrac{1}{3!}x^3-\dfrac{1}{5!}x^5-\dfrac{1}{7!}x^7+...$

(D) $\dfrac{1}{x}+\dfrac{1}{2!}x+\dfrac{1}{4!}x^3+\dfrac{1}{6!}x^5+...$

(E) $\dfrac{1}{x}-\dfrac{1}{2!}x+\dfrac{1}{4!}x^3-\dfrac{1}{6!}x^5+...$

3. The coefficient of x^6 in the Taylor series expansion of e^{-x^2} about $x=0$ is

(A) $-\dfrac{1}{6}$ (B) 0 (C) $\dfrac{1}{120}$ (D) $\dfrac{1}{6}$ (E) 1

4. What value is obtained when using the fourth-degree Taylor polynomial for $\cos x$ about $x=0$ to approximate $\cos 1$?

(A) $1-\dfrac{1}{2}+\dfrac{1}{4}$

(B) $1-\dfrac{1}{2}+\dfrac{1}{24}$

(C) $1-\dfrac{1}{3}+\dfrac{1}{5}$

(D) $1-\dfrac{1}{4}+\dfrac{1}{720}$

(E) $1-\dfrac{1}{6}+\dfrac{1}{120}$

183

5. If the fourth-degree Taylor polynomial for $\cos x$ about $x = 0$ is used to approximate $\cos 1$, then the smallest number that is larger than the error in this approximation is

(A) $\dfrac{1}{7!}$ (B) $\dfrac{1}{6!}$ (C) $\dfrac{1}{5!}$ (D) $\dfrac{1}{4!}$ (E) $\dfrac{1}{3!}$

6. The Maclaurin series for e^t is $1 + t + \dfrac{1}{2!}t^2 + \dfrac{1}{3!}t^3 + \cdots$. Let g be a function such that $g'(x) = xe^x$. What is the coefficient of x^6 in the Maclaurin series for $g(x)$?

(A) $\dfrac{1}{4!}$ (B) $\dfrac{1}{4}$ (C) $\dfrac{1}{6}$ (D) $\dfrac{1}{30}$ (E) $\dfrac{1}{144}$

7. Let f be the function given by $f(x) = \ln x$. The third order Taylor polynomial for $f'(x)$ centered at $x = 1$ is

(A) $1 - (x-1) + (x-1)^2 - (x-1)^3$ (B) $1 + (x-1) + (x-1)^2 + (x-1)^3$

(C) $(x-1) - \dfrac{1}{2}(x-1)^2 + \dfrac{1}{3}(x-1)^3$ (D) $(x-1) + \dfrac{1}{2}(x-1)^2 + \dfrac{1}{3}(x-1)^3$

(E) $(x-1) + \dfrac{1}{2!}(x-1)^2 + \dfrac{1}{3!}(x-1)^3$

8. $\displaystyle\sum_{n=0}^{\infty} \dfrac{2^n x^n}{n!}$ is the Taylor series about $x = 0$ for

(A) e^x (B) e^{-2x} (C) e^{2x} (D) $\sin 2x$ (E) $\cos 2x$

9. $\displaystyle\sum_{n=0}^{\infty} \frac{(-1)^n}{n!} =$

(A) $\sin\left(\dfrac{\pi}{4}\right)$ (B) $\dfrac{1}{e}$ (C) e (D) $\cos\left(\dfrac{\pi}{6}\right)$ (E) $\tan\left(\dfrac{\pi}{6}\right)$

10. $P(x) = x - \dfrac{1}{6}x^3$ is the third order Taylor polynomial for $\sin x$ about $x = 0$. The maximum value of $\left|P(x) - \sin x\right|$ for $0 \le x \le \dfrac{\pi}{3}$ is

(A) 0.010   (B) 0.201   (C) 0.373   (D) 0.838   (E) 0.967

11. The function f has the Maclaurin series expansion $2x - \dfrac{2^3 x^3}{3!} + \dfrac{2^5 x^5}{5!} - \dfrac{2^7 x^7}{7!} + \ldots$.

The graphs of $y = f(x)$ and $y = \dfrac{1}{2}$ intersect at $x =$

(A) $\dfrac{\pi}{12}$ (B) $\dfrac{\pi}{6}$ (C) $\dfrac{\pi}{4}$ (D) $\dfrac{\pi}{3}$ (E) $\dfrac{\pi}{2}$

12. For how many values of x, where $0 \le x \le 10$, is $\displaystyle\sum_{n=0}^{\infty} \frac{(-1)^n x^n}{n!} = \sum_{n=0}^{\infty} \frac{(-1)^n x^{2n}}{(2n)!}$?

(A) 2   (B) 3   (C) 4   (D) 5   (E) more than 5

13. The Taylor series centered at $x = 2$ for the function g is given by $\displaystyle\sum_{n=0}^{\infty} \frac{(-1)^n (x-2)^n}{(n+1)!}$.

What is $g^{(20)}(2)$, the 20th derivative of g at $x = 2$?

(A) $-\dfrac{1}{21!}$ (B) $-\dfrac{1}{21}$ (C) $\dfrac{1}{21!}$ (D) $\dfrac{1}{21}$ (E) $\dfrac{1}{20}$

14. $g(x) = \sum_{n=0}^{\infty} \dfrac{x^{3n}}{n!}$ for all real values of x. $g'(x) =$

(A) $g(x)$ (B) $3 \cdot g(x)$ (C) $3x \cdot g(x)$ (D) $3x^2 \cdot g(x)$ (E) $3x^3 \cdot g(x)$

15. Let P be the third order Taylor polynomial centered at $x = 1$ for the function $\dfrac{1}{x}$, then

$P(x) =$

(A) $(x-1) + \dfrac{1}{2}(x-1)^2 + \dfrac{1}{3}(x-1)^3$
     (B) $(x-1) - \dfrac{1}{2}(x-1)^2 + \dfrac{1}{3}(x-1)^3$

(C) $1 - (x-1) + (x-1)^2 - (x-1)^3$
     (D) $1 + (x-1) + \dfrac{1}{2!}(x-1)^2 + \dfrac{1}{3!}(x-1)^3$

(E) $1 + (x-1) - \dfrac{1}{2!}(x-1)^2 + \dfrac{1}{3!}(x-1)^3$

16. $f(x) = \sum_{n=0}^{\infty} c_n (x-2)^n$ for all real values of x. $f'(3) =$

(A) 0 (B) c_1 (C) $\sum_{n=0}^{\infty} c_n$ (D) $\sum_{n=1}^{\infty} n \cdot c_n$ (E) $\sum_{n=1}^{\infty} n \cdot c_n^{n-1}$

17. Let P be the second order Taylor polynomial centered at $x = 4$ for $f(x) = \sqrt{x}$. $P(x) =$

(A) $2 + (x-4) + (x-4)^2$
     (B) $2 + \dfrac{1}{4}(x-4) - \dfrac{1}{64}(x-4)^2$

(C) $2 + \dfrac{1}{4}(x-4) - \dfrac{1}{32}(x-4)^2$
     (D) $2 + \dfrac{1}{4}(x-4) + \dfrac{1}{32}(x-4)^2$

(E) $2 + \dfrac{1}{4}(x-4) + \dfrac{1}{32}(x-4)^2$

18. The Maclaurin series expansion of $\ln(1 + x)$ is $\sum_{n=1}^{\infty} \frac{(-1)^{n+1}}{n} x^n$. The sum of the first four nonzero terms in the Maclaurin series expansion of $\ln\sqrt{1 + x^2}$ is

(A) $x^2 - \frac{1}{2}x^4 + \frac{1}{3}x^6 - \frac{1}{4}x^8$

(B) $x^2 + \frac{1}{2}x^4 + \frac{1}{3}x^6 + \frac{1}{4}x^8$

(C) $\frac{1}{2}x^2 - \frac{1}{4}x^4 + \frac{1}{6}x^6 - \frac{1}{8}x^8$

(D) $\frac{1}{2}x^2 + \frac{1}{4}x^4 + \frac{1}{6}x^6 + \frac{1}{8}x^8$

(E) $x^2 - \frac{1}{2!}x^4 + \frac{1}{3!}x^6 - \frac{1}{4!}x^8$

19. The Maclaurin series expansion of $\frac{x^3}{1 + x^2}$ is

(A) $1 + x^3 + x^5 + x^7 + \cdots$

(B) $1 - x^3 + x^5 - x^7 + \cdots$

(C) $x^3 + x^5 + x^7 + x^9 + \cdots$

(D) $x^3 - x^5 + x^7 - x^9 + \cdots$

(E) $\frac{1}{3}x^3 + \frac{1}{5}x^5 + \frac{1}{7}x^7 + \frac{1}{9}x^9 + \cdots$

20. The Taylor series for x near zero for e^{-x} is $1 - x + \frac{1}{2!}x^2 - \frac{1}{3!}x^3 + \ldots$. What is the maximum error when the third-degree Taylor polynomial from this series is used to approximate e^{-x} for $-1 \le x \le 1$?

(A) 0.035　　　(B) 0.052　　　(C) 0.132　　　(D) 0.140　　　(E) 0.218

21. The Maclaurin series for $\dfrac{3}{2+x}$ is

(A) $1 - \dfrac{1}{2}x + \dfrac{1}{4}x^2 - \dfrac{1}{8}x^3 + \cdots$

(B) $1 + \dfrac{1}{2}x + \dfrac{1}{4}x^2 + \dfrac{1}{8}x^3 + \cdots$

(C) $\dfrac{3}{2} - \dfrac{3}{4}x + \dfrac{3}{8}x^2 - \dfrac{3}{16}x^3 + \cdots$

(D) $\dfrac{3}{2} + \dfrac{3}{4}x + \dfrac{3}{8}x^2 + \dfrac{3}{16}x^3 + \cdots$

(E) $\dfrac{3}{2} - \dfrac{3}{2}x + \dfrac{3}{2}x^2 - \dfrac{3}{2}x^3 + \cdots$

22. The fourth-degree Taylor polynomial centered at $x = 0$ for the function $\dfrac{\sin x}{1+x}$ is

(A) $x - x^2 + \dfrac{5}{6}x^3 - \dfrac{5}{6}x^4$

(B) $x + x^2 + \dfrac{5}{6}x^3 + \dfrac{5}{6}x^4$

(C) $-x + x^2 - \dfrac{5}{6}x^3 + \dfrac{5}{6}x^4$

(D) $x - x^2 + x^3 - x^4$

(E) $-x + x^2 - x^3 + x^4$

23. The function f has derivatives of all orders and $f(2) = 1$, $f'(2) = 3$, $f''(2) = 6$, $f'''(2) = -12$. The Taylor polynomial of degree three for f near $x = 2$ is

(A) $1 + 3(x-2) + 6(x-2)x^2 - \dfrac{9}{2}(x-2)^3$

(B) $1 + 3(x-2) + 3(x-2)x^2 - 2(x-2)^3$

(C) $1 + \dfrac{1}{3}(x-2) + \dfrac{1}{3}(x-2)^2 - \dfrac{1}{2}(x-2)^3$

(D) $1 - 3(x-2) + 3(x-2)x^2 - 2(x-2)^3$

(E) $1 - 3(x-2) + 6(x-2)x^2 - \dfrac{9}{2}(x-2)^3$

24. The function g has the property that $\left|g^{(4)}(x)\right| < 4$ for all values of x, where $g^{(4)}$ means the fourth derivative of g. When the third order Taylor polynomial for g centered at $x = 2$ is used to approximate the value of $g(1.8)$, the best error bound is

(A) 0.00001   (B) 0.00007   (C) 0.00027   (D) 0.43740   (E) 1.74960

25. The sixth order Taylor polynomial centered at $x = \pi$ for the function $\sin x$ is

(A) $(x-\pi) - \dfrac{1}{3!}(x-\pi)^3 + \dfrac{1}{5!}(x-\pi)^5$ (B) $(x-\pi) + \dfrac{1}{3!}(x-\pi)^3 + \dfrac{1}{5!}(x-\pi)^5$

(C) $\pi - \dfrac{1}{2!}(x-\pi)^2 + \dfrac{1}{4!}(x-\pi)^4 - \dfrac{1}{6!}(x-\pi)^6$ (D) $\pi + \dfrac{1}{2!}(x-\pi)^2 + \dfrac{1}{4!}(x-\pi)^4 + \dfrac{1}{6!}(x-\pi)^6$

(E) $-(x-\pi) + \dfrac{1}{3!}(x-\pi)^3 - \dfrac{1}{5!}(x-\pi)^5$

Chapter 10 Multiple Choice Questions

Question	Answer	AB	BC	No Calculator	Calculator Required	Neutral Calculator
1	E		x	x		
2	A		x	x		
3	A		x	x		
4	B		x	x		
5	B		x	x		
6	E		x	x		
7	A		x	x		
8	C		x	x		
9	B		x	x		
10	A		x		x	
11	A		x	x		
12	C		x	x		
13	D		x	x		
14	D		x	x		
15	C		x	x		
16	D		x	x		
17	B		x	x		
18	C		x	x		
19	D		x	x		
20	B		x		x	
21	C		x	x		
22	A		x	x		
23	B		x			x
24	C		x		x	
25	E		x	x		

Chapter 10 Free Response Questions

1. Let g be the function defined by $g(x) = \sum_{n=0}^{\infty} a_n x^n$, where $a_0 = 3$ and $a_n = \left(-\dfrac{1}{n}\right) a_{n-1}$.

   (a) Write the series for $g(x)$ showing the first four terms and the general term.

   (b) Determine the interval of convergence for this power series.

   (c) Express $g(x)$ as a familiar function not involving a series.

   (d) Express the value of $g'(1)$ both as a series and not as a series.

2. Let f be the function defined by $f(x) = \sqrt[3]{1+x}$.

   (a) Find the first four nonzero terms in the Taylor series expansion of f centered at $x = 0$.

   (b) Use the result of part (a) to approximate the value of $\sqrt[3]{1.1}$.

   (c) Use the result of part (a) to find the first four nonzero terms in the Taylor series expansion of $g(x) = \sqrt[3]{1+x^3}$ centered at $x = 0$.

   (d) Find the first four nonzero terms in the Taylor series expansion of h centered at $x = 0$ given that $h(0) = 3$ and $h'(x) = g(x) = \sqrt[3]{1+x^3}$.

3. Let f and H be the functions given by $f(t) = \dfrac{1}{1+t^2}$ and $H(x) = \displaystyle\int_0^x \dfrac{t}{1+t^2}\,dt$.

   (a) Find the first 4 nonzero terms and general term in the Maclaurin series expansion of f.

   (b) Find the first 4 nonzero terms and general term in the Maclaurin series expansion of H.

   (c) Determine the interval of convergence for the series in part (b). Justify your answer.

   (d) Express H without using a series.

4. Let f be a function that has derivatives of all orders for all real numbers. Assume $f(2)=2$, $f'(2)=4$, $f''(2)=-6$, $f'''(2)=12$ and $\left|f^{(4)}(x)\right|<2$ for all real numbers x.

   (a) Write the second order Taylor polynomial for f about $x=2$ and use it to approximate the value of $f(1.8)$.

   (b) Write the third order Taylor polynomial for f about $x=2$ and use it to approximate the value of $f(2.3)$.

   (c) Write the second order Taylor polynomial for f', the derivative of f, about $x=2$ and use it to approximate the value of $f'(2.3)$.

   (d) Use the Lagrange error bound on your approximation for $f(2.3)$ found in part (b) to explain why $2.983 < f(2.3) < 2.985$.

5. The Maclaurin series for $f(x)$ is given by

$$f(x) = \frac{1}{2} - \frac{x^2}{4!} + \frac{x^4}{6!} - \frac{x^6}{8!} + \ldots + \frac{(-1)^{n+1} x^{2n-2}}{(2n)!} + \ldots$$

   (a) Find the interval of convergence for the series. Justify your answer.

   (b) Let $h(x) = x^2 \cdot f(x)$. Write the first four nonzero terms and the general term of the Maclaurin series for $h(x)$.

   (c) Write $h(x)$ in terms of a familiar function.

   (d) Write $f(x)$ in terms of the same familiar function.

Chapter 10 Free Response Questions

Question	AB	BC	No Calculator	Calculator Required	Neutral Calculator
1		x			x
2		x	x		
3		x	x		
4		x		x	
5		x	x		

Chapter 10 Solutions to Free Response Questions

1.

(a) $a_0 = 3$, $a_1 = -3$, $a_2 = \dfrac{3}{2!}$, $a_3 = -\dfrac{3}{3!}$, $a_n = \dfrac{(-1)^n \cdot 3}{n!}$

$$g(x) = \sum_{n=0}^{\infty} \frac{(-1)^n \cdot 3}{n!} x^n = 3 - 3x + \frac{3}{2!} x^2 - \frac{3}{3!} x^3 + \cdots + \frac{(-1)^n \cdot 3}{n!} x^n + \cdots$$

(b) Ratio Test: $L = \lim\limits_{n \to \infty} |x| \dfrac{n!}{(n+1)!} = |x| \cdot \lim\limits_{n \to \infty} \dfrac{1}{n+1} = 0$. $L < 1$ for all real numbers, so the interval of convergence is all real numbers.

(c) $g(x) = \sum\limits_{n=0}^{\infty} \dfrac{(-1)^n \cdot 3}{n!} x^n = 3 \sum\limits_{n=0}^{\infty} \dfrac{(-1)^n}{n!} x^n = 3e^{-x}$.

(d) $g(x) = \sum\limits_{n=0}^{\infty} \dfrac{(-1)^n \cdot 3}{n!} x^n \Rightarrow g'(x) = \sum\limits_{n=1}^{\infty} \dfrac{(-1)^n \cdot 3}{(n-1)!} x^{n-1} = -3 + 3x - \dfrac{3}{2!} x^2 + \dfrac{3}{3!} x^3 - \cdots$

$g'(1) = -3 + 3 - \dfrac{3}{2!} + \dfrac{3}{3!} - \dfrac{3}{4!} + \cdots$ and $g'(x) = -3e^{-x} \Rightarrow g'(1) = -\dfrac{3}{e}$.

2.

(a) $f(x) = (1+x)^{\frac{1}{3}}$, $f(x) = \dfrac{1}{3}(1+x)^{-\frac{2}{3}}$, $f''(x) = \dfrac{1}{3} \cdot \dfrac{-2}{3}(1+x)^{-\frac{5}{3}}$, $f'''(x) = \dfrac{1}{3} \cdot \dfrac{-2}{3} \cdot \dfrac{-5}{3}(1+x)^{-\frac{8}{3}}$

$a_0 = 1 \cdot \dfrac{1}{0!} = 1$, $a_1 = \dfrac{1}{3} \cdot \dfrac{1}{1!} = \dfrac{1}{3}$, $a_2 = \dfrac{1}{3} \cdot \dfrac{-2}{3} \cdot \dfrac{1}{2!} = -\dfrac{1}{9}$, $a_3 = \dfrac{1}{3} \cdot \dfrac{-2}{3} \cdot \dfrac{-5}{3} \cdot \dfrac{1}{3!} = \dfrac{5}{81}$

$f(x) \approx T_4(x) = 1 + \dfrac{1}{3}x - \dfrac{1}{9}x^2 + \dfrac{5}{81}x^3$

(b) $f(1.1) \approx T_4(0.1) = 1 + \dfrac{1}{3}(0.1) - \dfrac{1}{9}(0.1)^2 + \dfrac{5}{81}(0.1)^3$

(c) $g(x) = f(x^3) \approx T_4(x^3) = 1 + \dfrac{1}{3}(x^3) - \dfrac{1}{9}(x^3)^2 + \dfrac{5}{81}(x^3)^3 = 1 + \dfrac{1}{3}x^3 - \dfrac{1}{9}x^6 + \dfrac{5}{81}x^9$

(d) $h(x) = 3 + \int_0^x h'(t)\,dt = 3 + \int_0^x g(t)\,dt \approx 3 + \int_0^x \left(1 + \frac{1}{3}t^3 - \frac{1}{9}t^6 + \frac{5}{81}t^9\right)dt$

$$h(x) \approx 3 + x + \frac{1}{12}x^4 - \frac{1}{63}x^7.$$

3.

(a) $\dfrac{1}{1+t^2}$ is the sum of an infinite geometric series with a first term of 1 and a ratio of $-t^2$.

$$f(t) = 1 - t^2 + t^4 - t^6 + \cdots + (-1)^n t^{2n} + \cdots = \sum_{n=0}^{\infty} (-1)^n t^{2n}.$$

(b) $H(x) = \int_0^x t\,f(t)\,dt = \int_0^x \left(t - t^3 + t^5 - t^7 + \cdots\right) dt$

$$H(x) = \frac{1}{2}x^2 - \frac{1}{4}x^4 + \frac{1}{6}x^6 - \frac{1}{8}x^8 + \cdots + \frac{(-1)^{n-1}}{2n}x^{2n} + \cdots = \sum_{n=1}^{\infty} \frac{(-1)^{n-1}}{2n}x^{2n}$$

(c) Ratio Test: $L = \lim_{n\to\infty} |x^2| \dfrac{2n}{2n+2} = x^2$. $L < 1$ for $-1 < x < 1$. At both endpoints the series is

$\displaystyle\sum_{n=1}^{\infty} \frac{(-1)^{n-1}}{2n}$. This is a convergent alternating series because its terms alternate in sign and the

magnitude of the terms is monotonically decreasing to zero. The interval of convergence is $-1 \le x \le 1$.

(d) $H(x) = \int_0^x \dfrac{t}{1+t^2}\,dt = \dfrac{1}{2}\int_0^x \dfrac{2t\,dt}{1+t^2} = \dfrac{1}{2}\ln(1+t^2)\Big|_0^x = \dfrac{1}{2}\left(\ln(1+x^2) - \ln 1\right)$

$$H(x) = \frac{1}{2}\ln(1+x^2).$$

4.

(a) $f(x) \approx T_2(x) = 2 + 4(x-2) - \dfrac{6}{2!}(x-2)^2 = 2 + 4(x-2) - 3(x-2)^2;$

$$f(1.8) \approx T_2(1.8) = 2 + 4(-0.2) - 3(-0.2)^2 = 1.08$$

(b) $f(x) \approx T_3(x) = 2 + 4(x-2) - \dfrac{6}{2!}(x-2)^2 + \dfrac{12}{3!}(x-2)^3 = 2 + 4(x-2) - 3(x-2)^2 + 2(x-2)^3$

$f(2.3) \approx T_3(2.3) = 2 + 4(0.3) - 3(0.3)^2 + 2(0.3)^3 = 2.984$

(c) $f'(x) \approx T_3'(x) = 4 - 6(x-2) + 6(x-2)^2$

$f'(2.3) \approx T_3'(2.3) = 4 - 6(0.3) + 6(0.3)^2 = 2.74$

(d) $E_3 < \dfrac{2}{4!}(2.3-2)^4 = 0.000675 \Rightarrow 2.984 - 0.000675 < f(2.3) < 2.984 + 0.000675$

$2.983 < 2.983325 < f(2.3) < 2.984675 < 2.985$

$2.983 < f(2.3) < 2.985$

5.

(a) Ratio Test: $L = \lim\limits_{n \to \infty} |x^2| \dfrac{(2n)!}{(2n+2)!} = x^2 \lim\limits_{n \to \infty} \dfrac{1}{(2n+2)(2n+1)} = 0$. $L < 1$ for all real numbers.

The interval of convergence is all real numbers.

(b) $h(x) = x^2 \cdot f(x) = \dfrac{x^2}{2} - \dfrac{x^4}{4!} + \dfrac{x^6}{6!} - \dfrac{x^8}{8!} + \cdots + \dfrac{(-1)^{n+1} x^{2n}}{(2n)!} + \cdots$

(c) $\cos x = 1 - \dfrac{x^2}{2} + \dfrac{x^4}{4!} - \dfrac{x^6}{6!} + \cdots + \dfrac{(-1)^{n+1} x^n}{(2n)!} + \cdots$

$\cos x = 1 - \left(\dfrac{x^2}{2} - \dfrac{x^4}{4!} + \dfrac{x^6}{6!} - \dfrac{x^8}{8!} + \cdots + \dfrac{(-1)^{n+1} x^{2n}}{(2n)!} + \cdots \right) = 1 - h(x)$

$$h(x) = 1 - \cos x$$

(d) $\quad h(x) = 1 - \cos x = x^2 \cdot f(x)$

$$f(x) = \begin{cases} \dfrac{1 - \cos x}{x^2} & \text{for} \quad x \neq 0 \\[3mm] \dfrac{1}{2} & \text{for} \quad x = 0 \end{cases}$$

AP Teacher Tips
Chapter 11: Differential Equations

The AP Calculus AB and BC curricula require students to analytically solve first order separable differential equations from modeled phenomenon or from symbolically stated differential equations with or without boundary conditions. The graphical interpretation of solutions via slope fields was included in both Calculus AB and BC syllabi starting in the 2003-2004 academic year for the 2004 AP Examinations. However, the numerical approximation technique, Euler's Method, is currently a BC-only topic, as is the study of logistic growth. Thus the following guide should be used in referencing appropriate AP coverage in Chapter 11:

Calculus AB: Sections 1, 2, 4, 5, 6
Calculus BC: Sections 1 - 7 all

Also in introducing Chapter 11, you may want to review the first elementary concepts of differential equations presented in Chapter 6, Section 3.

In case an AP teacher might be inclined to avoid problems which involve differential equations of higher order than the first order or to avoid any type that is not separable, it is advised that these constraints were placed on analytical solutions in the AP syllabus. Certainly students should be able to verify solutions as in problems 9 - 16 on pages 525 - 526, and to analyze solutions on a slope field as in problems 3 and 4 on page 530, and BC students to should be able to find numerical approximations via Euler's Method as in problems 1, 4, 8 on pages 534 - 535. All of the above-cited problems involve differential equations which are not first order separable, but in none of the problems is the student asked to analytically solve the differential equation. The rich experience of analyzing a slope field and/or applying Euler's Method for numerical approximations allows students to "see beyond" the analytical knowledge they possess and to propose characteristics of a solution.

In Section 2, slope fields are presented via computer drawings; however, the student experience with drawing a slope field at specified points on the coordinate plane have been frequently tested on the free-response sections of recent AP exams. Because it can be a tedious process to draw a slope field by hand and produce a sufficient number of tangent segments to see the generalized field, try the following class exercise:

- Give each student a coordinate point position on a [-3, 3] x [-3, 3] coordinate grid. In terms of integer-valued coordinate points this would mean a maximum 49 points are available. If your class is 24 or fewer students you may want to give two coordinate points to each student.

- Project a [-3, 3] x [-3, 3] coordinate lattice on your chalkboard or white board from your overhead-graphing calculator. If this is not possible you may construct an overhead transparency grid or chalkboard grid.

- Choose a differential equation for students to model as a slope field. For example if the equation is $\frac{dy}{dx} = x - y$, instruct each student to compute the slope, $\frac{dy}{dx}$, at their coordinate point position. Thus, if a student has coordinate point (1, -1) then the slope at that point is $\frac{dy}{dx} = x - y = 1 - (-1) = 2$.

- When each student has computed his/her slope ask them to come to the board and draw a short line segment with the coordinate point as midpoint and having the slope determined by the differential equation. You may want to provide a ruler or meterstick to assist students in making appropriate slope measurements.

- When all have recorded their data graphically, stand back and have the students review the result. Typically individual errors will be glaringly obvious upon inspection.

- Choose a student point to be the point on a solution curve, have them draw their solution curve on the board. Challenge all students to find "their solution curve." Compare and contrast solutions.

This is a dynamic exercise that involves the entire class and takes relatively little time as compared to an individual student attempting to draw the same. While still "sitting" on their coordinate points you might ask the students to compute the concavity at their point and check for consistency with the proposed solution curve through their point. Or have students find all other peers with the same slope, thereby identifying isoclines in the field. Or ask if there are any unusual slope situations and what does this imply about a solution curve? The fun and challenges are endless…

In Section 3, Euler's Method (BC topic) could also be a "class draw" similar to the suggested activity for slope fields above. However in this activity the class could:

- Identify a point on the solution curve, example $\frac{dy}{dx} = x - y$ at point (1, -1).

- Ask a student to come to the board and draw a tangent line from point (1, -1) which extends to $x = 1.5$. That student should then hand the chalk to another student to draw a new tangent line in the slope field at $x = 1.5$ for this differential equation and extend it to $x = 2$. The y value at $x = 2$ obtained from the process above is the Euler's Method approximation for $y(2)$ for the differential equation. Students should analyze the process and declare whether the approximation is an overestimate or an underestimate of the actual solution value at the point.

- You could now (with grid enlargement) ask 4 students to do the same Euler's process, but this time with each student moving over only 0.25, that is, from $x = 1$ to $x = 1.25$ and from $x = 1.25$ to $x = 1.5$ and so on until $x = 2$. The four line segments drawn have iterated a new solution for $y(2)$, and the question to consider is whether this is a better approximation.

- Finally a larger number of iterations could be accomplished by passing a card of information from one student to the next where the Δx, incremental change could be determined by the number of students involved. In this case the numerical iterations would be emphasized over the graphics as the size of Δx becomes difficult to draw. In the end check the $y(2)$ solution (if doing the problem above) against the true solution which in this case is

$y(2) = 1 - \dfrac{1}{e} \approx 0.63212...$ (Note: the AP exam requires an answer correct to the thousandths place, however, students should be wary of intermediate rounding to the third decimal place in developing this final answer.) You could check students' answers with an Euler approximation program on the graphing calculator thus leading into a discussion of the use of a calculator or computer program. Caution: do this exercise first before using an Euler program, but allow the use of calculators for the numerical efficiency they bring. If answers go astray (when later checked) there is much to be learned from the process, for example the above mentioned errors in rounding and other mistakes which are obvious departures from the slope field trend, steps made too large or too small for the corresponding y-result, etc.

In Section 4 the analytical technique of separation of variables is reviewed and reinforced while Sections 5-7 emphasize modeling verbal descriptions as differential equations and subsequently solving by the analytic method of Section 4.

Chapter 11 Multiple Choice Questions

1. Determine the maximum value of the solution to the initial value problem:

$$\frac{dy}{dt} = y - 2yt, \ y(0) = 1.$$

(A) $e^{-\frac{1}{2}}$ (B) $e^{-\frac{1}{4}}$ (C) 1   (D) $e^{\frac{1}{4}}$ (E) $e^{\frac{1}{2}}$

2. For what value of the constant k does $y = x^2 + 2x + k$ satisfy the differential equation $xy' - y = x^2 + 1$?

(A) -1 (B) 0   (C) $\frac{1}{2}$

(D) 1   (E) cannot be determined

3. If $\frac{dP}{dt} = P(50 - 0.5P)$, then $\lim\limits_{t \to \infty} P =$

(A) 0   (B) 25   (C) 50   (D) 100   (E) 200

4. If $\frac{dy}{dx} = x - y$ then at the point (0, 1), the solution curve is:

(A) increasing and concave up
(B) increasing and concave down
(C) decreasing and concave up
(D) decreasing and concave down
(E) not differentiable

5. If $\frac{dy}{dt} = -2ty$ with boundary condition $y(-1) = -1$, the functional solution $y(t) =$

(A) $-e^{-t^2}$ (B) e^{1-t^2} (C) $-e^{1-t^2}$ (D) $e^{-t^2} + 1$ (E) $1 - e^{-t^2}$

6. If $y' = \dfrac{2x}{x+y}$, then the slope field for this differentiable equation is:

(A)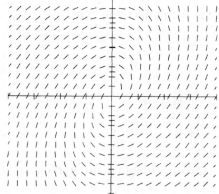

(B)

(C)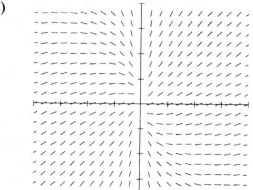

(D)

(E)

7. Use Euler's Method with $\Delta x = \dfrac{1}{2}$ to approximate the value of y at $x = 1$ for the solution curve to the differential equation $\dfrac{dy}{dx} = 2x^2 - y^2$ which passes through $(0, 1)$.

(A) $\dfrac{1}{4}$ (B) $\dfrac{3}{8}$ (C) $\dfrac{1}{2}$ (D) $\dfrac{5}{8}$ (E) $\dfrac{7}{8}$

x	$f(x)$	$f'(x)$
1	2	-1
1.5		-2
2		

8. A table of values for a continuous function f and its derivative f' is shown above. Given that $f(1) = 2$, and using Euler's method to compute the missing table values, an approximate value for $f(2)$ is

(A) $\dfrac{1}{4}$ (B) $\dfrac{1}{2}$ (C) $\dfrac{3}{4}$ (D) 1   (E) $\dfrac{3}{2}$

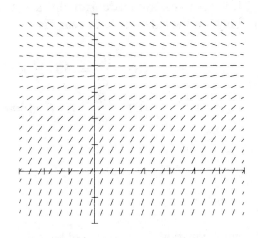

9. The slope field shown above is best analytically described as

(A) $\dfrac{dy}{dx} = e^{y-4}$ (B) $\dfrac{dy}{dx} = 4 - \ln|x|$ (C) $\dfrac{dy}{dx} = 2 - \dfrac{y}{2}$

(D) $\dfrac{dy}{dx} = y^2 - 4y$ (E) $\dfrac{dy}{dx} = (y-4)^2$

203

10. The motion of a particle moving along the x-axis is determined by the differential equation $\frac{dx}{dt} = x^2 - 2t^2$ where $x(t)$ represents the position of a particle at time t. If a particle is at $x = 4$ at time $t = 2$, what is the acceleration of the particle at this time?

(A) −128 (B) −8 (C) 0 (D) 48 (E) 56

11. The rate of change with respect to time in the volume, V, of a sphere is inversely proportional, with proportionality constant k, to the square of the sphere's radius, r. A differential equation representing the change in the radius with respect to time is:

(A) $\frac{dr}{dt} = \frac{k}{\pi r^2}$
(B) $\frac{dr}{dt} = k\pi r^4$
(C) $\frac{dr}{dt} = \frac{k}{4\pi r^4}$

(D) $\frac{dr}{dt} = k\pi r^2$
(E) $\frac{dr}{dt} = \frac{k}{r^2}$

12. A deposit of \$10,000 is made into an account paying 7.5% interest compounded annually. Withdrawals totaling \$1,000 per year are made from this account. The differential equation describing the rate of change of the balance, B, in year t is:

(A) $\frac{dB}{dt} = 10,000 - 1000t$
(B) $\frac{dB}{dt} = 750 - 1000t$

(C) $\frac{dB}{dt} = 10,000 - 250t$
(D) $\frac{dB}{dt} = 750B - 1000$

(E) $\frac{dB}{dt} = 0.075B - 1000$

13. A solution to the differential equation $\frac{dy}{dx} = 5y$ could be

(A) $y = \ln|5x|$
(B) $y = \ln|x + 5|$
(C) $y = -\frac{1}{5}e^{-5x}$

(D) $y = e^{5x-1}$
(E) $y = 5x$

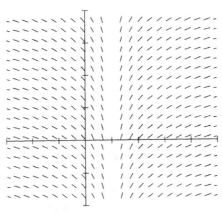

14. A slope field for a differential equation $\dfrac{dy}{dx} = f(x, y)$ is shown above. Which of the following could be a solution?

(A) $y = (x-1)^2$

(B) $y = -\dfrac{1}{|x-1|}$

(C) $y = \dfrac{1}{e^{|1-x|}}$

(D) $y = -\dfrac{1}{(x-1)^2}$

(E) $y = \ln|x-1|$

15. A rumor spreads through a high school population at the rate $\dfrac{dy}{dt} = 0.1y(1-y)$, where y is the fraction of the population that heard the rumor at time t. Which of the following statements are true for this logistic differential equation?

  I. If initially $\dfrac{1}{2}$ of the students have heard the rumor, then the rumor will spread thereafter at a decreasing rate.

  II. The rumor always spreads at an increasing rate.

  III. The time of most rapid spread of the rumor occurs when $\dfrac{1}{20}$ of the population has heard the rumor.

(A) I only

(B) II only

(C) III only

(D) I and III only

(E) II and III only

205

16. If $\dfrac{dy}{dx} = \dfrac{y-2}{x+1}$ and $y(1) = -2$ then $y(2) =$

(A) –4   (B) –3   (C) –2   (D) –1   (E) 0

17. A car travels at a constant speed, then uniformly brakes until it stops. Which of the following graphs would best represent the car's position $s(t)$?

(A)

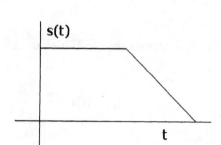

(B)

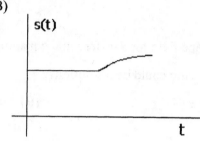

(C)

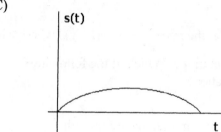

(D)

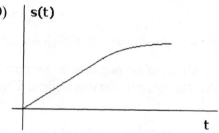

(E)

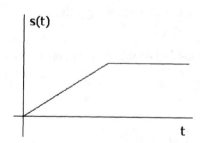

18. If $\frac{dy}{dt} = y(1-y)(2-y)$, then which of the following are true:

    I.   If $y(0) = \frac{1}{2}$ then $\lim_{t \to \infty} y(t) = 0$

    II.   If $y(1) = \frac{3}{2}$ then $\lim_{t \to \infty} y(t) = 1$

    III. If $y(2) = \frac{5}{2}$ then $\lim_{t \to \infty} y(t) = 2$

(A) I only   (B) II only   (C) III only

(D) II and III only   (E) I, II, and III

19. For what value of the constant r is $y = e^{rx}$ a solution to the differential equation $y' + \frac{y}{2} = 0$?

(A) -2 (B) $-\frac{1}{2}$ (C) 0   (D) $\frac{1}{2}$ (E) 2

20. A heated cup of coffee of temperature 130°F is placed in a room of constant temperature 70°F. Newton's Law of Cooling describes the cooling process of the coffee temperature T with respect to time t as:

(A) $\frac{dT}{dt} = kT$ (B) $\frac{dT}{dt} = k(T-60)$ (C) $\frac{dT}{dt} = \frac{130k}{T}$

(D) $\frac{dT}{dt} = k(T-70)$ (E) $\frac{dT}{dt} = k(130-T)$

Chapter 11 Multiple Choice Questions

Question	Answer	AB	BC	No Calculator	Calculator Required	Neutral Calculator
1	D	x	x			x
2	A	x	x			x
3	D		x			x
4	C	x	x			x
5	C	x	x			x
6	E	x	x	x		
7	D		x	x		
8	B		x			x
9	C	x	x	x		
10	E	x	x			x
11	C	x	x			x
12	E	x	x			x
13	D	x	x			x
14	E	x	x			x
15	A		x			x
16	A	x	x			x
17	D	x	x			x
18	B		x			x
19	B	x	x			x
20	D	x	x			x

Chapter 11 Free Response Questions

1. Given the differential equation $\dfrac{dy}{dx} = x(1-y)$

    (a) Find the general solution for y.

    (b) Find the particular solution whose tangent line at $x = 1$ has slope 4.

2. Let $P(t)$ be the population of rabbits in a nature park at time t, where t is measured in years. The rabbit population in the park is increasing at a rate directly proportional to $1000 - P(t)$. The initial population was 50 and the population doubled by the end of the first half-year.

    (a) Find a function for $P(t)$

    (b) Find the time (in years) when the population will reach 500 rabbits.

    (c) Find $\lim\limits_{x \to \infty} P(t)$

3. The volume of a cube is increasing at a rate proportional to the reciprocal of its side length x. At time $t = 0$ minutes, the side length is 1 cm, and at time $t = 9$ minutes the length is 2 cm.

    (a) Find the side length, x, of the cube as a function of time.

    (b) At what time is the numerical rate of change of the volume of the cube changing at five times the numerical rate of change in the side length x?

4. If $\dfrac{dy}{dx} = x + y$

    (a) Sketch a slope field for the given differential equation at the points indicated on the grid below.

    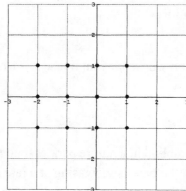

    (b) Let $y = f(x)$ be the particular solution to the given differential equation with the condition that $f(-2) = 1$. Use Euler's Method starting at $x = -2$ and use a step size of 0.5 to approximate $f(0)$.

    (c) Discuss how you think the Euler approximation you obtained for $f(0)$ compares to the actual solution value of $f(0)$.

5. A first rumor spreads through a school population P according to the following logistic differential equation where time t is measured in days.

    Rumor 1: $\dfrac{dP}{dt} = 20P - \dfrac{P^2}{50}$

    A second rumor spreads through the same school population according to the following differential equation, with time t measured in days.

    Rumor 2: $\dfrac{dP}{dt} = 25P - \dfrac{P^2}{40}$

    (a) What is the population, P, of the school?

    (b) Which rumor will spread the fastest through the entire population and why?

    (c) What is the difference in the time it takes the two rumors to spread through half of the population if, for both rumors, they begin with 10 people knowing the rumors?

Chapter 11 Free Response Questions

Question	AB	BC	No Calculator	Calculator Required	Neutral Calculator
1	x	x	x		
2	x	x			x
3	x	x			x
4		x	x		
5		x		x	

Chapter 11 Solutions to Free Response Questions

1.

(a) $\dfrac{dy}{dx} = x(1-y)$

$\displaystyle\int \dfrac{dy}{1-y} = \int x\,dx$

$-\ln|1-y| = \dfrac{x^2}{2} + C$

$\ln|1-y| = -\dfrac{x^2}{2} + C$

$e^{\ln|1-y|} = e^{-\frac{x^2}{2}+C} = e^{-\frac{x^2}{2}} \cdot e^C$

Let $A = e^C$

$\therefore |1-y| = Ae^{-\frac{x^2}{2}}$

$y = 1 + ke^{-\frac{x^2}{2}}$

(b) $4 = 1(1-y)$

$4 = 1 - y$

$-3 = y$

Point is (1, -3)

$4 = Ae^{-\frac{1}{2}}$

$4\sqrt{e} = A$

$1 - y = (4\sqrt{e})e^{-\frac{x^2}{2}}$

$y = 1 - 4e^{\frac{1-x^2}{2}}$

2.

(a) $\dfrac{dP}{dt} = k(1000 - P)$

$\dfrac{dP}{1000 - P} = k\,dt$

$-\ln|1000 - P| = kt + C$

$\ln|1000 - P| = -kt + C$

212

$$|1000 - P| = e^{-kt+C}$$

Let $A = e^C$

$$|1000 - P| = Ae^{-kt}$$

At $t = 0,\ 1000 - 50 = Ae^0$

$$950 = A$$

$$1000 - P = 950e^{-kt}$$

At $t = \dfrac{1}{2},\ 900 = 950e^{-\frac{1}{2}k}$

$$\dfrac{18}{19} = e^{-\frac{1}{2}k}$$

$$\ln\dfrac{18}{19} = -\dfrac{1}{2}k$$

$$-2\ln\left(\dfrac{18}{19}\right) = k$$

$$\therefore 1000 - P = 950e^{2\ln\left(\frac{18}{19}\right)t}$$

$$P = 1000 - 950e^{2t\ln\left(\frac{18}{19}\right)}$$

or

$$P = 1000 - 950\left(\dfrac{18}{19}\right)^{2t}$$

(b) $$500 = 1000 - 950\left(\dfrac{18}{19}\right)^{2t}$$

$$-500 = -950\left(\dfrac{18}{19}\right)^{2t}$$

$$\dfrac{10}{19} = \left(\dfrac{18}{19}\right)^{2t}$$

$$\ln\left(\dfrac{10}{19}\right) = 2t\ln\left(\dfrac{18}{19}\right)$$

$$\dfrac{1}{2}\dfrac{\ln\left(\dfrac{10}{19}\right)}{\ln\left(\dfrac{18}{19}\right)} = t \approx 5.936 \text{ years}$$

(c) $\lim\limits_{t \to \infty} P(t) = 1000$

because $\lim\limits_{t \to \infty} 1000 - 950\left(\dfrac{18}{19}\right)^{2t} = 1000 - 0 = 1000$

3.

(a) $\dfrac{dV}{dt} = \dfrac{k}{x}$

We know that $V = x^3$

Thus, $\dfrac{dV}{dt} = 3x^2 \dfrac{dx}{dt}$

$\therefore 3x^2 \dfrac{dx}{dt} = \dfrac{k}{x}$

$\dfrac{dx}{dt} = \dfrac{k}{3x^3}$

$\int 3x^3 dx = \int k \, dt$

$\dfrac{3x^4}{4} = kt + C$

$\dfrac{3}{4} = C$

$\dfrac{3}{4} x^4 = kt + \dfrac{3}{4}$

$x^4 = \dfrac{4}{3} kt + 1$

$16 = \dfrac{4}{3} k(9) + 1$

$15 = 12k$

$\dfrac{5}{4} = k$

$x^4 = \dfrac{5}{3} t + 1$

$x = \sqrt[4]{\dfrac{5}{3} t + 1}$

(b)   From part (a), $\dfrac{dV}{dt} = 3x^2 \dfrac{dx}{dt}$ and $x = \sqrt[4]{\dfrac{5}{3}t + 1}$

$\therefore \dfrac{dV}{dt} = 3\left(\sqrt[4]{\dfrac{5}{3}t + 1}\right)^2 \dfrac{dx}{dt}$

$\dfrac{dV}{dt} = 3\sqrt{\dfrac{5}{3}t + 1}\,\dfrac{dx}{dt}$

$3\sqrt{\dfrac{5}{3}t + 1}\,\dfrac{dx}{dt} = 5\dfrac{dx}{dt}$

$3\sqrt{\dfrac{5}{3}t + 1} = 5$

$\dfrac{5}{3}t + 1 = \dfrac{25}{9}$

$\dfrac{5}{3}t = \dfrac{16}{9}$

$t = \dfrac{16}{15}\,\text{min}$

4.
(a)

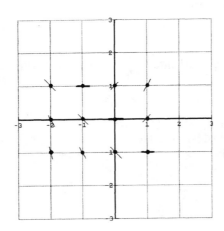

(b)

x	y	$\Delta y = (x+y)\Delta x = (x+y)(0.5)$
-2	1	-1(0.5) = -0.5
-1.5	0.5	-1(0.5) = -0.5
-1	0	-1(0.5) = -0.5
-0.5	-0.5	-1(0.5) = -0.5
0	-1	

$\therefore f(0) = -1$

(c)   Note in part (b) above that Euler's approximation computes a constant delta y for each increment. Thus the iterated values of y all fall on the line $y = -x - 1$. Looking at the slope field, all points that are on the line $y = -x - 1$ have slopes of -1. It is apparent graphically that a solution curve through (-2,-1) would follow along the line $y = -x - 1$. Furthermore, as shown below, $y = -x - 1$ meets the differential equation's specifications.

$$\frac{dy}{dx} = -1, \quad y(-2) = 1$$

$$\frac{dy}{dx} = x + y = -2 + 1 = -1$$

Thus, the Euler approximation for $f(0)$ is the same as the actual solution $f(0)$.

5.   Rumor 1: $\dfrac{dP}{dt} = 20P - \dfrac{P^2}{50} = \dfrac{1}{50} P(1000 - P)$

Rumor 2: $\dfrac{dP}{dt} = 25P - \dfrac{P^2}{40} = \dfrac{1}{40} P(1000 - P)$

(a)   The school's population is 1000 since $\dfrac{dP}{dt} = 0$ when P = 1000

(b)   Rumor 2 will spread the fastest because $\dfrac{dP}{dt}$ is greater for the value k = $\dfrac{1}{40}$ compared to the value k = $\dfrac{1}{50}$.

(c) $\dfrac{dP}{dt} = kP(1000 - P)$

$$\int \frac{dP}{P(1,000 - P)} = \int k \, dt$$

By partial fractions decomposition
$$\frac{1}{P(1000 - P)} = \frac{A}{P} + \frac{B}{1000 - P} = \frac{A(1000 - P) + BP}{P(1000 - P)}$$

When $A = \dfrac{1}{1000}$ and $B = \dfrac{1}{1000}$

$$\int \frac{\frac{1}{1000}}{P} + \frac{\frac{1}{1000}}{1000-P}\, dP = kt + C$$

$$\frac{1}{1000}\left(\ln P - \ln|1000 - P|\right) = kt + C$$

$$\ln \frac{P}{1000-P} = 1000(kt + C)$$

When $t = 0$, $P = 10$

$$\ln \frac{10}{990} = 1000C$$

$$\frac{1}{1000}\ln \frac{1}{99} = C$$

$$\ln \frac{P}{1000-P} = 1000\left(kt + \frac{1}{1000}\ln \frac{1}{99}\right)$$

$$\ln \frac{P}{1000-P} = 1000kt + \ln \frac{1}{99}$$

Rumor 1: P = 500 and k = $\frac{1}{50}$ $\qquad$ $\ln \frac{500}{500} = \frac{1000}{50}t + \ln \frac{1}{99}$ $\qquad$ $t = 0.22975599$ days

Rumor 2: P = 500 and k = $\frac{1}{40}$ $\qquad$ $\ln \frac{500}{500} = 25t + \ln \frac{1}{99}$ $\qquad$ $t = 0.18380479$ days

The difference in time is 0.046 days.

1. The average value of $f(x) = e^{-x^2}$ on the interval $-1 \leq x \leq 1$ is nearest to

   (A) 0.60   **(B)** 0.65   **(C)** 0.70   **(D)** 0.75   **(E)** 0.80

2. If the line $x = c$ divides in half the area under the graph of $f(x) = x^2 + 1$ from $x = 0$ to $x = 1$, then c is nearest to

   (A) 0.58   **(B)** 0.60   **(C)** 0.62   **(D)** 0.64   **(E)** 0.66

3. The maximum value of $f(x) = x(x - 5)(x - 10)$ on the interval $0 \leq x \leq 11$ is nearest to

   (A) 48   **(B)** 54   **(C)** 60   **(D)** 66   **(E)** 72

4. If the maximum value of $f(x) = x(x - 1)(x - 2)$ on the interval $0 \leq x \leq b$ occurs both at the endpoint $x = b$ and at another point inside the interval, then b is nearest to

   (A) 2.05   **(B)** 2.15   **(C)** 2.25   **(D)** 2.35   **(E)** 2.45

5. The absolute minimum value of $f(x) = 100e^{-x} \sin x$ for $x \geq 0$ is nearest to

   (A) -10 **(B)** -7 **(C)** -4 **(D)** -1 **(E)** f has no absolute minimum value for $x \geq 0$

6. If $f'(x) = \sin(x^2)$ for all x and $f(1) = 3$ then $f(2)$ is nearest to

   (A) 2.0   **(B)** 2.5   **(C)** 3.0   **(D)** 3.5   **(E)** 4.0

7. The number of inflection points for the graph of $f(x) = x + \cos(x^2)$ in the interval $0 \leq x \leq 5$ is

   (A) 6   **(B)** 7   **(C)** 8   **(D)** 9   **(E)** 10

8. The velocity of a weight attached to a spring is given by $v(t) = e^{-t} \sin 4t$. The total distance traveled by the weight from time $t = 0$ to time $t = 1$ is nearest to

   (A) 0.30   **(B)** 0.32   **(C)** 0.34   **(D)** 0.36   **(E)** 0.38

9. The position of a weight attached to a spring is given by $x(t) = e^{-t} \sin 4t$. The total distance traveled by the weight from time $t = 0$ to $t = 1$ is nearest to

   (A) 1.3   **(B)** 1.4   **(C)** 1.5   **(D)** 1.6   **(E)** 1.7

10. Suppose that $x \geq 0$ and $x + 4 \geq x^4$. Then which of the following is the largest value that could be x?

    (A) 1.52   **(B)** 1.53   **(C)** 1.54   **(D)** 1.55   **(E)** 1.56

11. The largest interval containing $x = 1$ such that the tangent line approximation to $f(x) = \ln x$ at $x = 1$ has error at most 0.1 has length

    (A) 0.90   **(B)** 0.95   **(C)** 1.00   **(D)** 1.05   **(E)** 1.10

12. The total area enclosed between the graphs of $y = 3 \sin x$ and $y = x + 1$ is

    (A) 5.2   **(B)** 5.3   **(C)** 5.4   **(D)** 5.5   **(E)** 5.6

13. Suppose that c is a positive number such that $x^3 - x = c$ has exactly two roots. Then the positive root is nearest to

    (A) 1.2   **(B)** 1.3   **(C)** 1.4   **(D)** 1.5   **(E)** 1.6

14. What is the area of the largest rectangle with its base on the x-axis that can be inscribed under the graph of $y = \cos x$, for $\frac{-\pi}{2} \leq x \leq \frac{\pi}{2}$?

    (A) 1.10   **(B)** 1.12   **(C)** 1.14   **(D)** 1.16   **(E)** 1.18

15. The graph of $y = \frac{\sin x}{x}$ has

    (I) A vertical asymptote at $x = 0$

    (II) A horizontal asymptote at $y = 0$

    (III) An infinite number of zeroes

    (A) I only   **(B)** II only   **(C)** III only   **(D)** I and III only   **(E)** II and III only

16. Two particles start at $t = 0$ and move along the x-axis. For $0 \leq t \leq 2\pi$, their respective position functions are given by
$$x_1 = \cos(2t) \qquad \text{and} \qquad x_2 = e^{\frac{t-3}{2}} - 0.75$$
For how many values of t do the particle have the same velocity?

    (A)   0   **(B)**   1   **(C)**   2   **(D)**   3   **(E)**   4

17. The area of the region bounded above by the curve $y = \arctan x$ and below by the curve $y = x^2 + 3x$ is approximately

    (A)   2.06   **(B)**   2.12   **(C)**   2.18   **(D)**   2.24   **(E)**   2.30

18. How many inflection points does the graph of $y = \sin x - \frac{1}{3}\sin(3x) - \frac{1}{5}\sin(5x)$ have on the interval $0 < x < \pi$?

    (A)   0   **(B)**   1   **(C)**   2   **(D)**   4   **(E)**   5

19. The average rate of change of the function $f(x) = \int_0^x \sqrt{1 + \sin(t^2)}\, dt$ over the interval $1 \leq x \leq 3$ is nearest to

    (A)   1.02   **(B)**   1.04   **(C)**   1.06   **(D)**   1.08   **(E)**   1.10

20. A car's velocity function $v(t)$ is displayed in the following graph:

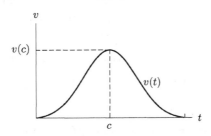

Figure 1

    which of the following is *not* necessarily true?

    I At time $t = c$, the car is stopped.
    II At time $t = c$, the car's acceleration is 0.
    III Over the time interval from 0 to c, the car's average velocity can be measured by evaluating the integral $\dfrac{1}{c}\displaystyle\int_0^c v(t)\, dt.$

    (A)   I only   **(B)**   II only   **(C)**   III only
    (D)   I and II only   **(E)**   all of the above are not necessarily true.

21. If $\displaystyle\lim_{x \to 4} \frac{x^2 - ax - 4}{x - 4}$ exists and $a \neq 0$, then that limit is:

    (A) -4 **(B)**   1   **(C)**   3
    (D)   5   **(E)**   cannot be determined from the given information

22. If $f(x)$ is an even function and $f(a) = b$, then $f(-a) =$

    (A)   0   **(B)** b **(C)** $-b$ **(D)** $2b$ **(E)** $-2b$

23. Which of the following is true if $f(x) = \displaystyle\int_0^x (\sin t + 1)\, dt?$

    I $f(x) > 0$ if $x > 0$ and $f(x) < 0$ if $x < 0$
    II $f'(x) > 0$ if $x > 0$ and $f'(x) < 0$ if $x < 0$
    III $f(x) \neq 0$

    (A)   I only   **(B)**   II only   **(C)**   I and II only   **(D)**   II and III only   **(E)**   I and III only

24. Given the following values of $f(x)$ and $f'(x)$:

Table 1

x	$f(x)$	$f'(x)$
0	1	5
1	3	−2
2	6	−1
4	0	2

If $f(x)$ is a continuous and differentiable function for all values of x and $g(x) = f(x^2)$, then $g'(2) =$

(A) −4   **(B)** 0   **(C)** 2   **(D)** 4   **(E)** 8

25. If a trapezoidal sum approximation (using n subdivisions) to $\int_a^b f(x)\,dx$ underestimates the true values of the integral, then which of the following must be true?

(A) $f(x)$ is always increasing for $a < x < b$
(B) $f(x)$ is always concave up for $a < x < b$
(C) The midpoint approximation (using n subdivisions) to $\int_a^b f(x)\,dx$ will overestimate the value of the integral
(D) $f(x) > 0$ for $a < x < b$
(E) None of the above

26. If $f'(x) = g'(x)$ for all x on $a < x < b$, then which of the following must be true?

  I $f(x) = g(x)$ for all $a < x < b$
  II $f''(x) = g''(x)$ for all $a < x < b$
  III $\int_a^b f'(x),\,dx = \int_a^b g'(x)\,dx$

(A) I only   **(B)** II only   **(C)** III only   **(D)** I and II   **(E)** II and III

27. For any real number a, $\int_{-b}^b |ax|\,dx =$

(A) $\dfrac{ab^2}{2}$ **(B)** ab^2 **(C)** $2ab^2$ **(D)** $|2ab|$ **(E)** $|a| \cdot b^2$

28. If $\int_0^2 f(x)\,dx = 3$ and $\int_0^{-1} f(x)\,dx = 4$, then $\int_{-1}^2 f(x)\,dx =$

 (A) −1   **(B)** 1   **(C)** 5   **(D)** 7   **(E)** 12

29. The following slope field represents possible solutions to a differential equation. (See Figure 2.)

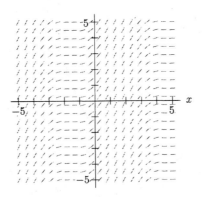

Figure 2

If $f(x)$ is a specific solution to that differential equation where $f(0) = -1$, then $f(5)$ is closest to:

(A) -1 (B) 0 (C) 1

(D) 4 (E) cannot be determined from given information

30. $\displaystyle\int e^{bx}\, dx =$

(A) $e^{bx} + C$ (B) $be^{bx} + C$ (C) $\dfrac{e^{bx}}{b} + C$

(D) $\dfrac{e^{bx+1}}{bx+1} + C$ (E) none of the above

31. $\displaystyle\int \sin 2\theta\, d\theta =$

(A) $\sin^2 \theta + C$ (B) $\cos 2\theta + C$ (C) $2\cos 2\theta + C$

(D) $\dfrac{\cos 2\theta}{2} + C$ (E) $\dfrac{\sin^2 2\theta}{2} + C$

32. Pictured below is a graph of the velocity, v, of a particle at a given time t.

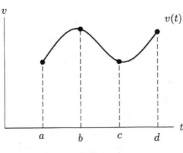

Figure 3

The maximum distance travelled by the particle over the time interval $[a, d]$ occurs at time $t =$

(A) a (B) b (C) c

(D) d (E) cannot be determined from the given information

33. Pictured below is a graph of the velocity, v, of a particle at a given time t.

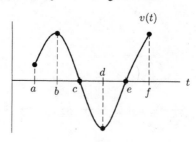

Figure 4

The maximum displacement of the particle over the time interval $[a, f]$ occurs at time $t =$

(A) f (B) b (C) c (D) d (E) e

34.

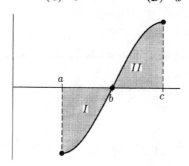

Figure 5

Pictured above is the graph of the function $f(x)$ with the areas of two regions labeled as I and II.
$\int_a^c f(x)\, dx =$

(A) $I + II$ (B) $I - II$ (C) $-(I + II)$ (D) $-(I - II)$ (E) $\dfrac{I + II}{2}$

35. Let v be the volume of the solid generated when revolving the region R (below) about the x-axis:

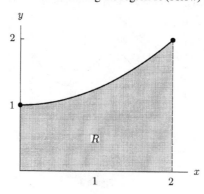

Figure 6

The best upper bound for v that can be determined from the given information is:

(A) π (B) 2π (C) $\dfrac{14}{3}\pi$ (D) $\dfrac{9}{2}\pi$ (E) 8π

222

36. A vase is constructed by rotating the function $g(y)$ about the y-axis, as pictured below, where a represents the height of water in the vase at any given time t.

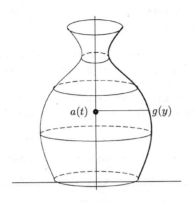

Figure 7

Water is being poured into the vase at a constant rate, $\dfrac{dv}{dt}$, which would be represented by which of the following?

(A) $g'(a) \cdot \dfrac{da}{dt}$

(B) $\pi(g(a))^2 \dfrac{da}{dt}$

(C) $\pi g(a)g'(a)\dfrac{da}{dt}$

(D) $2\pi(g(a))g'(a)\dfrac{da}{dt}$

(E) cannot be determined from given information

37. If $f'(x) = g'(x)$ for all x in their domains, which of the following must be true?

  I $f(x) > g(x)$ for all x in their domains
  II $f(x) - g(x) = C_1$ for some constant C_1
  III $f(x) = C_2 \cdot g(x)$ for some constant C_2

  (A) I only   (B) II only   (C) I and II only   (D) II and III only   (E) I, II, and III

38. How many of the following graphs represent functions which appear to be differentiable on the interval $[a, b]$?

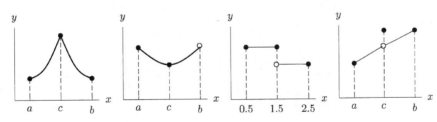

Figure 8

(A) 0   (B) 1   (C) 2   (D) 3   (E) 4

39. Consider the differential equation $\dfrac{dy}{dx} = \dfrac{x}{y}$. A possible solution is:

  I. $y = x$ II. $x^2 + y^2 = 1$ III. $x^2 - y^2 = 1$

  (A) I only   (B) II only   (C) III only   (D) I and III only   (E) II and III only

223

40. Bacteria grow in an exponential fashion, as modeled by the equation $B = Pe^{rt}$ where

$$P = \text{initial number of bacteria present}$$
$$r = \text{rate of growth, in bacteria per hour, of bacteria}$$
$$t = \text{time elapsed, in hours}$$

Suppose that at time $t = 0$ two slices of pizza—one refrigerated and the other at room temperature—have the same number of bacteria on them. The bacteria on the refrigerated pizza have a growth rate of r, while the non-refrigerated one's growth rate is k times that.

If one slice of pizza is put into the refrigerator while the other is left on the counter, how long will it be before the unrefrigerated slice has k times the number of bacteria as the refrigerated slice has on it?

(A) (kt) hours

(B) $\left(\dfrac{\ln k}{r - kr}\right)$ hours

(C) $\left(\dfrac{\ln k}{r(k-1)}\right)$ hours

(D) $\ln k(r(k-1))$ hours

(E) cannot be determined from the given information

41. Given a continuous function $f(x)$ which is concave up over the interval (a, b), which of the following approximations, each using the same finite number of subintervals, will overestimate the true value of $\displaystyle\int_a^b f(x)\,dx$?

I left-hand endpoint approximation
II trapezoidal approximation
III midpoint approximation

(A) I only (B) II only (C) III only (D) I and II (E) I and III

42. The volume of the solid which is bounded above by the function $f(x)$ (as shown below) and whose cross sections are squares is:

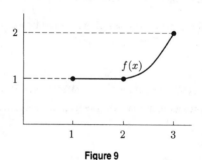

Figure 9

(A) $2\frac{1}{3}$

(B) $2\frac{1}{2}$

(C) $\displaystyle\int_1^3 \pi(f(x))^2\,dx$

(D) $1 + \displaystyle\int_2^3 (f(x))^2\,dx$

(E) $\displaystyle\int_1^3 f(x)\,dx$

43. The curve $y = 2^x$ and $y = x^2$ have the same slope when $x =$

(A) 0.4851 (B) 2 (C) 3.4212 (D) 3.6124

(E) the curves never have the same slope

44. If $f(t)$ is measured in dollars per hour and t is measured in seconds, which of the following integrals has units measured in dollars?

(A) $\displaystyle\int tf(t)\,dt$

(B) $\displaystyle\int 3600f(t)\,dt$

(C) $\displaystyle\int (60 + f(t))\,dt$

(D) $\displaystyle\int \dfrac{f(t)}{3600}\,dt$

(E) $\displaystyle\int \dfrac{tf(t)}{3600}\,dt$

45. A particle moves in the xy-plane according to the parametric equations

$$x = t^3 + 2t^2, \qquad y = t^3 - 3t$$

For time $-3 \le t \le 3$, there is exactly one point that the particle passes through twice at different times. The x-coordinate of that point is nearest to

(A) 0.2   (B) 0.4   (C) 0.6   (D) 0.8   (E) 1.0

46. The curve given by the parametric equations

$$x = t^2 - 1, \qquad y = t^2 + t$$

intersects the y-axis twice. The length of the portion of the curve between the two y-intercepts is nearest to

(A) 1.101   (B) 1.202   (C) 3.457   (D) 3.547   (E) 3.652

47. Suppose that

$$f(x) = \sum_{n=1}^{\infty} (-1)^{n+1} \frac{x^n}{n}.$$

Then $f(0.8)$ is nearest to

(A) 0.582   (B) 0.584   (C) 0.586   (D) 0.588   (E) 0.590

48. $\lim\limits_{x \to 0} \dfrac{ax}{\sin bx} =$

(A) 0   (B) a (C) $\dfrac{a}{b}$ (D) ab (E) the limit does not exist

49. If the 5th degree Taylor polynomial for $\sin x$ centered at $x = 0$ is used to approximate $\sin x$ for $\frac{-\pi}{2} \le x \le \frac{\pi}{2}$, then the largest error is nearest to

(A) 0.002   (B) 0.004   (C) 0.006   (D) 0.008   (E) 0.010

50. The arclength of one arch of the graph of $y = \sin x$ is nearest to

(A) 1.91   (B) 2.83   (C) 3.82   (D) 4.44   (E) 7.64

51. The fourth term of the Taylor series for e^{2x} expanded about $x = 1$ is:

(A) $\dfrac{e^{6x}}{6}$ (B) $\dfrac{32}{3}x^3$ (C) $e^2(x-1)^3$ (D) $\dfrac{e^2}{6}(x-1)^3$ (E) $\dfrac{4e^2}{3}(x-1)^3$

52. $\displaystyle\int (1 + x^2)^{-1}\, dx =$

(A) $\ln(1 + x^2) + C$ (B) $C + x - \dfrac{x^3}{3} + \dfrac{x^5}{5} - \cdots$ (C) $\tan x + C$

(D) $\dfrac{-1}{(1+x^2)^2} + C$ (E) $\dfrac{-2x}{(1+x^2)^2} + C$

53. The area inside the polar curve $r = a \sin 3\theta$ (where $a > 0$) is represented by which of the following integrals?

(A) $\displaystyle\int_0^\pi a \sin 3\theta\, d\theta$ (B) $\displaystyle\int_0^{2\pi} a \sin 3\theta\, d\theta$ (C) $\displaystyle\int_0^\pi \frac{(a \sin 3\theta)^2}{2}\, d\theta$

(D) $\displaystyle\int_0^{2\pi} \frac{(a \sin 3\theta)^2}{4}\, d\theta$ (E) $\displaystyle\int_0^{2\pi} \frac{1}{2} a \sin^2 3\theta\, d\theta$

54. $\displaystyle\int \frac{1}{x(4-x)}\, dx =$

(A) $\dfrac{1}{4} \displaystyle\int \left(\frac{1}{x} + \frac{1}{4-x}\right) dx$ (B) $\dfrac{1}{4} \displaystyle\int \left(\frac{1}{x} + \frac{1}{x-4}\right) dx$ (C) $\displaystyle\int \left(\frac{1}{4x} + \frac{1}{4(4-x)}\right) dx$

(D) $\displaystyle\int \left(\frac{4}{x} + \frac{4}{4-x}\right) dx$ (E) none of the above

1. D

2. B

   Hint: Just solve $\frac{c^3}{3} + c = \left(\frac{1}{2}\right)\left(\frac{4}{3}\right)$.

3. D

4. B

   Hint: Graph f, move cursor to relative max between 0 and 1, then move cursor horizontally to the right until it meets the curve again.

5. D

6. D

   Hint: Compute $3 + \int_1^2 \sin(x^2)\, dx$.

7. C

8. E

9. E

   Hint: Plot x versus t. There is one max and one min for $0 \le t \le 1$.

10. B

11. A

    Hint: The tangent line is $y = x - 1$ so plot $x - 1 - \ln x$ and find x-coordinates when function first exceeds 0.1.

12. E

13. A

    Hint: This is like Question 4. Put cursor at the relative maximum between -1 and 0. Then move cursor horizontal to the right until it meets the curve again.

14. B

    Hint: Just sketch $2x \cos x$ and trace to max.

15. E

16. E

17. C

18. D

19. A

    Hint: $\frac{(f(3) - f(1))}{2} = \left(\frac{1}{2}\right) \int_1^3 \sqrt{1 + \sin(t^2)}\, dt$.

20. A. From the graph, it can be determined that:

    $$v(c) \ne 0 \implies I \text{ is false}$$

    $v(t)$ is at a maximum at $t = c$. Thus, $a(c) = 0 \implies II$ is true.

    And, by the mean value theorem III is true.

21. D. Since the limit exists, $x - 4$ must be a factor of $x^2 - ax - 4$.

    $$(x - 4)(x + ?) = x^2 - ax - 4$$

    by long division (or observation), it can be determined that the other factor must be $x + 1$. Thus

    $$\lim_{x \to 4} \frac{x^2 - ax - 4}{x - 4} = \lim_{x \to 4} \frac{(x - 4)(x + 1)}{x - 4} = \lim_{x \to 4} x + 1 = 5.$$

22. B. Even functions are symmetric over the y-axis.

23. A. Since $\sin t + 1 \geq 0$ for all values of t, I must be true. $f'(x) = \sin x + 1$ which is always ≥ 0, so II is false. III is also false, since $f(0) = 0$.

24. E. If $g(x) = f(x^2)$, then $g'(x) = f'(x^2) \cdot 2x$. So, $g'(2) = f'(4) \cdot 4 = 8$.

25. E. By counterexample, A can be false. See Figure 1.1.

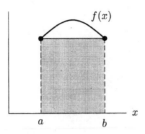

Figure 1.1

B can be false. See Figure 1.1. C can be false. See Figure 1.2.

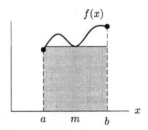

Figure 1.2

D can be false. See Figure 1.3

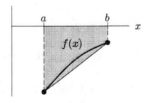

Figure 1.3

26. E. If $f'(x) = g'(x)$, the *slopes* of $f(x)$ and $g(x)$ are equal, thus II and III will be true, but I is not necessarily true.

27. E. $\displaystyle\int_{-b}^{b} |ax|\, dx = |a| \int_{-b}^{b} |x|\, dx$. Considering $\displaystyle\int_{-b}^{b} |x|\, dx$ gives two cases, where $b > 0$ and $b < 0$. In both cases, $\displaystyle\int_{-b}^{b} |x|\, dx = b^2$. So, $\displaystyle\int_{-b}^{b} |ax|\, dx = |a|b^2$.

227

28.

$$A. \int_{-1}^{2} f(x)\,dx = \int_{-1}^{0} f(x)dx + \int_{0}^{2} f(x)\,dx$$

$$= -\int_{0}^{-1} f(x)\,dx + \int_{0}^{2} f(x)\,dx$$

$$= -4 + 3$$

$$= -1$$

29. D

30. C. Let $u = bx$

$$du = b\,dx$$

$$dx = \frac{1}{b}du$$

$$\int e^{bx}\,dx = \int e^{u} \cdot \frac{1}{b}du$$

$$= \frac{1}{b}\int e^{u}\,du$$

$$= \frac{1}{b}(e^{u} + C)$$

$$= \frac{1}{b}e^{bx} + C$$

31.

$$A. \int \sin 2\theta\,d\theta = 2\int \sin\theta\cos\theta\,d\theta$$

$$= 2\left(\frac{\sin^2\theta}{2} + C\right)$$

$$= \sin^2\theta + C$$

32. D. Since velocity is always positive, distance travelled increases as t moves from a to d.

33. C. Displacement is net signed area. After time $t = c$, velocity is negative and the particle moves backwards. At $t = e$, the particle regains forward motion, but (via the diagram) the distance travelled over $e < t < f$ does not make up for the displacement lost over $c < t < e$.

34. D

35. C. The upper bound can be found by revolving the line joining $(0, 1)$ and $(2, 2)$ about the x-axis to form a frustum. The volume of that frustum is:

$$\int_{0}^{2} \pi\left(\frac{x}{2} + 1\right)^2 dx$$

$$= \pi \int_{0}^{2} \left(\frac{x^2}{4} + x + 1\right) dx$$

$$= \pi\left(\frac{x^3}{12} + \frac{x^2}{2} + x\right)\bigg|_{0}^{2}$$

$$= \frac{14}{3}\pi$$

The next lower choice, 2π can be eliminated, as it represents the volume of the cylinder formed by revolving the line $y = 1$ about the x-axis, which is completely contained within the solid.

36. B. Since $v = \int_0^{a(t)} \pi(g(y))^2 \, dy$, by the Second Fundamental Theorem,

$$\frac{dv}{dt} = \pi(g(a(t)))^2 \cdot \frac{d(a(t))}{dt}.$$

37. B. Since $f'(x) = g'(x)$, the functions must have the same slope.
I would be false if $g(x)$ were greater than or equal to $f(x)$
II is true
III would be false, unless $C_2 = 0$ or 1.

38. A. A function is differentiable if it is continuous and a tangent line can be drawn at every point. In the first graph, no tangent line can be drawn when $x = c$. Each of the other graph are discontinuous over $[a, b]$.

39.

$$\text{D. Since } \frac{dy}{dx} = \frac{x}{y}$$
$$y \, dy = x \, dx$$
$$\int y \, dy = \int x \, dx$$
$$\frac{y^2}{2} = \frac{x^2}{2} + C_1$$
$$\frac{x^2}{2} - \frac{y^2}{2} = C_2$$

and $x^2 - y^2 = C_3$ for some constants C_1, C_2, C_3. Thus III is a possible solution, while II is not. If $C_3 = 0$, then

$$x^2 - y^2 = 0$$
$$x^2 = y^2$$

and $x = y$ is a possible solution.

40. C. Let Pe^{rt} be the number of bacteria on the refrigerated slice of pizza, and Pe^{rt} be the number of bacteria on the slice left on the counter at any time t. Consider the equation $k(Pe^{rt}) = Pe^{(kr)t}$, we have

$$\ln(kPe^{rt}) = \ln Pe^{krt}$$
$$\ln k + \ln P + (rt)\ln e = \ln Pe^{krt}$$
$$\ln k = (k-1)rt$$
$$t = \frac{\ln k}{r(k-1)}$$

41. B. The left-hand endpoint approximation could underestimate the true value of the integral, depending on how the function is increasing and decreasing over the interval. Since the function is continuously concave up, the trapezoidal approximation will overestimate and the midpoint approximation will underestimate the integral's true value.

42. D. Each "slice" has volume $(f(x))^2 \Delta x$, so

$$\text{total volume is} = \int_1^3 (f(x))^2 \, dx$$
$$= \int_1^2 (f(x))^2 \, dx + \int_2^3 (f(x))^2 \, dx.$$

Since the function is linear on the interval $1 \le x \le 2$, that part of the solid is a $1 \times 1 \times 1$ unit^3 cube, thus, total volume is $= 1 + \int_2^3 (f(x))^2 \, dx$.

43. A. For $y = 2^x$, $\dfrac{dy}{dx} = 2^x \ln 2$; and for $y = x^2$, $\dfrac{dy}{dx} = 2x$, setting $2x = 2^x \ln 2$, then $2x - 2^x \ln 2 = 0$. By graphing calculator, a solution occurs at $x = 0.4851$.

44. D. $\int f(t) \text{dollars/hour} * dt \text{ seconds} * \dfrac{1}{60} \dfrac{\text{minutes}}{\text{seconds}} * \dfrac{1}{60} \dfrac{\text{hours}}{\text{minutes}} = \int \dfrac{1}{3600} f(t) \, dt$.

45. B

46. C

47. D

Hint: $f(x) = \ln(1 + x)$ so either do lots of terms of the series (say 50) or compute $\ln 1.8$.

48. C. By L'Hopital's Rule: $\lim\limits_{x \to 0} \dfrac{ax}{\sin bx} = \lim\limits_{x \to 0} \dfrac{a}{b \cos bx} = \dfrac{a}{b}$

49. B

Hint: The alternating series error estimate is $\dfrac{(\frac{\pi}{2})^7}{7!} = 0.00468$. The actual largest error is $\sin x - x + \dfrac{x^3}{6} - \dfrac{x^5}{120}$ evaluated at $\frac{\pi}{2}$ which is about 0.00452. Both give same key.

50. Notice that A and B are clearly too small since the interval has length π so the answer must be larger than π. If the sin curve went straight up one unit, over π units, then down one unit, its length would be $\pi + 2 = 5.14$, so E is clearly too large. Even D is suspiciously close to the 5.14 upper bound.

51. E The fourth term of e^{2x} about $x = 0$ is $2^3 x^3 / 3!$, so the fourth term of $e^{2(x-1)}$ about $x = 1$ is $2^3 (x-1)^3 / 3!$. Thus, the fourth term of e^{2x} about $x = 1$ is $e^2 2^3 (x-1)^3 / 3!$.

52. B.

$$\int (1 + x^2)^{-1} \, dx = \int \frac{1}{1 + x^2} \, dx$$
$$= \arctan x + C$$
$$= x - \frac{x^3}{3} + \frac{x^5}{5} - \cdots + C$$

53. C. Although $r < 0$ over specific intervals, it will not have an effect on polar area here, which uses the formula $\int_a^b \dfrac{1}{2} r^2 \, d\theta$.

54. C. Using partial fractions, let $\dfrac{1}{x(4 - x)} = \dfrac{A}{x} + \dfrac{B}{4 - x}$, then

$$\frac{1}{x(4 - x)} = \frac{(4 - x)A + x(B)}{x(4 - x)}$$
$$1 = (4 - x)A + x \cdot B$$
$$1 = 4A - xA + xB$$
$$A = \frac{1}{4} \quad \text{and} \quad x(B - A) = 0$$
$$B - A = 0$$
$$B = A$$
$$B = \frac{1}{4},$$

so

$$\int \frac{1}{x(4 - x)} \, dx = \int \left(\frac{1}{4x} + \frac{1}{4(4 - x)} \right) dx.$$

Lab #1
Definition of the Derivative

In this activity, you will use the difference quotient definition of derivative to find the value of the derivative of a function at a point. You will make a graph of the difference quotient over an interval of inputs on the same axes as the graph of the original function and explore relationships between the graphs. Finally, you will look at points where the derivative fails to exist and, hopefully, see why.

With your graphing calculator in function mode, define Y1 = X^3 and
Y2 = (Y1(X+H)-Y1(X))/H.
Note that Y2 is a difference quotient, defining an approximation for the derivative of Y1 at X.

Note: On the TI-83 or TI-82, in defining Y2, you need to choose Y1 from the Function category of the Y-VARS menu.

On the home screen, we will use Y2 to approximate the derivative of Y1 at X = 0.5 by storing successively smaller values into H and computing Y2(0.5) for each. Fill in the table below. To get the first entry, store 0.1 into H, then evaluate Y2(0.5). Again, on the TI-83 or TI-82, to evaluate Y2(0.5), you need to choose Y2 from the Function category of the Y-VARS menu. To get the rest of the table entries, just store a new value into H, and evaluate Y2(0.5) for each.

H	Y2(0.5)	H	Y2(0.5)
0.1		-0.1	
0.01		-0.01	
0.001		-0.001	
0.0001		-0.0001	

Look at the data in your table to answer these questions.

1. What do you think $\lim\limits_{H \to 0^+} \dfrac{(0.5+H)^3 - 0.5^3}{H}$ (i.e. the right hand limit) is? _____

2. What do you think $\lim\limits_{H \to 0^-} \dfrac{(0.5+H)^3 - 0.5^3}{H}$ (i.e. the left hand limit) is? _____

3. Do your answers to 1 and 2 agree? _____ They should! If they don't, check your work.

This value is called the *derivative of X^3 at $X = 0.5$.* It represents the slope of the line tangent to the graph of $Y = X^3$ at $X = 0.5$.

Now we'll try to approximate the derivative at $X = -0.5$. Evaluate Y2(-0.5). (*H* should be as you left it, probably with the value -0.0001).

4. What do you think the value of the derivative of X^3 at $X = -0.5$ is? _____

As before, your answer to number 4 gives the slope of the line tangent to the graph of $Y = X^3$ at $X = -0.5$.

From your Y= screen, select Y1 and de-select Y2. Then graph Y1 in the decimal viewing window (by pressing zoom decimal). Trace over to X = 0.5. Use your calculator to graph the tangent line at X = 0.5. On the TI-83, the command to draw a tangent line is on the DRAW menu. On the TI-86 or TI-89, the command to draw a tangent line is on the MATH menu of the graph screen. The calculator will tell you the value of dy/dx (the derivative) at this X coordinate. Some calculators will show the equation of the tangent line. The slope of that tangent line is the value of the derivative at the point in question. Compare this value with your answers to numbers 1 and 2. Then draw another tangent line at X = -0.5.

5. What do you notice about the two tangent lines? _____

_____

6. Try to offer an explanation for the result you discovered in number 5. Try to generalize.

_____

_____

_____

_____

Now go back to the **Y=** menu and select both Y1 and Y2 to graph. Press **GRAPH** and you'll see the graph of Y1=X^3 as well as Y2 (its approximate derivative for the entire interval of inputs on your graph). Copy your graph onto the axes below.

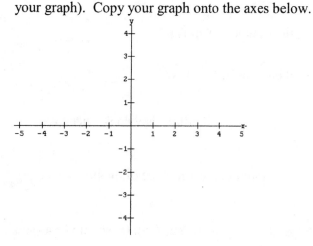

Trace along Y2 to 0.5 and then to -0.5. For any given X, the Y coordinate on the graph of Y2 tells you the slope of the line tangent to the graph of Y1 at that particular X.

7.   For what values of X is Y2 > 0?   _____

8.   For what values of X is the slope of the line tangent to the graph of Y1 greater than 0?

_____

Now you will repeat the activity above for the new function, Y1 = 1+abs(cos(πX/2)) at X = 1. Store this function in Y1 from the Y= menu (you shouldn't need to touch Y2), go to the HOME screen, store 0.1 in H, evaluate Y2(1). To get the rest of the table entries, just store a new value into H, and evaluate Y2(1) for each. Fill in the table.

H	Y2(1)	H	Y2(1)
0.1		-0.1	
0.01		-0.01	
0.001		-0.001	
0.0001		-0.0001	

9.   What is $\lim\limits_{H \to 0^-} \dfrac{(1+ABS(COS(\pi(1+H)/2)))-(1+ABS(COS(\pi*1/2)))}{H}$?   _____

10.   What is $\lim\limits_{H \to 0^+} \dfrac{(1+ABS(COS(\pi(1+H)/2)))-(1+ABS(COS(\pi*1/2)))}{H}$?   _____

11.   What is $\lim\limits_{H \to 0} \dfrac{(1+ABS(COS(\pi(1+H)/2)))-(1+ABS(COS(\pi*1/2)))}{H}$?   _____

You should see that the two-sided limit (and hence the derivative) does not exist for Y1 = 1+abs(cos(πX/2)) at X = 1. Now investigate this conclusion graphically. Select both Y1 and Y2 to graph and graph them in the decimal window. Copy your graphs onto the axes below.

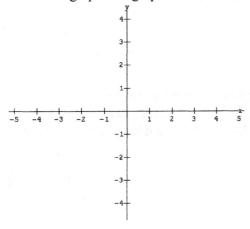

233

12. How does the graph of Y2 differ from the previous example, where Y1 = X^3?

_____

_____

_____

13. Try to draw the tangent line to the graph of Y1 at X=1. What happens?

_____

_____

_____

To understand how the calculator gets its result, you need to know what's going on "under the hood" when it computes a derivative. The TI-83 and TI-82 actually evaluate derivatives using the *symmetric difference quotient*, defined this way:

$$F'(X) = \lim_{H \to 0} \frac{F(X+H) - F(X-H)}{2H}$$

Most of the time, this symmetric difference quotient will give a better numeric approximation to the derivative than the "one sided" difference quotient, so it is not surprising that calculators use it. See the picture below to help you see why it's better. However, it causes problems for the unwary user when you attempt to use it at a place where the derivative doesn't exist!

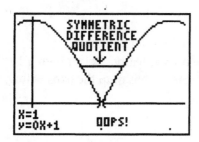

The TI-86 and TI-89 both try to find the derivative using analytic methods rather than the numeric approximation using the symmetric difference quotient. Thus, each of them gives a message that you cannot draw the tangent line at X = 1. In fact, the derivative doesn't exist for Y1 at X=1 (nor at any odd integer)

Teacher Notes and Answers

This activity can be used with students shortly after the definition of derivative at a point is introduced.

H	Y2(0.5)	H	Y2(0.5)
0.1	0.91	-0.1	0.61
0.01	0.7651	-0.01	0.7351
0.001	0.751501	-0.001	0.748501
0.0001	0.75015001	-0.0001	0.74985001

1. 0.75
2. 0.75
3. yes
4. 0.75
5. The two tangent lines are parallel. Each has slope 0.75. On the TI-83, the calculator may give a slope that is close to, but not exactly, 0.75.
6. Since $Y=X^3$ is an odd function, the slope at $X = A$ will be the same as the slope at $X = -A$. This will be true for any odd function.

This is the graph of $Y1=X^3$ and Y2, its derivative.

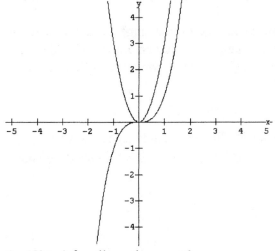

7. Y2 > 0 for all numbers $x \neq 0$.
8. Slope of tangent line > 0 for all numbers $x \neq 0$.

H	Y2(1)	H	Y2(1)
0.1	1.564345	-0.1	-1.564345
0.01	1.570732	-0.01	-1.570732
0.001	1.570796	-0.001	-1.570796
0.0001	1.570796	-0.0001	-1.570796

9. Approximately 1.570796 or $\pi/2$

10. Approximately -1.570796 or -π/2
11. The limit doesn't exist since the two one-sided limits disagree.

This is the graph of Y1 = 1+abs(cos(πX/2)) and Y2, its derivative

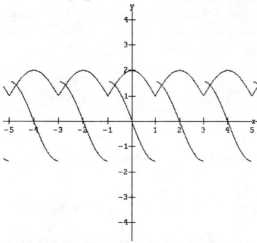

Calculator produced graphs may appear continuous if graphed in "Connected" mode.

12. This graph of the difference quotient has a discontinuity at every odd integer. The previous graph was continuous everywhere.
13. On the TI-83 or TI-82, the calculator draws a horizontal line for the tangent at $x = 1$. The TI-86 and TI-89 give an error message indicating that a tangent cannot be drawn. The '86 and '89 calculate a symbolic derivative, while the '82 and '83 use the symmetric difference quotient.

Caution students against trying too small of a value for h. There is a tendency just to try $h = 10^{-20}$ for example, which would then give you 0 for $f'(1)$, since $1 + h = 1$ on the calculator.

Lab #2
An Investigation into the Accuracy of the Tangent Line Approximation

In this activity, you will investigate why the tangent line is called the "best" linear approximation to a function at a point. Notice from the figure below that *any* line that intersects the graph of a function at a point could be used to approximate the function close to that point.

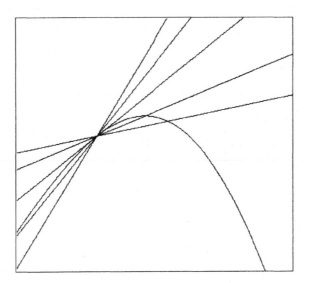

Of all those lines, why exactly is the tangent line the best? That's the question we'll answer in this activity.

You will go through the first part of the activity with the help of your teacher. Here we'll explain and define the concept of *power zooming*.

If you zoom in to the graph of any linear function with equal horizontal and vertical "zoom factors", the shape of your graph remains unchanged. Try it!

First, define any linear function, set a viewing window where you can see its graph, set the Xres variable in your Window menu to 1. Draw the graph.

Check that your zoom factors are equal. On the TI-83, you do this from the ZOOM Memory menu, on the TI-86, from the ZFACT menu, and on the TI-89, from the ZOOM...Set Factors... menu.

Press Trace to position the cursor on the pixel halfway across the graph, then zoom in to the graph repeatedly. You should see no change in the slope of the line as you zoom in. Look at the screens below for an example:

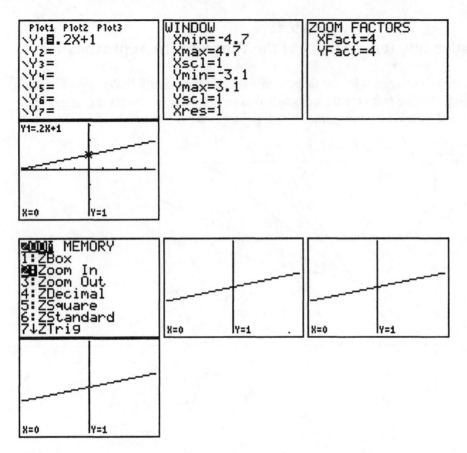

Now, suppose you wanted to zoom in to a parabola, like $y = x^2$, and see the same effect: the shape of the graph stay the same as you zoom in. Start at the decimal window (Zoom 4 on the TI83 and '89, ZOOM…ZDECM on the '86). Then try zooming in to the graph of $y = x^2$ with equal zoom factors at (0, 0).

1. What happened to the graph of $y = x^2$ as you zoomed in? _____

_____

Now, change your zoom factors so that the y factor is the square of the x factor. For example, try zoom factors of XFact = 3 and YFact = 9. Start again at the decimal window, and try zooming in with these factors.

2. What happened to the graph as you zoomed in this time?   ? _____

_____

A zoom like you just did will be called a *power zoom of degree 2*. The degree is 2 because the y-factor is the square of the x-factor. Now, try zooming in to your graph of $y = x^2$ with a degree 3 power zoom. For example, set XFact = 2 and YFact = 8. Start again from the decimal window, and zoom in a few times with this degree 3 power zoom.

3. What happened to the graph of $y = x^2$ as you zoomed in with a degree 3 power zoom?

_____

_____

Let's see if these observations might generalize. Clear out Y1, define Y2 = X^2, Y3 = X^3, and Y4 = X^4, and set your viewing window to [-5, 5] horizontally by [-25, 25] vertically. Leave your zoom factors set for a degree 3 power zoom. You might also want to set a different graphing style for Y2, Y3, and Y4 so you can tell the graphs apart. Zoom in repeatedly to these three graphs.

4. Which graph kept the same shape as you zoomed in? _____

5. Which graph flattened out as you zoomed in? _____

6. Which graph got steeper as you zoomed in? _____

In general, zooming in at the origin to the graph of $y = x^n$ with a power zoom of degree m will cause the graph to get steeper if $n < m$, stay the same shape if $n = m$, and flatten out if $n > m$. The same effect will be seen if you zoom in to the graph of $y = (x - a)^n$ at the point $(a, 0)$. Try it.

Now, let's get back to our question about the tangent line.

We'll take a look at how the _error_ functions for different linear approximations to a curve behave. To that end, define Y1 = e^(X). Then, in Y2, define the tangent line to the graph of $y = e^x$ at the point $(0,1)$. That is, set Y2 = X + 1.

Then, in Y3, we'll define another line that intersects Y1 at $(0,1)$, but has a slope that is slightly different from the slope of the tangent line at that point. We'll use Y3 = 1.2X+1, though any slope other than 1 will work.

Now, define Y4 to be the error in the tangent line approximation. That is, set Y4 = Y2(X) − Y1(X). Set Y5 to be the error from using the other line to approximate e^x. That is, set Y5 = Y3(X)-Y1(X). Select only Y4 and Y5 for graphing, and graph them in the decimal window.

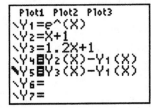

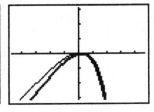

7. Explain why both error functions pass through the origin. _____

_____

_____

8. What is magnitude (absolute value) of the error from using the tangent line to approximate $\sqrt{e}$ at $x = 0.5$? _____

9. What is magnitude (absolute value) of the error from using the line with slope 1.2 to approximate $\sqrt{e}$? _____

Notice that the line with slope 1.2 actually does a better job at approximating $\sqrt{e}$! However, 0.5 is pretty far from 0, and the behavior we're looking for isn't discernible unless we look at these graphs very close to the point of interest.

Set your zoom factors so that the x-factor is 2 and the y-factor is 4.

10. What degree power zoom are we about to do? _____

Zoom in at the origin until you can see the different behavior with the two error functions.

11. Describe your observations _____

_____

_____

_____

_____

You should have seen that the error from the line with slope 1.2 got steeper, while the error in the tangent line approximation kept the same shape. This is evidence that the tangent line approximation error behaves like a degree two power function, while the other line's error behaves like a lower degree. In fact it behaves like a line, degree 1.

Repeat the activity, choosing some other function whose tangent line you can produce. Make sure your "other" line passes through the point of tangency with the wrong slope.

12. Does the error in the tangent line always behave like a degree 2 power function? _____

13. Does the error in the "other" line approximation always behave like a degree 1 function? _____

14. Explain why a higher degree error function is superior to a lower degree. _____

_____

_____

_____

Teacher Notes and Answers

This activity was inspired by a talk delivered by Donald Kreider from Dartmouth College at the Technology Intensive Calculus for Advanced Placement (TICAP) workshop. The concept of power zooming appears in Calculus of a Single Variable, by Dick and Patton, 1994 PWS Publishing Company, Boston.

This activity can be done with students any time after they have covered the tangent line as the best linear approximation to a function at a point. For BC students, it foreshadows Taylor Series nicely. A follow-up activity extends the idea to higher degrees.

You should guide the students through the first six questions of the activity, up to the investigation of the tangent line. Students must know the result stated after question 6. Here's an investigation into the graph of $y = (x-1)^2$, $y = (x-1)^3$, and $y = (x-1)^4$. The screen shots here were taken from the TI-83. The procedure is easily translated to other models.

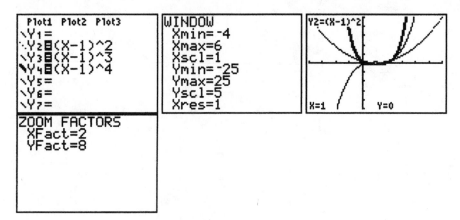

Now we do a degree 3 power zoom:

Notice that the quadratic (degree less than the degree of the power zoom) got steeper, the cubic stayed the same shape, and the quartic (degree greater than the degree of the power zoom) got flatter.

1. When you zoom in to the graph of $y = x^2$ with equal factors at $(0, 0)$, the graph gets flatter. Under these conditions, the graph of $y = x^2$ becomes more and more linear, approaching the graph of the tangent line at $(0, 0)$, namely the line $y = 0$.

2. When you zoom in to the graph of $y = x^2$ with the y-factor the square of the x-factor, say 16 and 4, the shape of the parabola stays the same. To understand why, think about the fact that we are repeatedly dividing Xmin and Xmax by 4, and Ymin and Ymax by 16. If we used to have an ordered pair at the top left corner of our graph, $(oldX, oldY) = (oldX, oldX^2)$, after we zoom in, we'll still have an ordered pair at $(newX, newY) = (oldX/4, (oldX/4)^2) = (oldX/4, oldX^2/16)$.

3. As you zoom in to the graph of $y = x^2$ with a degree 3 power zoom, the graph becomes steeper.

4. Y3 = X^3

5. Y4 = X^4

6. Y2 = X^2

7. Each tangent line contains the point $(0, 1)$. The graph of Y1 = e^X also contains $(0, 1)$, so the error at that point is zero for both linear approximations.

8. Approximately 0.1487

9. Approximately 0.0487

10. The y-factor is the square of the x-factor, so this is a degree two power zoom.

11. Both error functions always pass through the origin. After a few zooms, the shape of the error from the tangent line approximation remains unchanged, indicating degree 2 behavior. The error in the line with the "wrong" slope becomes steeper, indicating behavior less than degree two. The tangent line error is always negative, indicating that the tangent line is always underneath the curve.

Here's a similar investigation with a different function and different tangent lines. Here, we're using $y = \sin(x)$ at $x = \pi/4$. Notice that the window is centered at $\pi/4$ by subtracting and adding 2 from $\pi/4$ to get Xmin and Xmax, respectively.

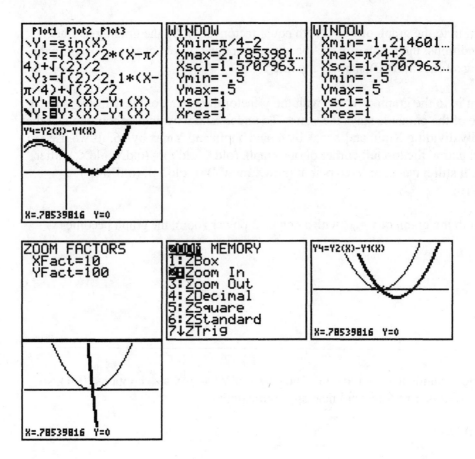

Here we've cranked up the zoom factors in the interest of getting to the point more quickly!

12. Yes.

13. Yes, it gets steeper. Steep error functions are bad!

14. Higher degree power functions stay near zero longer than lower degree power functions. This is because the more times a number whose absolute value is less than 1 is multiplied by itself, the closer the product is to 0. Error functions that stay near zero for a long time are obviously more desirable than those that do not.

Lab #3
A Numeric Investigation into the Accuracy
of the Tangent Line Approximation

This activity is meant to supplement an earlier activity titled "An Investigation into the Accuracy of the Tangent Line Approximation". In that activity we looked at the error from using the tangent line at $x = 0$ to approximate e^x. We used the tool of power zooming to explore how the error in the tangent line approximation behaved and how the error from using a different line with a slope that was just slightly "wrong" behaved. We discovered that the error from using the tangent line exhibited degree 2 behavior, while the error from using the other line exhibited degree 1 behavior.

Here we'll investigate that result from a purely numeric perspective, using tables of values and the idea of relative error.

The curve we'll use is $f(x) = e^x$ at $x = 0$. So, define $Y1 = e^\wedge(X)$. One line that could approximate e^x near 0 is $y = f(0)$. So define the constant function, $Y2(X) = 1$, whose output agrees with Y1 at $X = 0$. Then, in Y4, define the relative error from using $Y2(X)$ as an approximation to $Y1(X)$. That is, set $Y4(X) = (Y1(X)-Y2(X))/X$. Notice that $Y4(X) = \dfrac{f(x) - f(0)}{x}$. Select Y4 and deselect Y1 and Y2. See the screen below.

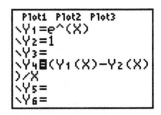

Set up you table of values so that it starts at $X = 0$ and has a step size, ΔTbl, of 0.1. Then look at the table.

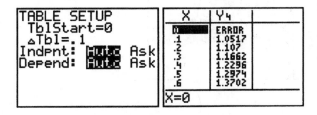

1. Why is the relative error, Y4, undefined at $X = 0$? _____

2. Change the table step, ΔTbl, to 0.01 and look again at the table. Then change it to 0.0001 and look again.

   Does it appear that the relative error has a limit as X approaches 0? _____
   What is the limit? _____

3. Notice that $\lim\limits_{x\to 0} Y4(X) = \lim\limits_{x\to 0} \dfrac{f(x)-f(0)}{x}$. Remember the definition of the derivative? Explain why Y4(X) approaches 1 as X approaches 0.

_____

_____

_____

We've seen that our relative error, $Y4(X) = \dfrac{f(x)-f(0)}{x}$, approaches $f'(0) = 1$ as x approaches 0. This suggests that since $\dfrac{f(x)-f(0)}{x} \approx f'(0)$ for values of x near 0, we could better approximate $f(x)$ by simply solving that approximation for $f(x)$. That is, use $f(x) \approx f(0) + xf'(0)$. To parallel the investigation from the earlier tangent line activity, we'll also look at the relative error from using the line whose output agrees with e^x at $x = 0$, but whose slope is slightly different. Define functions as shown below, except choose your own value for the slope of the line in Y3 (any slope other than 1 will work).

```
Plot1 Plot2 Plot3
\Y₁=e^(X)
\Y₂=1+X
\Y₃=1+1.2X
\Y₄■(Y₁(X)-Y₂(X)
)/X
\Y₅■(Y₁(X)-Y₃(X)
)/X
```

Reset your table so that it start at X=0, with a step size, ΔTbl, of 0.1. Take a look at the table of values. Then set ΔTbl, of 0.0001 and take another look. See the screens below.

```
TABLE SETUP
TblStart=0
ΔTbl=.1
Indpnt: Auto Ask
Depend: Auto Ask
```

X	Y₄	Y₅
0	ERROR	ERROR
.1	.05171	-.1483
.2	.10701	-.093
.3	.1662	-.0338
.4	.22956	.02956
.5	.29744	.09744
.6	.3702	.1702

X=0

```
TABLE SETUP
TblStart=0
ΔTbl=.0001
Indpnt: Auto Ask
Depend: Auto Ask
```

X	Y₄	Y₅
0	ERROR	ERROR
1E-4	5E-5	-.1999
2E-4	1E-4	-.1999
3E-4	1.5E-4	-.1998
4E-4	2E-4	-.1998
5E-4	2.5E-4	-.1997
6E-4	3E-4	-.1997

X=0

4. What differences do you see between the behavior of the tangent line relative error and the relative error from the line with different slope?

_____

_____

_____

5. From the table, what do you guess is the value of $\lim_{x \to 0} Y5(X)$? _____

Repeat the activity, choosing some other function whose tangent line you can produce. Make sure your "other" line passes through the point of tangency with the wrong slope. Note that if you choose a value for x other than 0, say $x = a$, you'll have to divide by $x - a$ instead of X in Y4 and Y5. Check your parentheses carefully!

6. Does the relative error in the tangent line always approach 0 as x approaches the x-coordinate of the point of tangency? _____

7. Does the relative error in the "other" line approximation always approach a constant other than 0? _____

The only line whose relative error approaches 0 as x approaches the point where we are approximating is the tangent line!

Teacher Notes and Answers

This activity was inspired by a discussion with Tom Tucker, Professor of Mathematics at Colgate University. It can be done with students any time after they have covered the idea that the value of the derivative at a point tells you the slope at that point. It also requires an understanding of the definition of derivative. For BC students, the activity and the accompanying graphical investigation using power zooming foreshadow Taylor Series nicely. A follow-up activity, "A Numeric Investigation into the Accuracy of Polynomial Approximations to Transcendental Functions" extends the idea to higher degrees.

1. The relative error is undefined at X = 0 because we are dividing by X.

2. Yes, 1.

3. $\lim\limits_{x \to 0} Y4(X) = \lim\limits_{x \to 0} \dfrac{f(x) - f(0)}{x} = f'(0)$. For $f(x) = e^x$, $f'(0) = 1$

4. It appears that the values in Y4 approach 0 as X approaches 0, while the values in Y5 approach -0.2 as X approaches 0. It also appears that the values in Y4 approach 0 at a constant rate (though students may not observe this). The latter observation is good ground to start from when motivating the extension to higher degree approximations.

5. -0.2

6. Yes, it appears to always approach 0.

7. Yes, it appears to approach the difference in slope between the curve we are approximating and the line we are approximating with. In fact, this is why the relative error in the tangent line approaches 0!

Lab #4
Fundamental Theorem Investigation

In this activity, you will explore the Fundamental Theorem of Calculus from numeric and graphic perspectives. The version of the Fundamental Theorem covered by this activity says that, if *f* is a function continuous on the closed interval, [a,b], and *x* is any number in [a,b], then the function $F(x) = \int_a^x f(t)dt$ is an antiderivative for *f*. Another way to say this is

$$\frac{d}{dx} \int_a^x f(t)dt = f(x).$$

Define `Y1=0.5-1.5sin(X^2)` and `Y2=fnInt(Y•(T),T,Xmin,X)`. (On the TI-83, you have to find the variable `Xmin` in the VARS...Window... menu. You can type it directly on the TI-86 or TI-89.)

Make sure your calculator is in radian mode, and set up your viewing window as [-2.5, 1.5] x [-2, 2]. Note that Y2 is a function defined by a definite integral. That is,

$$Y(X) = \int_{X\min}^X 0.5 - 1.5\sin(t^2)dt.$$

Also note that Y2 measures the accumulated *signed* area from Xmin to X. Draw a graph of Y1 (deselect Y2 first!). Your graph should look like this one:

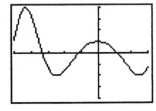

If it doesn't, check that you've entered Y1 correctly, that your window is correct, and that you are in radian mode.

Now you will generate a list of inputs running from the left to the right edge of your graphing window, and store that list in L1 (or c1 on the TI-89). These numbers will be inputs into Y2. That is, they will be upper limits of integration.

Go to the List Editor (Data/Matrix Editor on the TI-89), and use the `seq` command (from LIST OPS on the TI-83) to generate the list. The syntax (for all the calculators) looks like this: `seq(T,T,Xmin,Xmax,2*ΔX)`. (On the TI-83, you have to find the variables `Xmin`, `Xmax`, and `ΔX` in the VARS...Window... menu. You can type them directly on the TI-86 or TI-89.) Then define a new list of data as Y2(L1) on the '83 or y2(L1) on the '86). To calculate c2 on the TI-89, you'll need to use the seq command. On any of the calculators, it could take several minutes of calculations to fill the output list, since each value requires that your calculator evaluate a definite integral. Additionally, you should substitute c1 and c2 for L1 and L2 respectively for the rest of the activity. See the screen snapshots below:

TI-83:

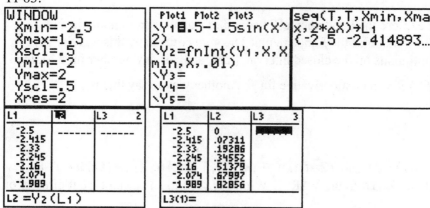

TI-86:

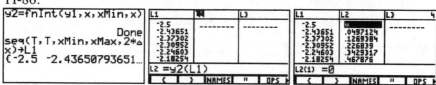

TI-89

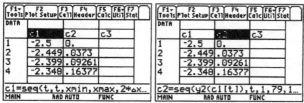

Each element of the output list (L2 or c2) results from the evaluation of a definite integral. For example, when the second component of L1 is plugged into Y2 on the TI-83, we get

$$\int_{X_{\min}}^{-2.415} 0.5 - 1.5\sin(t^2)\,dt$$ which is the second element of L2.

1. Why is the first component of L2 = 0? _____

Look at the graph of the integrand function, Y1(X). Use the graph to answer question 2:

2. Why is the second component of L2 greater than 0? _____

_____

Go to the STAT EDIT screen (or Data/Matrix editor on the TI-89) and look at the table of inputs and outputs, L1 and L2 respectively.

3. Why is the third value in L2, which represents $\int_{X\min}^{-2.33} 0.5 - 1.5\sin(t^2)dt$, greater than the second

value in L2, which represents $\int_{X\min}^{-2.415} 0.5 - 1.5\sin(t^2)dt$? _____

_____

_____

For the TI-86, the third value of L2 represents $\int_{x\text{Min}}^{-2.373} 0.5 - 1.5\sin(t^2)dt$ and the second

is $\int_{x\text{Min}}^{-2.437} 0.5 - 1.5\sin(t^2)dt$, and for the TI-89, the third is $\int_{x\min}^{-2.3987} 0.5 - 1.5\sin(t^2)dt$ and the second

is $\int_{x\min}^{-2.449} 0.5 - 1.5\sin(t^2)dt$.

4. Looking again at the table of values for L2, the values of the area accumulation function, for

what value of x does $Y2(X) = \int_{X\min}^{X} 0.5 - 1.5\sin(t^2)dt$ reach its first local maximum? _____

5. Explain why the 21st value of L2 (or c2) is smaller than the 20th value of L2 (or c2) . (Keep in mind that Y2 is measuring *signed* area)

_____

_____

_____

6. For what value of X does $Y2(X) = \int_{X\min}^{X} 0.5 - 1.5\sin(t^2)dt$ reach its first local minimum? _____

Set up a scatter plot of L2 versus L1. Select just Y1 for graphing, then look at the graph:

TI-83:

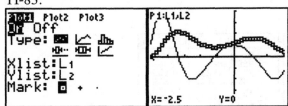

TI-86:   TI-89:

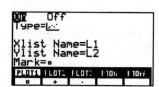   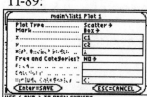

7. Use your calculator to find the two negative X-intercepts on the graph of Y1 in the viewing window defined at the beginning of this activity: _____ and

_____

8. Compare the answers to number 7 to the answers to numbers 4 and 6. Carefully explain why

they are similar. _____

_____

_____

_____

9. Find the X coordinate of the positive root (X-intercept) of Y1.

_____

10. What happens with Y2 at the point found in number 9? _____

_____

(Verify your answer numerically by looking at the table of values for Y2 in L2)

Go back to the Y= menu and define Y3=fnInt(Y•(T),T,-2,X), thus changing the lower limit of integration from Xmin, which was -2.5, to-2. Then, evaluate Y3 at all the inputs in L1, and store the results in L3 (or c3 on the TI-89):

TI-83:

Plot1 Plot2 Plot3	Y3(L1)→L3	L1	L2	L3 3
\Y1◼.5-1.5sin(X^2)	{-.8113881184 -...	-2.5	0	-.81388
\Y2=fnInt(Y1,X,Xmin,X)		-2.415	.07311	-.7383
		-2.33	.19286	-.6185
		-2.245	.34552	-.4659
\Y3=fnInt(Y1,X,-2,X)		-2.16	.51379	-.2976
		-2.074	.67997	-.1314
\Y4=		-1.989	.82856	.01717
		L3(1)= -.811388118...		

TI-86:

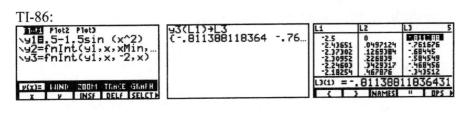

TI-89:

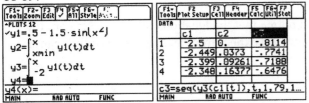

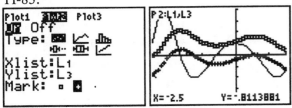

Define PLOT2 as a scatter plot of L3 versus L1, and select PLOT1, PLOT2, and Y1 for graphing. Study the graph and table:

TI-83:

```
Plot1  Plot2  Plot3
On  Off
Type: 🔲 📈 📊
     📊 📊 📈
Xlist:L₁
Ylist:L₃
Mark: □ ■ ·
```

```
P 2:L1,L3




X=-2.5        Y=-.8113881
```

TI-86:   TI-89:

```
On    Off
Type=📈

Xlist Name=L1
Ylist Name=L3
Mark=+
FLOT1 PLOT2 PLOT3 F10n F10ff
  □    +    ·
```

```
              main\list1 Plot 2
Plot Type.................. Scatter →
Mark...................... Plus →
x......................... c1
y......................... c3
x[P. O:...:x] :...:x...... A
Free and Categories? NO →
f:...:...................
[...:]..................
[...:]..............  C:
 Enter=SAVE           ESC=CANCEL
USE ← AND → TO OPEN CHOICES
```

11. Why is the graph of L3 versus L1 below the graph of L2 versus L1 (remember, the only difference between the two is the lower limit of integration)?

_____

_____

_____

12. Explain why plots 1 and 2 have the same shape.

_____

_____

_____

Look at the table of values for L2 and L3, and notice that the locations of the extrema are the same for both accumulation functions (as you would expect from an inspection of the scatter plots).

13. (Challenge for the experts). Find the locations of any points of inflection on PLOT1 and PLOT2. Explain what these locations have in common with features on the graph of Y1.

_____

_____

_____

Teacher Notes and Answers

This activity can be done anytime after students have learned about a function defined by a definite integral, like $F(x) = \int_a^x g(t)dt$. Students should know such functions will be positive when the integrand is positive and $x > a$, and negative when the integrand is negative and $x > a$. The exploration gives students some hands-on experience with how accumulation functions behave, and the connections with the behavior of the integrand.

1. The first component of the output list represents $\int_{-2.5}^{-2.5} Y1(X)dX$ and so is zero. There is no area from -2.5 to -2.5.

2. The second value in the output list is positive since the integrand is positive for all x from -2.5 to the second value of L1. Thus, positive area has been accumulated.

3. The third value in the output list is greater than the second since the integrand is positive for all x between the second value of the input list and the third. Thus, more positive area has been accumulated.

4. Answers will vary depending on the calculator used: TI-83: -1.649; TI-86: -1.6746; TI-89: -1.68987

5. The integrand is negative for all numbers x between L1(20) and L1(21) (or c1[20] and c1[21] on the TI-89). Thus, negative area has been accumulated, and the values of the accumulation function are decreasing.

6. Answers will vary depending on the calculator used: TI-83: -0.5426; TI-86: -0.5952; TI-89: -0.5759

7. -1.6738 and -0.5830

8. At the first x-intercept, -1.6738, the integrand changes from positive to negative. Thus the accumulation function, Y2, has a local maximum there. We stop accumulating positive area, and start accumulating negative area at that point. Similarly, at $x = -0.5830$, the integrand changes from negative to positive. Thus, we stop accumulating negative area and start accumulating positive area at that point, producing a local minimum on the graph of the accumulation function..

9. $x = 0.5830$

10. The accumulation function has a maximum there. This can be seen in the table of values for Y2 and Y3 as well.

L1	L2	L3	2
.2234	.71035	-.101	
.30851	.74381	-.0676	
.39362	.77059	-.0408	
.47872	.28893	-.0225	
.56383		-.0142	
.64894	.79377	-.0176	
.73404	.77755	-.0338	

L2(37)=.797161281...

11. There could be many correct explanations for this. Focusing on the left endpoint of the graphing window, $Y2(-2.5) = \int_{Xmin}^{-2.5} .5 - 1.5\sin(t^2)dt$ is zero, since the upper and lower limits of integration are equal.. However, $Y3(-2.5) = \int_{-2}^{-2.5} .5 - 1.5\sin(t^2)dt < 0$, since the integrand is positive, but we are integrating from "right to left". This makes the graph of Y3 below the graph of Y2.

12. Plots 1 and 2 have the same shape since each increases where the integrand is positive, and each decreases where the integrand is negative. In fact, at each value of x, the two plots are changing at exactly the same rate, since each accumulates area under the graph of Y1. The Fundamental Theorem says that the two accumulation functions, Y2 and Y3, have the same derivative, Y1.

13. Points of inflection occur at $x = -2.1708$, $x = -1.2533$, $x = 0$, and $x = 1.2533$. These are the extrema on the graph of Y1. It is at these points that the accumulation functions change the fastest.

Lab #5
Exploration of Integrals
Using Integration by Parts

Let $B_{m,n} = \displaystyle\int_0^1 x^m (1-x)^n \, dx$ for positive integers m, n.

1. Evaluate $B_{m,0}$ and $B_{0,n}$.

2. Using substitution, show that $B_{m,n} = B_{n,m}$.

3. There are two recurrence relations that can be derived using integration by parts. One is

$$B_{m,n} = \frac{m}{n+1} \, B_{m-1,n+1} \, .$$

   Show that this is true and derive the other one.

4. Use your work from questions #1 and #3 repeatedly to evaluate $B_{2,5}$ and $B_{2,n}$ and $B_{3,n}$.

5. Generalize your answer to question #4 to get a formula for $B_{m,n}$.

Teacher Notes and Answers

1.   Setting $n = 0$, we have

$$B_{m,0} = \int_0^1 x^m (1-x)^0\, dx = \int_0^1 x^m\, dx = \frac{x^{m+1}}{m+1}\bigg|_0^1 = \frac{1}{m+1}\ .$$

Setting $m = 0$, we have

$$B_{0,n} = \int_0^1 x^0 (1-x)^n\, dx = \int_0^1 (1-x)^n\, dx = \frac{-(1-x)^{n+1}}{n+1}\bigg|_0^1 = \frac{1}{n+1}\ .$$

2.   We substitute $w = 1 - x$ into $B_{m,n}$. Then $dw = -dx$ and $x = 1 - w$.
        When $x = 0$, $w = 1$ and when $x = 1$, $w = 0$, so

$$B_{m,n} = \int_0^1 x^m (1-x)^n\, dx = \int_1^0 (1-w)^m w^n\, (-dw)$$

$$= -\int_1^0 w^n (1-w)^m\, dw = \int_0^1 w^n (1-w)^m\, dw = B_{n,m}\ .$$

3.   To integrate by parts, we first choose $u = x^m$, $v' = (1-x)^n$, so $u' = mx^{m-1}$ and
        $v = -(1-x)^{n+1}/(n+1)$. Then

$$B_{m,n} = \int_0^1 x^m (1-x)^n\, dx = -x^m \frac{(1-x)^{n+1}}{n+1}\bigg|_0^1 + \int_0^1 mx^{m-1}\frac{(1-x)^{n+1}}{n+1}\, dx\ .$$

Notice that $x^m (1-x)^{n+1}\big|_0^1 = 1^m \cdot 0^{n+1} - 0^m \cdot 1^{n+1} = 0$, so we get the result given:

$$B_{m,n} = \int_0^1 x^m (1-x)^n\, dx = \frac{m}{n+1}\int_0^1 x^{m-1}(1-x)^{n+1}\, dx = \frac{m}{n+1} B_{m-1,n+1}\ .$$

To find the other recurrence relation, we choose u and v' the other way around.

Let $v' = x^m$ and $u = (1-x)^n$. Then $v = x^{m+1}/(m+1)$ and $u' = -n(1-x)^{n-1}$, so

$$B_{m,n} = \int_0^1 x^m (1-x)^n \, dx = \frac{x^{m+1}}{m+1}(1-x)^n \bigg|_0^1 - \int_0^1 \frac{x^{m+1}}{m+1}\left(-n(1-x)^{n-1}\right) dx$$

$$= \frac{1^{m+1}}{m+1} \cdot 0^n - \frac{0^{m+1}}{m+1} \cdot 1^n + \frac{n}{m+1} \int_0^1 x^{m+1}(1-x)^{n-1} \, dx = \frac{n}{m+1} B_{m+1,n-1} \, .$$

Thus, the other recurrence relation is

$$B_{m,n} = \frac{n}{m+1} B_{m+1,n-1} \, .$$

4.　For $B_{2,5}$, we have $m = 2$, $n = 5$. Then $m - 1 = 1$, $n + 1 = 6$, so question #3 gives

$$B_{2,5} = \frac{2}{6} B_{1,6} \, .$$

Using question #3 again, this time with $m = 1$, $n = 6$, we get

$$B_{1,6} = \frac{1}{7} B_{0,7} \, .$$

From question #1 with $n = 7$, we have

$$B_{0,7} = \frac{1}{8} \, .$$

Therefore we have

$$B_{1,6} = \frac{1}{7} \cdot \frac{1}{8} = \frac{1}{56} \, ,$$

so, putting all this together we have

$$B_{2,5} = \frac{2}{6} \cdot \frac{1}{56} = \frac{1}{168} \, .$$

For $B_{2,n}$, we follow similar reasoning as for $B_{2,5}$. Using question #3 twice gives

$$B_{2,n} = \frac{2}{n+1} B_{1,n+1} = \frac{2}{n+1}\left(\frac{1}{n+2} B_{0,n+2}\right) = \frac{2}{(n+1)(n+2)} B_{0,n+2}$$

Since, from question #1 with n replaced by $n + 2$, we have $B_{0,n+2} = 1/(n+3)$, we have

$$B_{2,n} = \frac{2}{(n+1)(n+2)} \cdot \frac{1}{n+3} = \frac{2}{(n+1)(n+2)(n+3)} \, .$$

For $B_{3,n}$, we use question #3 three times, as follows.

$$B_{3,n} = \frac{3}{n+1} B_{2,n+1} = \frac{3}{n+1}\left(\frac{2}{n+2} B_{1,n+2}\right) = \frac{6}{(n+1)(n+2)}\left(\frac{1}{n+3} B_{0,n+3}\right) .$$

Since from question #1, we have $B_{0,n+3} = 1/(n+4)$, we have

$$B_{3,n} = \frac{6}{(n+1)(n+2)(n+3)} \cdot \frac{1}{n+4} = \frac{6}{(n+1)(n+2)(n+3)(n+4)} .$$

5. Notice that the numerator for the expression for $B_{3,n}$ can be rewritten so that the expression for $B_{3,n}$ is

$$B_{3,n} = \frac{3 \cdot 2 \cdot 1}{(n+1)(n+2)(n+3)(n+4)} .$$

Generalizing gives

$$B_{4,n} = \frac{4 \cdot 3 \cdot 2 \cdot 1}{(n+1)(n+2)(n+3)(n+4)(n+5)}$$

and

$$B_{m,n} = \frac{m(m-1)(m-2)\cdots 2 \cdot 1}{(n+1)(n+2)(n+3)\cdots(n+m)(n+m+1)} .$$

This expression for $B_{m,n}$ can be rewritten using factorials as

$$B_{m,n} = \frac{m!}{(n+1)(n+2)(n+3)\cdots(n+m)(n+m+1)} .$$

It can be further rewritten using the fact that

$$(n+1)(n+2)(n+3)\cdots(n+m)(n+m+1) = \frac{(n+m+1)!}{n!} ,$$

giving us

$$B_{m,n} = \frac{m!}{(n+m+1)!/n!} = \frac{m!n!}{(n+m+1)!} .$$

Short Answers

1. $B_{m,0} = 1/(m+1)$
   $B_{0,n} = 1/(n+1)$

2. No short answer

3. $B_{m,n} = \dfrac{n}{m+1} B_{m+1,n-1}$

4. $B_{2,5} = 1/168$
   $B_{2,n} = 2/((n+1)(n+2)(n+3))$
   $B_{3,n} = 6/((n+1)(n+2)(n+3)(n+4))$

5. $B_{m,n} = \dfrac{m(m-1)\cdots 2\cdot 1}{(n+1)(n+2)\cdots(n+m)(n+m+1)}$

Lab #6
Using a Spreadsheet to Investigate Series Convergence

The purpose of this activity is to examine graphically the convergence or divergence of certain series. For each series, create a spreadsheet with a column of the numbers $k = 1, 2, 3, ...$; a column for the sequence $f(k)$; and a column for the series $\sum f(k)$.

Then make a graph (called a "chart" on the spreadsheet) plotting both the sequence and the series against the numbers $1, 2, 3,...$ on the same graph. After looking at all the graphs, answer the following questions:

1.   What is the behavior of the sequence graphs? Give one answer, covering all graphs.

2.   What is the behavior of the series graphs? Give one answer covering the convergent series, and one answer covering the divergent series.

3.   Can you tell by looking at the graphs if the series converges or diverges? Explain.

The series:

a) $\sum \dfrac{1}{k}$

b) $\sum \dfrac{1}{k^p}$, for a p of your choice which is less than 1

c) $\sum \dfrac{1}{k^p}$, for a p of your choice which is greater than 1

(Note: At this point you may wish to plot the three above series (without their sequences) on the same chart and compare them.)

d) $\sum \dfrac{1}{\ln k}$

e) $\sum \dfrac{\sin k}{2^k}$

f) $\sum \dfrac{(-2)^k}{k!}$

Teacher Notes and Answers

The series spreadsheets and their graphs are designed to show how one might or might not be able to discern convergence simply by looking at the graphs of the series as the partial sums grow. Clearly series E and F seem strongly to converge, as their partial sums go back and forth above and below the ultimate sum. In the p-series with $p > 1$, as in series C, there is also strong visual evidence for convergence. However, in series A, B and D, while there is no immediately obvious evidence that the graphs "level off", perhaps we are looking at an early increase in the series graph, and later it will level off and approach some ceiling or horizontal asymptote. We know that these series diverge, but we have too little visual evidence to be sure of that from these graphs alone.

The following charts are part of the solutions provided by Harry Greene, Belmont Hill School, Class of 2003.

a) $f(k) = \dfrac{1}{k}$

k	$f(k)$	$\sum f(k)$
1	1	1
2	0.5	1.5
3	0.33333333	1.83333333
4	0.25	2.08333333
5	0.2	2.28333333
6	0.16666667	2.45
7	0.14285714	2.59285714
8	0.125	2.71785714
9	0.11111111	2.82896825
10	0.1	2.92896825
11	0.09090909	3.01987734
12	0.08333333	3.10321068
13	0.07692308	3.18013376
14	0.07142857	3.25156233
15	0.06666667	3.31822899
16	0.0625	3.38072899
17	0.05882353	3.43955252
18	0.05555556	3.49510808
19	0.05263158	3.54773966
20	0.05	3.59773966
21	0.04761905	3.6453587
22	0.04545455	3.69081325
23	0.04347826	3.73429151
24	0.04166667	3.77595818
25	0.04	3.81595818

b) $f(k) = \dfrac{1}{k^p}$

Let $p = 0.5$

k	$f(k)$	$\sum f(k)$
1	1	1
2	0.70710678	1.70710678
3	0.57735027	2.28445705
4	0.5	2.78445705
5	0.4472136	3.23167065
6	0.40824829	3.63991894
7	0.37796447	4.01788341
8	0.35355339	4.3714368
9	0.33333333	4.70477013
10	0.31622777	5.0209979
11	0.30151134	5.32250924
12	0.28867513	5.61118438
13	0.2773501	5.88853448
14	0.26726124	6.15579572
15	0.25819889	6.41399461
16	0.25	6.66399461
17	0.24253563	6.90653023
18	0.23570226	7.14223249
19	0.22941573	7.37164823
20	0.2236068	7.59525503
21	0.21821789	7.81347292
22	0.21320072	8.02667363
23	0.20851441	8.23518805
24	0.20412415	8.43931219
25	0.2	8.63931219

c) $f(k) = \dfrac{1}{k^p}$

Let $p = 2$

k	$f(k)$	$\sum f(k)$
1	1	1
2	0.25	1.25
3	0.11111111	1.36111111
4	0.0625	1.42361111
5	0.04	1.46361111
6	0.02777778	1.49138889
7	0.02040816	1.51179705
8	0.015625	1.52742205
9	0.01234568	1.53976773
10	0.01	1.54976773
11	0.00826446	1.55803219
12	0.00694444	1.56497664
13	0.00591716	1.5708938
14	0.00510204	1.57599584
15	0.00444444	1.58044028
16	0.00390625	1.58434653
17	0.00346021	1.58780674
18	0.00308642	1.59089316
19	0.00277008	1.59366324
20	0.0025	1.59616324
21	0.00226757	1.59843082
22	0.00206612	1.60049693
23	0.00189036	1.60238729
24	0.00173611	1.6041234
25	0.0016	1.6057234

a)

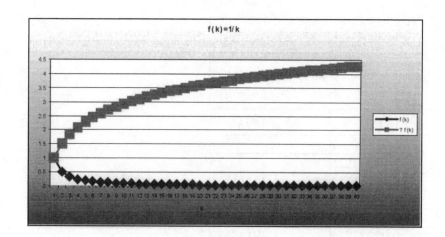

b)

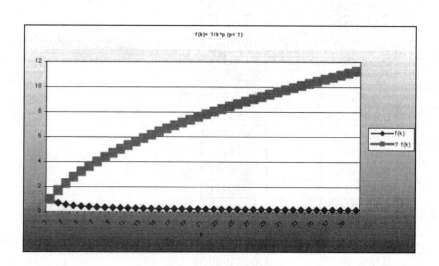

c)

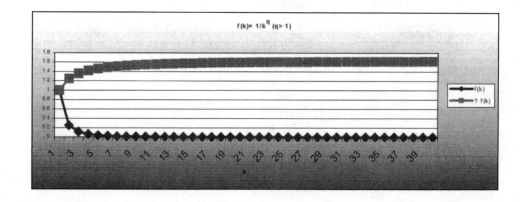

Lab #7
Convergence of Series

Let $A = \sum_{n=1}^{\infty} \frac{(0.9)^n}{n}$, $B = \sum_{n=1}^{\infty} \frac{(0.99)^n}{n}$, and $C = \sum_{n=1}^{\infty} \frac{(0.999)^n}{n}$

These series all converge. Why? It is interesting to note the relationship between the values of A, B, and C, $B = 2A$ and $C = 3A$. You could use your calculator or a spreadsheet to find approximations for the values of A, B, and C. However it would be necessary to sum 150 terms to approximate A to 9 decimal places and 16,000 terms to approximate C. After all this work we would be able to make a conjecture as to the relationship between A,B, and C; however, it is not yet clear why the relationship exists. For this reason we will do this problem entirely without our calculators.

How could we investigate to see what is actually happening? Sometimes if a problem is studied in a larger context it is easier to assign meaning to the specific case that is of interest. So with this idea in mind let's consider our problem in the context of a power series.

1. Let $f(x) = \sum_{n=1}^{\infty} \frac{x^n}{n}$.

    a) What is the interval of convergence?

    b) How is $f(0.9)$ related to our problem? How is $f(0.99)$ related to our problem? Are 0.9 and 0.99 in the interval of convergence for the power series?

    c) Find the series for $f'(x)$.

    d) This series for $f'(x)$ is geometric. Express $f'(x)$ in closed form.

    e) How can you find $f(x)$ from $f'(x)$? Express $f(x)$ in closed form.

    f) Use some algebra to explain why $B = 2A$ and $C = 3A$.

    g) Does a similar relationship exist between $\sum_{n=1}^{\infty} \frac{(0.8)^n}{n}$, $\sum_{n=1}^{\infty} \frac{(0.88)^n}{n}$, and $\sum_{n=1}^{\infty} \frac{(0.888)^n}{n}$?

2. Let $D = \sum_{n=1}^{\infty} \frac{(0.7)^n}{n}$, $E = \sum_{n=1}^{\infty} \frac{b^n}{n}$, and $F = \sum_{n=1}^{\infty} \frac{c^n}{n}$. Determine the values for b and c so that the same relationship that exists between A, B, & C will exist between D, E, & F. Use the closed form formula for f. A calculator is not necessary.

Teacher Notes and Answers

1. a) $-1 \le x < 1$

   b) $f(0.9) = A$ and $f(0.99) = B$; both 0.9 and 0.99 are in the interval of convergence

   c) $f'(x) = \sum_{n=1}^{\infty} x^n$

   d) $f'(x) = \dfrac{1}{1-x}$ for $-1 < x < 1$

   e) Antidifferentiate $f'(x) = \dfrac{1}{1-x}$. $f(x) = -\ln|1-x| = \ln\dfrac{1}{1-x}$ for $-1 \le x < 1$.

   f) $A = f(0.9) = \ln\dfrac{1}{1-0.9} = \ln 10$

   $B = f(0.99) = \ln\dfrac{1}{1-0.99} = \ln 100 = \ln 10^2 = 2\ln 10 = 2A$

   $C = f(0.999) = \ln\dfrac{1}{1-0.999} = \ln 1000 = \ln 10^3 = 3\ln 10 = 3A$

   g) No, the same relationship does not hold.

2. $D = \ln\dfrac{1}{1-0.7} = \ln\dfrac{10}{3}$

   $E = \ln\dfrac{1}{1-b} = 2E = 2\ln\dfrac{10}{3} = \ln\dfrac{100}{9} \Rightarrow b = 0.91$

   $F = \ln\dfrac{1}{1-c} = 3E = 3\ln\dfrac{10}{3} = \ln\dfrac{1000}{27} \Rightarrow c = 0.973$

   $b = 0.91$ and $c = 0.973$

Lab #8
Series Exploration

In this project you will consider the series $\sum_{n=1}^{\infty} \frac{n^2}{3^n}$ (we will refer to this as **A**) and use it as motivation for considering a related power series. In the process it is hoped that you will see how series can be manipulated to determine a series of interest.

1. Show that **A** converges using an appropriate test.

2. Use your calculator to convince yourself that **A** really does converges and to obtain an approximation for the sum. It appears that the **A** converges to what value?

3. This seems too good to be true, so let's consider **A** in a broader context, that is, as a Power Series for x equal to a certain value.

4. Consider the Power Series $\sum_{n=1}^{\infty} n^2 x^n$. For what value of x will the power series and **A** be the same?

5. For what values of x does the power series converge? Is the value you determined in (4) in this interval of convergence?

6. Our task now is to try to determine what function has this as a Power Series. We will manipulate a series that we can express in closed form, that is, know the function to which the series converges.

7. Consider the power series $\sum_{n=1}^{\infty} x^n$. Is this a geometric series? To what does it converge? What is its interval of convergence?

8. At this stage you should have determined that $\frac{x}{1-x} = \sum_{n=1}^{\infty} x^n$. If you cannot see this be sure to check with someone before continuing.

9. Differentiate both sides with respect to x and then multiply both sides by x. You should now know what function has $\sum_{n=1}^{\infty} nx^n$ as its power series representation for each x in the interval of convergence.

10. Repeat the previous step (9)   {that is all of step (9)}.

11. Call this function f.

12. Evaluate f at the x value that you determined in (4). Does this agree with the value you determined for the sum of **A**.

13. Use what you have learned to determine why $\sum_{n=1}^{\infty} \dfrac{n^3}{4^n} = 1.\overline{629}$

Your write-up of this project should include your work for 1, 2, 4, 5, 7, 9 - 12, answers to all questions that were asked. Include a paragraph in which you comment on what you have learned by completing this project.

Teacher Notes and Answers

1. Ratio Test: $L = \lim\limits_{n \to \infty} \dfrac{(n+1)^2}{3^{n+1}} \cdot \dfrac{3^n}{n^2} = \dfrac{1}{3} < 1$

2. $A = \dfrac{3}{2}$

4. $x = \dfrac{1}{3}$

5. The series is convergent for $-1 < x < 1$. Yes it is in the interval of convergence.

7. Yes, the series is geometric. The series converges to $\dfrac{x}{1-x}$.
    The interval of convergence is $-1 < x < 1$.

9. $\displaystyle\sum_{n=1}^{\infty} nx^n = \dfrac{x}{(x-1)^2}$

11. $f(x) = \displaystyle\sum_{n=1}^{\infty} n^2 x^n = \dfrac{x(x+1)}{(1-x)^3}$

12. $f\left(\dfrac{1}{3}\right) = \displaystyle\sum_{n=1}^{\infty} n^2 \left(\dfrac{1}{3}\right)^n = \displaystyle\sum_{n=1}^{\infty} \dfrac{n^2}{3^n} = \dfrac{3}{2}$ which agrees with the value of A found in #2.

13. $h(x) = \displaystyle\sum_{n=1}^{\infty} n^3 x^n = \dfrac{x(x^2 + 4x + 1)}{(x-1)^4}$

    $h\left(\dfrac{1}{4}\right) = \displaystyle\sum_{n=1}^{\infty} \dfrac{n^3}{4^n} = \dfrac{44}{27} = 1.\overline{629}$

Lab #9
An Investigation into the Accuracy of Polynomial Approximations
to Transcendental Functions

In this activity, you will investigate the behavior of the error in using various polynomials to approximate transcendental functions. That it is possible to make such approximations is startling enough. The mathematics that you can uncover by looking closely at the errors in these approximations is truly amazing. You should begin by recalling an earlier investigation into the accuracy of using the tangent line to approximate a function near the point of tangency. That activity looked closely at the consequences of the distinguishing features of the tangent line: that its output and its slope both agree with the function being approximated at the point of tangency.

The first investigation you'll make involves creating a second degree polynomial whose output, slope, *and concavity* all agree with a function we are trying to approximate. The function we'll approximate is $f(x) = e^x$ at the point (0, 1). Notice that $f(0) = 1$, $f'(0) = 1$, and $f''(0) = 1$. We are looking for a quadratic function, $q(x) = ax^2 + bx + c$ whose output, slope, and concavity all agree with those of e^x at $x = 0$.

1. Since $f(0) = 1$, we require $q(0) = 1$. Plug in 0 for x in the formula for $q(x)$ and set the result equal to 1. What is the value of c? _____

2. Since $f'(0) = 1$, we require $q'(0) = 1$. Using your value for c from number 1, calculate $q'(0)$ and set the result equal to 1. What is the value of b? _____

3. Since $f''(0) = 1$, we require $q''(0) = 1$. Using your value for c from number 1, calculate $q''(0)$ and set the result equal to 1. What is the value of a? _____

4. Use your values for a, b, and c and write down your formula for $q(x)$ here:
   _____
   Have your teacher initial here before proceeding. _____

5. Now find another quadratic polynomial, $r(x)$, whose output and slope agree with that of e^x at $x = 0$, but whose second derivative is slightly different from 1 at $x = 0$.

   Write down your formula for $r(x)$ here: _____
   Have your teacher initial before proceeding. _____

Now the fun starts! We'll take a close look at the behavior of the errors in using $q(x)$ and $r(x)$ to approximate e^x near $x = 0$. First, recall the result from your earlier investigation that used the idea of power zooming. A *power zoom* of degree m means, if the horizontal zoom factor is XFact (xFact on the TI-86 or TI-89) and the vertical zoom factor is YFact (xFact on the TI-86 or TI-89), then $(XFact)^m = YFact$. Zooming in to a graph of $y = x^n$ with a power zoom of degree m will cause the graph to get steeper if $n < m$, stay the same shape if $n = m$, and flatten out if $n > m$.

Now, on your calculator, enter e^x into Y1, your formula for $q(x)$ into Y2, and your $r(x)$ into Y3. Then define Y4 to be the error in using $q(x)$ to approximate e^x (that is, Y2(X) – Y1(X)), and define Y5 to be the error in using $r(x)$ to approximate e^x (that is, Y3(X) – Y1(X)). Remember that the difference between $q(x)$ and $r(x)$ was that q's output and first two derivatives agree with those of e^x at $x = 0$, while r's output and first derivative only agree. See the screen below. Select functions Y4 and Y5 for graphing, and deselect the others. Note the different graph styles chosen for the two error functions.

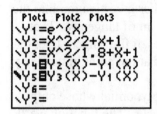

Draw the graph in the decimal window (Zoom 4 on the TI83 and '89, ZOOM…ZDECM on the '86). Set your zoom factors to do a degree 2 power zoom (factors of 5 and 25 work well). On the TI-83, you do this from the ZOOM Memory menu, on the TI-86, from the ZFACT menu, and on the TI-89, from the ZOOM…Set Factors… menu. Your graph should look like this:

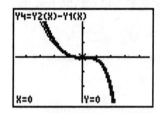

6. Explain why both error functions pass through (0, 0). _____

_____

_____

7. Now perform a degree 2 power zoom several times at (0, 0). Which graph flattened out?

_____

Remember that if a graph flattens out, this indicates that its behavior is greater in degree than that of the zoom.

8. What happened to the other error function after several zooms?_____

_____

Remember that if a graph remains unchanged upon a degree 2 power zoom, then it is exhibiting degree 2 behavior.

Now we'll try a degree 3 power zoom. Go back to the original zoom decimal window, and change the zoom factors to 5 for the x-factor and 125 for the y-factor.

9. Which graph flattened out, if any? _____

10. Which graph got steeper? _____

11. Which graph kept the same shape? _____

You should have seen that the error in using the function $q(x)$ to approximate e^x behaved like a degree 3 power function, and that the error in using the function $r(x)$ to approximate e^x behaved like a degree 2 power function. Also remember that steep error functions are bad! We would like error functions to stay near zero. Steep ones dart away from zero rapidly.

What happens if we extend this activity up one more degree? While we're at it, we'll try approximating a different function, too, just to see if our results might apply more generally. We will generate a cubic polynomial, $p(x) = ax^3 + bx^2 + cx + d$, to approximate $g(x) = \ln(x+1)$ at $x = 0$. We'll make the output and first *three* derivatives of $p(x)$ all agree with $f(x)$ at $x = 0$.

12. Verify that the cubic polynomial $p(x) = \dfrac{x^3}{3} - \dfrac{x^2}{2} + x$ satisfies the four

conditions $p(0) = g(0)$, $p'(0) = g'(0)$, $p''(0) = g''(0)$, and $p'''(0) = g'''(0)$.

_____

_____

_____

13. Verify that the cubic polynomial $r(x) = \dfrac{x^3}{2} - \dfrac{x^2}{2} + x$ satisfies the three conditions

$r(0) = f(0)$, $r'(0) = g'(0)$, and $r''(0) = g''(0)$ but fails to satisfy the fourth condition,
$r'''(0) = g'''(0)$.

_____

_____

_____

On your calculator, enter $\ln(x + 1)$ into Y1, the formula for $p(x)$ into Y2, and $r(x)$ into Y3. Then define Y4 to be the error in using $p(x)$ to approximate $\ln(x + 1)$ (that is, Y2(X) – Y1(X)), and define Y5 to be the error in using $r(x)$ to approximate $\ln(x + 1)$ (that is, Y3(X) – Y1(X)). Select functions Y4 and Y5 for graphing, and deselect the others. Remember that the difference between $p(x)$ and $r(x)$ was that p's output and first three derivatives agree with those of $\ln(x + 1)$

at $x = 0$, while r's output and first two derivatives only agree. See the screen below. Again, note the different graph styles chosen for the two error functions.

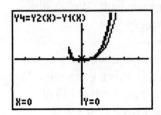

```
Plot1 Plot2 Plot3
\Y1=ln(X+1)
\Y2=X^3/3-X^2/2+
X
\Y3=X^3/2-X^2/2+
X
\Y4=Y2(X)-Y1(X)
\Y5=Y3(X)-Y1(X)
```

Draw the graphs in the decimal window. The graphs should look like this:

```
Y4=Y2(X)-Y1(X)



X=0              Y=0
```

14. Why do the graphs not extend to the left of $x = -1$? _____

_____

15. Verify that both error functions go through $(0, 0)$. Why must this be so? _____

_____

16. Now perform a degree 3 power zoom several times at $(0, 0)$. Remember to set your zoom factors so that YFact = $(XFact)^3$. Factors of 5 and 125 work well. Which graph flattened out? _____

Remember that if a graph flattens out, this indicates that its behavior is greater in degree than that of the zoom.

17. What happened to the other error function after several zooms? _____

_____

Remember that if a graph remains unchanged upon a degree 3 power zoom, then it is exhibiting degree 3 behavior.

Now we'll try a degree 4 power zoom. Go back to the original zoom decimal window, and change the zoom factors to 5 for the x-factor and 625 for the y-factor.

18. Which graph flattened out, if any? _____

19. Which graph got steeper? _____

20. Which graph kept the same shape? _____

You should have seen that the error in using the function $p(x)$ to approximate $\ln(x + 1)$ behaved like a degree 4 power function, and that the error in using the function $r(x)$ to approximate $\ln(x + 1)$ behaved like a degree 3 power function. Higher degree power functions stay near zero longer.

21. Try to generalize the results from the two parts of this activity.

_____

_____

_____

_____

Teacher Notes and Answers

This activity can be used with students as they begin their study of Taylor Polynomials. As students work through questions 4 and 5 you'll need to get around the room and make sure students have correct polynomials for $q(x)$ and $r(x)$. Otherwise, the rest of the activity won't make sense. That's why the students are asked to get the teacher's initials before proceeding past questions 4 and 5.

It would be a good idea to return to this activity when Taylor's Theorem with Remainder is covered. The fact that the error from using a degree n Taylor Polynomial to approximate a function behaves like a degree $n + 1$ function is key to understanding Taylor's Theorem.

1. $c = 1$

2. Since $q'(x) = 2ax + b$, $q'(0) = b$ and $b = 1$.

3. Since $q''(x) = 2a$, $q''(0) = 2a$ and $a = \dfrac{1}{2}$.

4. $q(x) = \dfrac{x^2}{2} + x + 1$

5. Any quadratic of the form $r(x) = \dfrac{x^2}{d} + x + 1$ with $d \neq 2$ will work. Choosing the constant d so that the concavity is just slightly "off" is more persuasive. For example, use

    $r(x) = \dfrac{x^2}{1.8} + x + 1$.

6. The outputs from $q(x) = Y2(X)$ and $r(x) = Y3(X)$ both agree with that of $F1(X) = e^x$ at $x = 0$. That is, $Y2(0) = Y3(0) = Y1(0) = 1$. So the errors are both 0 at $x = 0$.

7. The graph of $Y4(X)$, the error from using $q(x)$, flattened out. Remember that q's output, slope, and second derivative all agree with e^x at $x = 0$.

    Here is what the graphs might look like after 2 or 3 zooms:

    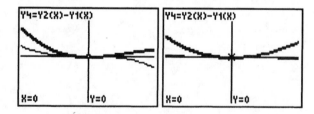

8. The other error function, $Y5(X)$, remained unchanged (and began to resemble a parabola).

9. Neither graph flattened out.

10. The graph of $Y5(X)$ got steeper.

11. The graph of Y4(X) kept the same shape (and resembled the graph of a degree 3 power function).

Here are the graphs after 2 or 3 zooms:

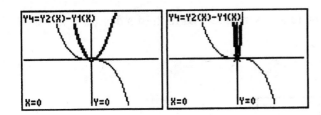

12. $p(0) = 0 = \ln(0+1)$; $p'(x) = x^2 - x + 1$ so $p'(0) = 1$. Also, $g'(x) = \dfrac{1}{x+1}$ and $g'(0) = 1$.

$p''(x) = 2x - 1$ so $p''(0) = -1$. Also, $g''(x) = \dfrac{-1}{(x+1)^2}$ and $g''(0) = -1$.

$p'''(x) = 2$ so $p'''(0) = 2$. Also, $g'''(x) = \dfrac{2}{(x+1)^3}$ and $g'''(0) = 2$.

13. $r(0) = 0 = \ln(0+1)$; $r'(x) = \dfrac{3x^2}{2} - x + 1$ so $r'(0) = 1$. Also, $g'(x) = \dfrac{1}{x+1}$ and $g'(0) = 1$.

$r''(x) = 3x - 1$ so $r''(0) = -1$. Also, $g''(x) = \dfrac{-1}{(x+1)^2}$ and $g''(0) = -1$.

$r'''(x) = 3$ so $r'''(0) = 3$. However, $g'''(x) = \dfrac{2}{(x+1)^3}$ and $g'''(0) = 2$. Thus $r'''(0) \neq g'''(0)$.

14. $\ln(x+1)$ is undefined when $x <= -1$. Each error function is defined in terms of $\ln(x+1)$.

15. $p(0) = r(0) = g(0) = 0$, so the errors are all 0 at 0.

16. The graph of Y4(X), the error from using $p(x)$, flattened out. Remember that p's output, first, second, and third derivatives all agree with $\ln(x+1)$ at $x = 0$.

Here is what the graphs might look like after 3 or 4 zooms:

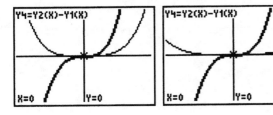

17. The other error function, Y5(X), remained unchanged (and began to resemble a cubic graph).

279

18. Neither graph flattened out.

19. The graph of Y5(X) got steeper.

20. The graph of Y4(X) kept the same shape (and resembled the graph of a degree 4 power function).

Here are the graphs after 2 or 3 zooms:

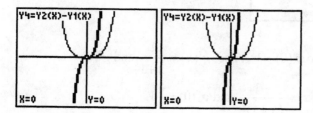

21. Suppose a degree n polynomial whose output and first n derivatives agree with a function f at a point is used to approximate f near that point. Then the error from that approximation behaves like a degree $n + 1$ power function.

Lab #10
A Numeric Investigation into the Accuracy of Polynomial Approximations to Transcendental Functions

In an earlier activity, "An Investigation into the Accuracy of Polynomial Approximations to Transcendental Functions", you used the tool of power zooming to look at the graphic behavior of polynomial approximations to a transcendental function. Here, you will investigate the same results from a numeric perspective. This activity follows ideas covered in an earlier activity, "A Numeric Investigation into the Accuracy of the Tangent Line Approximation."

If you did the lab investigating the accuracy of polynomial approximations, you generated a quadratic polynomial whose output, slope, and concavity all agreed with e^x at $x = 0$. Here we will produce the same quadratic polynomial by a different approach.

The tangent line that approximates $f(x) = e^x$ at the point $(0, 1)$ is $y = 1 + x$. In the lab that investigated the behavior of the relative error in using $x + 1$ to approximate e^x at $x = 0$, we saw that the relative error from using the tangent line approached 0. That is, we saw that

$\lim\limits_{x \to 0} \dfrac{e^x - (1+x)}{x} = 0$. This indicates that the error in the approximation approaches 0 faster than x

approaches 0. It would be even more remarkable if that error approached 0 faster than x^2 approached 0 (since x^2 approaches 0 faster than x does). So, let's take a look at the behavior of

$\lim\limits_{x \to 0} \dfrac{e^x - (1+x)}{x^2}$. Define functions as indicated by the screen below:

```
Plot1  Plot2  Plot3
\Y1=e^(X)
\Y2=1+X
\Y3=
\Y4=(Y1(X)-Y2(X)
)/X^2
\Y5=
\Y6=
```

Set up your table so that it starts at X=0, with a step size, ΔTbl, of 0.1. Take a look at the table of values.

1. Explain why the relative error is undefined at $x = 0$. _____

Now change the table step size, ΔTbl, to 0.01. Take a close look at the values for Y4 near 0. Then change the table step size, ΔTbl, to 0.0001. Look closely again at the values for Y4 near 0.

2. What does it appear the value of the error relative to x^2 is? That is, what is $\lim\limits_{x \to 0} \dfrac{e^x - (1+x)}{x^2}$?

_____

If $\lim\limits_{x\to 0}\dfrac{e^x-(1+x)}{x^2}=\dfrac{1}{2}$, we should be able to add a degree 2 term to our tangent line to compensate.

3. What is $\lim\limits_{x\to 0}\dfrac{\dfrac{x^2}{2}}{x^2}$? _____

4. What should the value of $\lim\limits_{x\to 0}\left[\dfrac{e^x-(1+x)}{x^2}-\dfrac{\dfrac{x^2}{2}}{x^2}\right]$ be? _____

Notice that $\lim\limits_{x\to 0}\left[\dfrac{e^x-(1+x)}{x^2}-\dfrac{\dfrac{x^2}{2}}{x^2}\right]=\lim\limits_{x\to 0}\dfrac{e^x-\left(1+x+\dfrac{x^2}{2}\right)}{x^2}$. So, let's look at the error relative to x^2

for $q(x)=1+x+\dfrac{x^2}{2}$. Edit Y2 as shown below:

```
Plot1  Plot2  Plot3
\Y1=e^(X)
\Y2=1+X+X^2/2
\Y3=
\Y4■(Y1(X)-Y2(X)
)/X^2
\Y5=
\Y6=
```

5. Let $f(x)=e^x$. Verify that $q(0)=f(0)$, $q'(0)=f'(0)$, and $q''(0)=f''(0)$.

_____

_____

_____

_____

We have found a quadratic polynomial whose output, slope, and concavity all agree with those of e^x at $x=0$. Amazing! Let's check out its error relative to x^2.

Reset your table so that it starts at X=0, with a step size, ΔTbl, of 0.1. Take a look at the table of values. Change the table step size, ΔTbl, to 0.01. Take a close look at the values for Y4 near 0. Then change the table step size, ΔTbl, to 0.0001. Look closely again at the values for Y4 near 0. You should be careful not to enter a very small value for ΔTbl right off the bat. Doing so could lead you to make false conclusions. Your calculator will display erroneous results because of its limited precision. See the screens below to confirm your results.

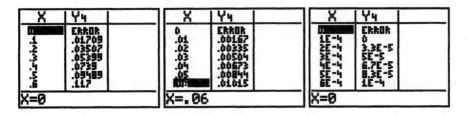

6. What does it appear the value of the error relative to x^2 is? That is, what is

$$\lim_{x \to 0} \frac{e^x - \left(1 + x + \dfrac{x^2}{2}\right)}{x^2}?$$ _____

We have found a way to approximate e^x so that the error in our approximation goes to 0 faster than x^2 goes to 0! This by itself is a remarkable achievement, but why should we stop there?

Let's look at the error relative to x^3. Check that your function definitions agree with those in the screen below.

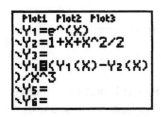

As before, look at the table of values with successively smaller values for ΔTbl, and try to see what the limit of the error relative to X^3 is. You should be careful not to use a ΔTbl value smaller than about 0.0001.

7. Write down your observations. _____

_____

You should have seen that the error relative to X^3 approached a number close to 0.166666. This is the decimal equivalent of 1/6. So, we could add on another term to our polynomial, a degree 3 term, so that we adjust for this constant. We were just looking at $\dfrac{e^x - \left(1 + x + \dfrac{x^2}{2}\right)}{x^3}$, and saw that it approaches 1/6 as x approaches 0.

8. What should happen, then, to $\dfrac{e^x - \left(1 + x + \dfrac{x^2}{2} + \dfrac{x^3}{6}\right)}{x^3}$ as x approaches 0?

_____

Let's check it out! Edit Y2, adding on the X^3/6 term to the end of your polynomial.

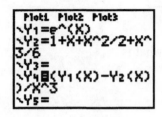

9. Verify that this new polynomial has the property that its output and first *three* derivatives all agree with e^x at $x = 0$.

_____

_____

_____

_____

Now let's look at our table of values again. As before, start off with ΔTbl = 0.1, and then change it to 0.01 and 0.001. You can't trust the results for values of x any closer to 0, again because of the calculator's limited numeric precision. However, we can see that the behavior of the error relative to X^3 is different from what it was with our degree 2 approximation.

10. What does the error relative to x^3 appear to be now? _____

We've found a cubic polynomial whose error in approximating e^x approaches 0 faster than x^3 approaches 0!

We could, of course, continue this process indefinitely for higher and higher degree polynomials, each time making one more derivative agree with the function we're approximating.

Teacher Notes and Answers

This activity could be used to introduce Taylor Polynomials. An accompanying lab, "An Investigation into the Accuracy of Polynomial Approximations to Transcendental Functions", looks at errors from a graphical perspective, while this one takes a numeric angle. Together, they provide invaluable experience with the nature and behavior of Taylor Polynomials. This one follows the spirit of a lab that you might have used early in the course investigating the error in tangent line approximations numerically.

1. The relative error is undefined at $x = 0$ because we are dividing by x.

2. $\dfrac{1}{2}$

3. $\dfrac{1}{2}$

4. 0

5. Note that $f(x) = f'(x) = f''(x) = e^x$ and $f(0) = f'(0) = f''(0) = e^0 = 1$

   $q(0) = 1 + 0 + 0 = 1$; $q'(x) = 1 + \dfrac{2x}{2} = 1 + x$; $q'(0) = 1$; $q''(x) = 1, q''(0) = 1$

6. 0

7. It appears there is a limit, and that the limit is about 0.166666.

8. $\dfrac{e^x - \left(1 + x + \dfrac{x^2}{2} + \dfrac{x^3}{6}\right)}{x^3}$ should approach 0 as x approaches 0.

9. Again note that $f(x) = f'(x) = f''(x) = f'''(x) = e^x$ and $f(0) = f'(0) = f''(0) = f'''(0) = e^0 = 1$

   $q(0) = 1 + 0 + 0 + 0 = 1$; $q'(x) = 1 + \dfrac{2x}{2} + \dfrac{3x^2}{6} = 1 + x + \dfrac{x^2}{2}$; $q'(0) = 1$; $q''(x) = 1 + \dfrac{2x}{2} = 1 + x, q''(0) = 1$;

   $q'''(x) = 1, q'''(0) = 1$

10. 0

Lab #11
An Exploration for Chapter 10

In this lab we will consider the function $f(x) = \cos\left(x^{\frac{2}{3}}\right)$ and its derivative at $x = 0$.

1. Use the Chain Rule to determine $f'(x)$.

2. What conclusion do you come to when you try to use this formula to determine $f'(0)$?

3. Look up the hypotheses for Chain Rule and explain why your conclusion might be invalid.

4. Use your calculator to look at the graph of $y = f(x)$.

5. Based on your graph, estimate the value of $f'(0)$.

6. Use the definition of the derivative to determine $f'(0)$.

7. Do your answers to questions 5 and 6 agree?

8. What is the Maclaurin Series expansion for $\cos t$?

9. Using the result of question 8, write a series expansion for $f(x)$. Explain why this series is not a power series.

10. Using the result of question 9, write a series expansion for $f'(x)$.

11. Using the result of question 10, what is the value of $f'(0)$.

12. What does this lab show about the use of series expansions of functions?

Teacher Notes and Answers

1. $f'(x) = -\sin\left(x^{\frac{2}{3}}\right)\left(\frac{2}{3}x^{-\frac{1}{3}}\right), \quad x \neq 0$

2. No conclusion about $f'(0)$ from the Chain Rule. The Chain Rule does not apply since the derivative of $x^{\frac{2}{3}}$ does not exist at $x = 0$.

5. From the graph of $y = f(x)$ it appears that $f'(0) = 0$.

6. $f'(0) = \lim_{x \to 0} \frac{f(x) - f(0)}{x - 0} = \lim_{x \to 0} \frac{\cos x^{\frac{2}{3}} - 1}{x} = \lim_{x \to 0} \frac{\cos x^{\frac{2}{3}} - 1}{x} \cdot \frac{\cos x^{\frac{2}{3}} + 1}{\cos x^{\frac{2}{3}} + 1}$

$f'(0) = \lim_{x \to 0} \frac{\cos^2\left(x^{\frac{2}{3}}\right) - 1}{x\left(\cos x^{\frac{2}{3}} + 1\right)} = -\lim_{x \to 0} \frac{\sin x^{\frac{2}{3}}}{x^{\frac{2}{3}}} \cdot \frac{\sin x^{\frac{2}{3}}}{x^{\frac{2}{3}}} \cdot \frac{x^{\frac{1}{3}}}{1 + \cos x^{\frac{2}{3}}} = -(1)(1)\left(\frac{0}{2}\right)$

$f'(0) = 0$

7. Yes, the answers agree.

8. $\cos t = 1 - \frac{1}{2!}t^2 + \frac{1}{4!}t^4 - \frac{1}{6!}t^6 + \dots$

9. $f(x) = \cos x^{\frac{2}{3}} = 1 - \frac{1}{2!}\left(x^{\frac{2}{3}}\right)^2 + \frac{1}{4!}\left(x^{\frac{2}{3}}\right)^4 - \frac{1}{6!}\left(x^{\frac{2}{3}}\right)^6 + \dots$

$f(x) = \cos x^{\frac{2}{3}} = 1 - \frac{1}{2!}x^{\frac{4}{3}} + \frac{1}{4!}x^{\frac{8}{3}} - \frac{1}{6!}x^{\frac{12}{3}} + \dots$

10. $f'(x) = -\frac{2}{3}x^{\frac{1}{3}} + \left(\text{only terms containing } x^{\text{pos.}}\right)$

11. $f'(0) = 0$

287

12. (Answers will vary) Power series representations of functions can help you see why certain relationships exist. In this case it was easy to see why $f'(0)=0$.

Lab #12
Euler's Method

For each of the differential equations listed below, set up a spreadsheet with six columns.

Hold Δx as a constant. Start Δx at 0.1, then repeat the spreadsheet for $\Delta x = 0.01$, then for $\Delta x = 0.001$.

The columns for your spreadsheet should be as follows:

A: x-values, starting with the given x-value from the initial condition

B: y-values on the estimated solution to the differential equation. Start with the given y-value from the initial condition.

C: The value of $\dfrac{dy}{dx}$ at the point (x, y)

D: The value of Δy according to Euler's method.

E: The value of y from the exact solution to the differential equation.

F: The difference between the estimated y-value and the exact y-value.

Each spreadsheet should show ten points computed via Euler's method.

(Extra Credit: Have the spreadsheet graph your estimated and real solutions.)

Use the following equations, subject to the given initial conditions:

1. $\dfrac{dy}{dx} = 3y, \quad y = 10$ when $x = 0$

2. $\dfrac{dy}{dx} = \dfrac{x^2}{y^2}, \quad y = 4$ when $x = 1$

3. $\dfrac{dy}{dx} = 4y(1-y), \quad y = 20$ when $x = 0$

4. $\dfrac{dy}{dx} = \cos(x), \quad$ through the origin

Teacher Notes and Answers

The following is a sample of the three spreadsheets for the first equation.

1. dy/dx=3y					
Delta x	Initial x	Initial y	Exact Solution		
0.1	0	10	y=10e^3x		
x	y	dy/dx	Delta y	Exact y	Exact y - Euler y
0	10	30	3	10	0
0.1	13	39	3.9	13.4986	0.4985881
0.2	16.9	50.7	5.07	18.2212	1.321188
0.3	21.97	65.91	6.591	24.596	2.6260311
0.4	28.56	85.68	8.568	33.2012	4.6401692
0.5	37.13	111.4	11.14	44.8169	7.6875907
0.6	48.27	144.8	14.48	60.4965	12.228385
0.7	62.75	188.2	18.82	81.6617	18.913182
0.8	81.57	244.7	24.47	110.232	28.658692
0.9	106	318.1	31.81	148.797	42.752324
1	137.9	413.6	41.36	200.855	62.996877

1. dy/dx=3y

Delta x	Initial x	Initial y	Exact Solution:		
0.01	0	10	y=10e^3x		

x	y	dy/dx	Delta y	Exact y	Exact y - Euler y
0	10	30	0.3	10	0
0.01	10.3	30.9	0.309	10.3045	0.0045453
0.02	10.61	31.83	0.318	10.6184	0.0093655
0.03	10.93	32.78	0.328	10.9417	0.0144728
0.04	11.26	33.77	0.338	11.275	0.0198804
0.05	11.59	34.78	0.348	11.6183	0.0256017
0.06	11.94	35.82	0.358	11.9722	0.0316507
0.07	12.3	36.9	0.369	12.3368	0.0380419
0.08	12.67	38	0.38	12.7125	0.0447907
0.09	13.05	39.14	0.391	13.0996	0.0519127
0.1	13.44	40.32	0.403	13.4986	0.0594243

1. dy/dx=3y

Delta x	Initial x	Initial y	Exact Solution:		
0.001	0	10	$y=10e^{3x}$		

x	y	dy/dx	Delta y	Exact y	Exact y - Euler y
0	10	30	0.03	10	0
0.001	10.03	30.09	0.03	10.03	5E-05
0.002	10.06	30.18	0.03	10.0602	9E-05
0.003	10.09	30.27	0.03	10.0904	1E-04
0.004	10.12	30.36	0.03	10.1207	2E-04
0.005	10.15	30.45	0.03	10.1511	2E-04
0.006	10.18	30.54	0.031	10.1816	3E-04
0.007	10.21	30.64	0.031	10.2122	3E-04
0.008	10.24	30.73	0.031	10.2429	4E-04
0.009	10.27	30.82	0.031	10.2737	4E-04
0.01	10.3	30.91	0.031	10.3045	5E-04

DISPLACEMENT VECTORS

Suppose you are a pilot planning a flight from Dallas to Pittsburgh. There are two things you must know: the distance to be traveled (so you have enough fuel to make it) and in what direction to go (so you don't miss Pittsburgh). Both these quantities together specify the displacement or *displacement vector* between the two cities.

> The **displacement vector** from one point to another is an arrow with its tail at the first point and its tip at the second. The **magnitude** (or length) of the displacement vector is the distance between the points, and is represented by the length of the arrow. The **direction** of the displacement vector is the direction of the arrow.

Figure 13.1 shows the displacement vectors from Dallas to Pittsburgh, from Albuquerque to Oshkosh, and from Los Angeles to Buffalo, SD. These displacement vectors have the same length and the same direction. We say that the displacement vectors between the corresponding cities are the same, even though they do not coincide. In other words

> Displacement vectors which point in the same direction and have the same magnitude are considered to be the same, even if they do not coincide.

Figure 13.1: Displacement vectors between cities

Notation and Terminology

The displacement vector is our first example of a vector. Vectors have both magnitude and direction; in comparison, a quantity specified only by a number, but no direction, is called a *scalar*.[1] For instance, the time taken by the flight from Dallas to Pittsburgh is a scalar quantity. Displacement is a vector since it requires both distance and direction to specify it.

In this book, vectors are written with an arrow over them, $\vec{v}$, to distinguish them from scalars. Other books use a bold **v** to denote a vector. We use the notation $\overrightarrow{PQ}$ to denote the displacement vector from a point P to a point Q. The magnitude, or length, of a vector $\vec{v}$ is written $\|\vec{v}\|$.

---

[1]So named by W. R. Hamilton because they are merely numbers on the *scale* from $-\infty$ to ∞.

Addition and Subtraction of Displacement Vectors

Suppose NASA commands a robot on Mars to move 75 meters in one direction and then 50 meters in another direction. (See Figure 13.2.) Where does the robot end up? Suppose the displacements are represented by the vectors $\vec{v}$ and $\vec{w}$, respectively. Then the sum $\vec{v} + \vec{w}$ gives the final position.

The **sum**, $\vec{v} + \vec{w}$, of two vectors $\vec{v}$ and $\vec{w}$ is the combined displacement resulting from first applying $\vec{v}$ and then $\vec{w}$. (See Figure 13.3.) The sum $\vec{w} + \vec{v}$ gives the same displacement.

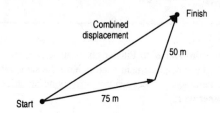

Figure 13.2: Sum of displacements of robots on Mars

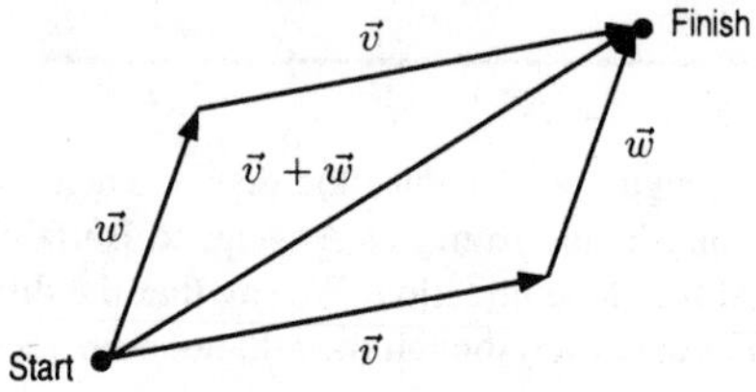

Figure 13.3: The sum $\vec{v} + \vec{w} = \vec{w} + \vec{v}$

Suppose two different robots start from the same location. One moves along a displacement vector $\vec{v}$ and the second along a displacement vector $\vec{w}$. What is the displacement vector, $\vec{x}$, from the first robot to the second? (See Figure 13.4.) Since $\vec{v} + \vec{x} = \vec{w}$, we define $\vec{x}$ to be the difference $\vec{x} = \vec{w} - \vec{v}$. In other words, $\vec{w} - \vec{v}$ gets you from $\vec{v}$ to $\vec{w}$.

The **difference**, $\vec{w} - \vec{v}$, is the displacement vector which, when added to $\vec{v}$, gives $\vec{w}$. That is, $\vec{w} = \vec{v} + (\vec{w} - \vec{v})$. (See Figure 13.4.)

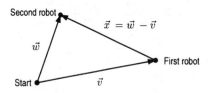

Figure 13.4: The difference $\vec{w} - \vec{v}$

If the robot ends up where it started, then its total displacement vector is the *zero vector*, $\vec{0}$. The zero vector has no direction.

The **zero vector**, $\vec{0}$, is a displacement vector with zero length.

Scalar Multiplication of Displacement Vectors

If $\vec{v}$ represents a displacement vector, the vector $2\vec{v}$ represents a displacement of twice the magnitude in the same direction as $\vec{v}$. Similarly, $-2\vec{v}$ represents a displacement of twice the magnitude in the opposite direction. (See Figure 13.5.)

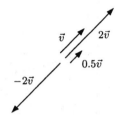

Figure 13.5: Scalar multiples of the vector $\vec{v}$

> If λ is a scalar and $\vec{v}$ is a displacement vector, the **scalar multiple of $\vec{v}$ by** λ, written $\lambda\vec{v}$, is the displacement vector with the following properties:
> - The displacement vector $\lambda\vec{v}$ is parallel to $\vec{v}$, pointing in the same direction if $\lambda > 0$, and in the opposite direction if $\lambda < 0$.
> - The magnitude of $\lambda\vec{v}$ is $|\lambda|$ times the magnitude of $\vec{v}$, that is, $\|\lambda\vec{v}\| = |\lambda|\,\|\vec{v}\|$.

Note that $|\lambda|$ represents the absolute value of the scalar λ while $\|\lambda\vec{v}\|$ represents the magnitude of the vector $\lambda\vec{v}$.

Example 1 Explain why $\vec{w} - \vec{v} = \vec{w} + (-1)\vec{v}$.

Solution The vector $(-1)\vec{v}$ has the same magnitude as $\vec{v}$, but points in the opposite direction. Figure 13.6 shows that the combined displacement $\vec{w} + (-1)\vec{v}$ is the same as the displacement $\vec{w} - \vec{v}$.

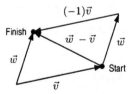

Figure 13.6: Explanation for why $\vec{w} - \vec{v} = \vec{w} + (-1)\vec{v}$

Parallel Vectors

Two vectors $\vec{v}$ and $\vec{w}$ are *parallel* if one is a scalar multiple of the other, that is, if $\vec{w} = \lambda\vec{v}$, for some scalar λ.

295

Components of Displacement Vectors: The Vectors $\vec{i}$ and $\vec{j}$

Suppose that you live in a city with equally spaced streets running east-west and north-south and that you want to tell someone how to get from one place to another. You'd be likely to tell them how many blocks east-west and how many blocks north-south to go. For example, to get from P to Q in Figure 13.7, we go 4 blocks east and 1 block south. If $\vec{i}$ and $\vec{j}$ are as shown in Figure 13.7, then the displacement vector from P to Q is $4\vec{i} - \vec{j}$.

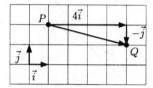

Figure 13.7: The displacement vector from P to Q is $4\vec{i} - \vec{j}$

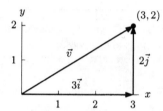

Figure 13.8: We resolve $\vec{v}$ into components by writing $\vec{v} = 3\vec{i} + 2\vec{j}$

Writing Displacement Vectors Using $\vec{i}$ and $\vec{j}$

Any displacement in the plane can be expressed as a combination of displacements in the coordinate directions. For example, Figure 13.8 shows that the displacement vector $\vec{v}$ from the origin to the point $(3, 2)$ can be written as a sum of displacement vectors along the x and y-axes:

$$\vec{v} = 3\vec{i} + 2\vec{j}.$$

This is called *resolving $\vec{v}$ into components*. In general:

> We **resolve** $\vec{v}$ into components by writing $\vec{v}$ in the form
> $$\vec{v} = v_1\vec{i} + v_2\vec{j}.$$
> We call $v_1\vec{i}$ and $v_2\vec{j}$ the **components** of $\vec{v}$.

An Alternative Notation for Vectors

Many people write a vector in 2-dimensions as a string of two numbers, that is, as

$$\vec{v} = (v_1, v_2) \quad \text{instead of} \quad \vec{v} = v_1\vec{i} + v_2\vec{j}.$$

Since the first notation can be confused with a point and the second cannot, we usually use the second form.

Example 2   Resolve the displacement vector, $\vec{v}$, from the point $P_1 = (2, 4)$ to the point $P_2 = (3, 7)$ into components.

Solution   To get from P_1 to P_2, we move 1 unit in the positive x-direction and 3 units in the positive y-direction. Hence $\vec{v} = \vec{i} + 3\vec{j}$.

Example 3   Decide whether the vector $\vec{v} = 2\vec{i} + 3\vec{j}$ is parallel to each of the following vectors:

$$\vec{w} = 4\vec{i} + 6\vec{j}, \quad \vec{a} = -\vec{i} - 1.5\vec{j}, \quad \vec{b} = 4\vec{i} + 5\vec{j}.$$

Solution   Since $\vec{w} = 2\vec{v}$ and $\vec{a} = -0.5\vec{v}$, the vectors $\vec{v}$, $\vec{w}$, and $\vec{a}$ are parallel. However, $\vec{b}$ is not a multiple of $\vec{v}$ (since, for example, $4/2 \neq 5/3$), so $\vec{v}$ and $\vec{b}$ are not parallel.

In general, Figure 13.9 shows us how to express the displacement vector between two points in components:

Components of Displacement Vectors

The displacement vector from the point $P_1 = (x_1, y_1)$ to the point $P_2 = (x_2, y_2)$ is given in components by

$$\overrightarrow{P_1 P_2} = (x_2 - x_1)\vec{i} + (y_2 - y_1)\vec{j}.$$

Position Vectors: Displacement of a Point from the Origin

A displacement vector whose tail is at the origin is called a *position vector*. Thus, any point (x_0, y_0) in space has associated with it the position vector $\vec{r}_0 = x_0\vec{i} + y_0\vec{j}$. (See Figure 13.10.) In general, a position vector gives the displacement of a point from the origin.

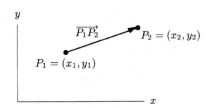

Figure 13.9: The displacement vector
$\overrightarrow{P_1 P_2} = (x_2 - x_1)\vec{i} + (y_2 - y_1)\vec{j}$

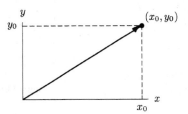

Figure 13.10: The position vector
$\vec{r}_0 = x_0\vec{i} + y_0\vec{j}$

The Components of the Zero Vector

The zero displacement vector has magnitude equal to zero and is written $\vec{0}$. So $\vec{0} = 0\vec{i} + 0\vec{j}$.

297

The Magnitude of a Vector in Components

For a vector, $\vec{v} = v_1\vec{i} + v_2\vec{j}$, the Pythagorean theorem is used to find its magnitude, $\|\vec{v}\|$. (See Figure 13.11.)

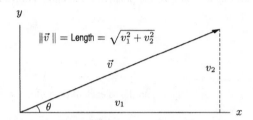

Figure 13.11: Magnitude, $\|\vec{v}\|$, of a 2-dimensional vector, $\vec{v}$

For instance, if $\vec{v} = 3\vec{i} - 4\vec{j}$, then $\|\vec{v}\| = \sqrt{3^2 + (-4)^2} = 5$.

Addition and Scalar Multiplication of Vectors in Components

Suppose the vectors $\vec{v}$ and $\vec{w}$ are given in components:

$$\vec{v} = v_1\vec{i} + v_2\vec{j} \quad \text{and} \quad \vec{w} = w_1\vec{i} + w_2\vec{j}.$$

Then

$$\vec{v} + \vec{w} = (v_1 + w_1)\vec{i} + (v_2 + w_2)\vec{j},$$

and

$$\lambda\vec{v} = \lambda v_1\vec{i} + \lambda v_2\vec{j}.$$

Figures 13.12 and 13.13 illustrate these properties. Finally, $\vec{v} - \vec{w} = \vec{v} + (-1)\vec{w}$, so we can write $\vec{v} - \vec{w} = (v_1 - w_1)\vec{i} + (v_2 - w_2)\vec{j}$.

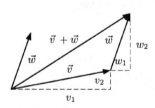

Figure 13.12: Sum $\vec{v} + \vec{w}$ in components

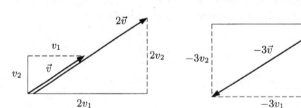

Figure 13.13: Scalar multiples of vectors showing $\vec{v}$, $2\vec{v}$, and $-3\vec{v}$

How to Resolve a Vector into Components

You may wonder how we find the components of a 2-dimensional vector, given its length and direction. Suppose the vector $\vec{v}$ has length v and makes an angle of θ with the x-axis, measured counterclockwise, as in Figure 13.14. If $\vec{v} = v_1\vec{i} + v_2\vec{j}$, Figure 13.14 shows that

$$v_1 = v\cos\theta \quad \text{and} \quad v_2 = v\sin\theta.$$

Thus, we resolve $\vec{v}$ into components by writing

$$\vec{v} = (v\cos\theta)\vec{i} + (v\sin\theta)\vec{j}.$$

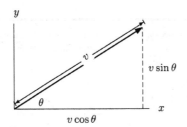

Figure 13.14: Resolving a vector: $\vec{v} = (v\cos\theta)\vec{i} + (v\sin\theta)\vec{j}$

Example 4   Resolve $\vec{v}$ into components if $\|\vec{v}\| = 2$ and $\theta = \pi/6$.

Solution   We have $\vec{v} = 2\cos(\pi/6)\vec{i} + 2\sin(\pi/6)\vec{j} = 2(\sqrt{3}/2)\,\vec{i} + 2(1/2)\vec{j} = \sqrt{3}\vec{i} + \vec{j}$.

Unit Vectors

A *unit vector* is a vector whose magnitude is 1. The vectors $\vec{i}$ and $\vec{j}$ are unit vectors in the directions of the coordinate axes. It is often helpful to find a unit vector in the same direction as a given vector $\vec{v}$. Suppose that $\|\vec{v}\| = 10$; a unit vector in the same direction as $\vec{v}$ is $\vec{v}/10$. In general, a unit vector in the direction of any nonzero vector $\vec{v}$ is

$$\vec{u} = \frac{\vec{v}}{\|\vec{v}\|}.$$

Example 5   Find a unit vector, $\vec{u}$, in the direction of the vector $\vec{v} = \vec{i} + 3\vec{j}$.

Solution   If $\vec{v} = \vec{i} + 3\vec{j}$, then $\|\vec{v}\| = \sqrt{1^2 + 3^2} = \sqrt{10}$. Thus, a unit vector in the same direction is given by

$$\vec{u} = \frac{\vec{v}}{\sqrt{10}} = \frac{1}{\sqrt{10}}(\vec{i} + 3\vec{j}) = \frac{1}{\sqrt{10}}\vec{i} + \frac{3}{\sqrt{10}}\vec{j} \approx 0.32\vec{i} + 0.95\vec{j}.$$

Example 6   Find a unit vector at the point (x, y) that points radially outward away from the origin.

Solution   The vector from the origin to (x, y) is the position vector

$$\vec{r} = x\vec{i} + y\vec{j}.$$

Thus, if we put its tail at (x, y) it will point away from the origin. Its magnitude is

$$\|\vec{r}\| = \sqrt{x^2 + y^2},$$

so a unit vector pointing in the same direction is

$$\frac{\vec{r}}{\|\vec{r}\|} = \frac{x\vec{i} + y\vec{j}}{\sqrt{x^2 + y^2}} = \frac{x}{\sqrt{x^2 + y^2}}\vec{i} + \frac{y}{\sqrt{x^2 + y^2}}\vec{j}.$$

Problems on Displacement Vectors

Exercises

For Exercises 1–5, perform the indicated operations on the following vectors:

$$\vec{c} = \vec{i} + 6\vec{j}, \quad \vec{x} = -2\vec{i} + 9\vec{j}, \quad \vec{y} = 4\vec{i} - 7\vec{j}.$$

1. $2\vec{c} + \vec{x}$

2. $\|\vec{y}\|$

3. $5c$

4. $\|x - c\|$

5. $c + x + y$

6. Resolve the vectors in Figure 13.15 into components.

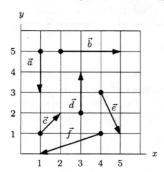

Figure 13.15

7. Resolve vector $\vec{v}$ into components if $\|\vec{v}\| = 8$ and the direction of $\vec{v}$ is shown in Figure 13.16.

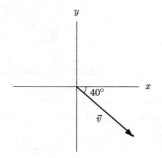

Figure 13.16

8. **(a)** Draw the position vector for $\vec{v} = 5\vec{i} - 7\vec{j}$.
   (b) What is $\|\vec{v}\|$?
   (c) Find the angle between $\vec{v}$ and the positive x-axis.

9. A vector starts at the point $Q = (4,6)$ and ends at the point $P = (1,2)$. Resolve the vector into its components.

Problems

10. **(a)** Find a unit vector from the point $P = (1,2)$ and toward the point $Q = (4,6)$.
   (b) Find a vector of length 10 pointing in the same direction.

11. Find all vectors $\vec{v}$ in 2 dimensions having $\|\vec{v}\| = 5$ and the $\vec{i}$-component of $\vec{v}$ is $3\vec{i}$.

12. A truck is traveling due north at 30 km/hr approaching a crossroad. On a perpendicular road a police car is traveling west toward the intersection at 40 km/hr. Both ve-

hicles will reach the crossroad in exactly one hour. Find the vector currently representing the displacement of the truck with respect to the police car.

13. Show that the medians of a triangle intersect at a point $\frac{1}{3}$ of the way along each median from the side it bisects.

14. Show that the lines joining the centroid (the intersection point of the medians) of a face of the tetrahedron and the opposite vertex meet at a point $\frac{1}{4}$ of the way from each centroid to its opposite vertex.

Solutions to Problems on Displacement Vectors ▬▬▬▬▬▬▬

Exercises

1. $2\vec{c} + \vec{x} = 2(\vec{i} + 6\vec{j}) + (-2\vec{i} + 9\vec{j}) = (2\vec{i} + 12\vec{j}) + (-2\vec{i} + 9\vec{j}) = (2-2)\vec{i} + (12+9)\vec{j} = 21\vec{j}$.

2. $\|\vec{y}\| = \sqrt{(4)^2 + (-7)^2} = \sqrt{16 + 49} = \sqrt{65}$.

3. $5c = 5i + 30j$

4. $\|x - c\| = \| -2i + 9j - (i + 6j)\| = \| -3i + 3j\| = 3\sqrt{2}$.

5. $c + x + y = i + 6j + -2i + 9j + 4i - 7j = 3i + 8j$.

6. $\vec{a} = -2\vec{j}$, $\vec{b} = 3\vec{i}$, $\vec{c} = \vec{i} + \vec{j}$, $\vec{d} = 2\vec{j}$, $\vec{e} = \vec{i} - 2\vec{j}$, $\vec{f} = -3\vec{i} - \vec{j}$.

7. Resolving $\vec{v}$ into components gives $\vec{v} = 8\cos(40°)\vec{i} - 8\sin(40°)\vec{j} = 6.13\vec{i} - 5.14\vec{j}$. Notice that the component in the $\vec{j}$ direction must be negative.

8. (a) See Figure 13.17.
   (b) $\|\vec{v}\| = \sqrt{5^2 + 7^2} = \sqrt{74} = 8.602$.
   (c) We see in Figure 13.18 that $\tan\theta = \frac{7}{5}$ and so $\theta = 54.46°$.

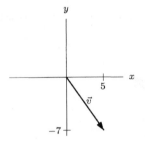

Figure 13.17

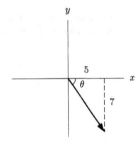

Figure 13.18

9. The vector we want is the displacement from Q to P, which is given by

$$\vec{QP} = (1-4)\vec{i} + (2-6)\vec{j} = -3\vec{i} - 4\vec{j}$$

Problems

10. (a) The displacement from P to Q is given by

$$\vec{PQ} = (4\vec{i} + 6\vec{j}) - (\vec{i} + 2\vec{j}) = 3\vec{i} + 4\vec{j}.$$

Since

$$\|\vec{PQ}\| = \sqrt{3^2 + 4^2} = 5,$$

a unit vector $\vec{u}$ in the direction of $\vec{PQ}$ is given by

$$\vec{u} = \frac{1}{5}\vec{PQ} = \frac{1}{5}(3\vec{i} + 4\vec{j}) = \frac{3}{5}\vec{i} + \frac{4}{5}\vec{j}.$$

(b) A vector of length 10 pointing in the same direction is given by

$$10\vec{u} = 10(\frac{3}{5}\vec{i} + \frac{4}{5}\vec{j}) = 6\vec{i} + 8\vec{j}.$$

11. Since the component of $\vec{v}$ in the $\vec{i}$-direction is 3, we have $\vec{v} = 3\vec{i} + b\vec{j}$ for some b. Since $\|\vec{v}\| = 5$, we have $\sqrt{3^2 + b^2} = 5$, so $b = 4$ or $b = -4$. There are two vectors satisfying the properties given: $\vec{v} = 3\vec{i} + 4\vec{j}$ and $\vec{v} = 3\vec{i} - 4\vec{j}$.

12.

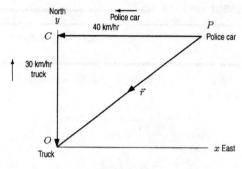

Figure 13.19

Since both vehicles reach the crossroad in exactly one hour, at the present the truck is at O in Figure 13.19; the police car is at P and the crossroads is at C. If $\vec{r}$ is the vector representing the line of sight of the truck with respect to the police car.

$$\vec{r} = -40\vec{i} - 30\vec{j}$$

13. In Figure 13.20 let O be the origin, points A, B, and C be the vertices of the triangle, point D be the midpoint of $\overline{BC}$, and Q be the point in the line segment $\overline{DA}$ that is $\frac{1}{3}|DA|$ away from D.

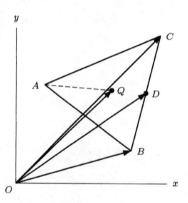

Figure 13.20

From Figure 13.20 we see that

$$\overrightarrow{OQ} = \overrightarrow{OD} + \overrightarrow{DQ} = \overrightarrow{OD} + \frac{1}{3}\overrightarrow{DA}$$

$$= \overrightarrow{OD} + \frac{1}{3}(\overrightarrow{OA} - \overrightarrow{OD})$$

$$= \overrightarrow{OD} + \frac{1}{3}\overrightarrow{OA} - \frac{1}{3}\overrightarrow{OD}$$

$$= \frac{1}{3}\overrightarrow{OA} + \frac{2}{3}\overrightarrow{OD}.$$

Because the diagonals of a parallelogram meet at their midpoint, and $2\overrightarrow{OD}$ is a diagonal of the parallelogram formed by $\overrightarrow{OB}$ and $\overrightarrow{OC}$, we have:

$$\overrightarrow{OD} = \frac{1}{2}(\overrightarrow{OB} + \overrightarrow{OC}),$$

so we can write:

$$\overrightarrow{OQ} = \frac{1}{3}\overrightarrow{OA} + \frac{2}{3}\left(\frac{1}{2}\right)(\overrightarrow{OB} + \overrightarrow{OC}) = \frac{1}{3}(\overrightarrow{OA} + \overrightarrow{OB} + \overrightarrow{OC}).$$

Thus a vector from the origin to a point $\frac{1}{3}$ of the way along median AD from D, the midpoint, is given by $\frac{1}{3}(\overrightarrow{OA}+\overrightarrow{OB}+\overrightarrow{OC})$.

In a similar manner we can show that the vector from the origin to the point $\frac{1}{3}$ of the way along any median from the midpoint of the side it bisects is also $\frac{1}{3}(\overrightarrow{OA}+\overrightarrow{OB}+\overrightarrow{OC})$. See Figure 13.21 and 13.22.

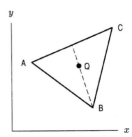

Figure 13.21

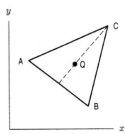

Figure 13.22

Thus the medians of a triangle intersect at a point $\frac{1}{3}$ of the way along each median from the side that each bisects.

14. We want to find an expression for a vector from the origin to a point that is $\frac{1}{4}$ of the way from a centroid to its opposite vertex.

In Figure 13.23 let O be the origin, A, B, C, and D be the vertices of a tetrahedron, P be the centroid of face BCD, and Q be the point on $\overline{PA}$ that is $|\frac{1}{4}\overline{PA}|$ away from P.

$$\begin{aligned}
\overrightarrow{OQ} &= \overrightarrow{OP} + \overrightarrow{PQ} \\
&= \overrightarrow{OP} + \frac{1}{4}\overrightarrow{PA} \\
&= \overrightarrow{OP} + \frac{1}{4}(\overrightarrow{OA} - \overrightarrow{OP}) \\
&= \overrightarrow{OP} + \frac{1}{4}\overrightarrow{OA} - \frac{1}{4}\overrightarrow{OP} \\
&= \frac{1}{4}\overrightarrow{OA} + \frac{3}{4}\overrightarrow{OP}.
\end{aligned}$$

In Problem 13 we showed that a vector from the origin to P, the centroid of a triangle, is

$$\overrightarrow{OP} = \frac{1}{3}(\overrightarrow{OB} + \overrightarrow{OC} + \overrightarrow{OD}).$$

Substituting this into our expression for $\overrightarrow{OQ}$ gives

$$\begin{aligned}
\overrightarrow{OQ} &= \frac{1}{4}\overrightarrow{OA} + \frac{3}{4}\left(\frac{1}{3}\right)(\overrightarrow{OB} + \overrightarrow{OC} + \overrightarrow{OD}) \\
&= \frac{1}{4}\overrightarrow{OA} + \frac{1}{4}(\overrightarrow{OB} + \overrightarrow{OC} + \overrightarrow{OD}) \\
&= \frac{1}{4}(\overrightarrow{OA} + \overrightarrow{OB} + \overrightarrow{OC} + \overrightarrow{OD}).
\end{aligned}$$

In a similar manner we can show that a vector from the origin to a point $\frac{1}{4}$ of the way from the centroid of *any* face to its opposite vertex is $\frac{1}{4}(\overrightarrow{OA} + \overrightarrow{OB} + \overrightarrow{OC} + \overrightarrow{OD})$. Thus, lines joining the centroid of each face to its opposite vertex all meet at a single point which is $\frac{1}{4}$ of the way from any centroid to its opposite face.

303

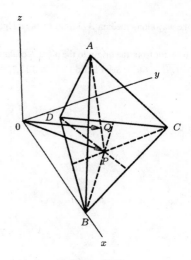

Figure 13.23

MOTION, VELOCITY, AND ACCELERATION

In this section we see how to find the vector quantities of velocity and acceleration from a parametric equation for the motion of an object.

The Velocity Vector

The velocity of a moving particle can be represented by a vector with the following properties:

> The **velocity vector** of a moving object is a vector $\vec{v}$ such that:
> - The magnitude of $\vec{v}$ is the speed of the object.
> - The direction of $\vec{v}$ is the direction of motion.
>
> Thus the speed of the object is $\|\vec{v}\|$ and the velocity vector is tangent to the object's path.

Example 1   A child is sitting on a ferris wheel of diameter 10 meters, making one revolution every 2 minutes. Find the speed of the child and draw velocity vectors at two different times.

Solution   The child moves at a constant speed around a circle of radius 5 meters, completing one revolution every 2 minutes. One revolution around a circle of radius 5 is a distance of 10π, so the child's speed is $10\pi/2 = 5\pi \approx 15.7$ m/min. Hence, the magnitude of the velocity vector is 15.7 m/min. The direction of motion is tangent to the circle, and hence perpendicular to the radius at that point. Figure 17.1 shows the direction of the vector at two different times.

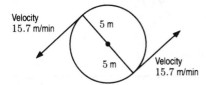

Figure 17.1: Velocity vectors of a child on a ferris wheel (Note that vectors would be in opposite direction if viewed from the other side)

Computing the Velocity

We find the velocity, as in one-variable calculus, by taking a limit. If the position vector of the particle is $\vec{r}(t)$ at time t, then the displacement vector between its positions at times t and $t + \Delta t$ is $\Delta\vec{r} = \vec{r}(t + \Delta t) - \vec{r}(t)$. (See Figure 17.2.) Over this interval,

$$\text{Average velocity} = \frac{\Delta\vec{r}}{\Delta t}.$$

In the limit as Δt goes to zero we have the instantaneous velocity at time t:

> The **velocity vector**, $\vec{v}(t)$, of a moving object with position vector $\vec{r}(t)$ at time t is
>
> $$\vec{v}(t) = \lim_{\Delta t \to 0} \frac{\Delta\vec{r}}{\Delta t} = \lim_{\Delta t \to 0} \frac{\vec{r}(t + \Delta t) - \vec{r}(t)}{\Delta t},$$
>
> whenever the limit exists. We use the notation $\vec{v} = \dfrac{d\vec{r}}{dt} = \vec{r}\,'(t)$.

305

Notice that the direction of the velocity vector $\vec{r}\,'(t)$ in Figure 17.2 is approximated by the direction of the vector $\Delta\vec{r}$ and that the approximation gets better as $\Delta t \to 0$.

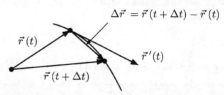

$$\Delta\vec{r} = \vec{r}\,(t + \Delta t) - \vec{r}\,(t)$$

Figure 17.2: The change, $\Delta\vec{r}$, in the position vector for a particle moving on a curve and the velocity vector $\vec{v} = \vec{r}\,'(t)$

The Components of the Velocity Vector

If we represent a curve parametrically by $x = f(t), y = g(t)$, then we can write its position vector as: $\vec{r}\,(t) = f(t)\vec{i} + g(t)\vec{j}$. Now we can compute the velocity vector:

$$
\begin{aligned}
\vec{v}\,(t) &= \lim_{\Delta t \to 0} \frac{\vec{r}\,(t + \Delta t) - \vec{r}\,(t)}{\Delta t} \\
&= \lim_{\Delta t \to 0} \frac{(f(t + \Delta t)\vec{i} + g(t + \Delta t)\vec{j}\,) - (f(t)\vec{i} + g(t)\vec{j}\,)}{\Delta t} \\
&= \lim_{\Delta t \to 0} \left(\frac{f(t + \Delta t) - f(t)}{\Delta t}\vec{i} + \frac{g(t + \Delta t) - g(t)}{\Delta t}\vec{j} \right) \\
&= f'(t)\vec{i} + g'(t)\vec{j} \\
&= \frac{dx}{dt}\vec{i} + \frac{dy}{dt}\vec{j}.
\end{aligned}
$$

Thus we have the following result:

The **components of the velocity vector** of a particle moving in space with position vector $\vec{r}\,(t) = f(t)\vec{i} + g(t)\vec{j}$ at time t are given by

$$\vec{v}\,(t) = f'(t)\vec{i} + g'(t)\vec{j} = \frac{dx}{dt}\vec{i} + \frac{dy}{dt}\vec{j}.$$

Example 2   Find the components of the velocity vector for the child on the ferris wheel in Example 1 using a coordinate system which has its origin at the center of the ferris wheel and which makes the rotation counterclockwise.

Solution   The ferris wheel has radius 5 meters and completes 1 revolution counterclockwise every 2 minutes. The motion is parameterized by an equation of the form

$$\vec{r}\,(t) = 5\cos(\omega t)\vec{i} + 5\sin(\omega t)\vec{j},$$

where ω is chosen to make the period 2 minutes. Since the period of $\cos(\omega t)$ and $\sin(\omega t)$ is $2\pi/\omega$, we must have

$$\frac{2\pi}{\omega} = 2, \quad \text{so} \quad \omega = \pi.$$

Thus, the motion is described by the equation

$$\vec{r}\,(t) = 5\cos(\pi t)\vec{i} + 5\sin(\pi t)\vec{j},$$

306

where t is in minutes. The velocity is given by

$$\vec{v} = \frac{dx}{dt}\vec{i} + \frac{dy}{dt}\vec{j} = -5\pi \sin(\pi t)\vec{i} + 5\pi \cos(\pi t)\vec{j}.$$

To check, we calculate the magnitude of $\vec{v}$,

$$\|\vec{v}\| = \sqrt{(-5\pi)^2 \sin^2(\pi t) + (5\pi)^2 \cos^2(\pi t)} = 5\pi\sqrt{\sin^2(\pi t) + \cos^2(\pi t)} = 5\pi \approx 15.7,$$

which agrees with the speed we calculated in Example 1. To see that the direction is correct, we must show that the vector $\vec{v}$ at any time t is perpendicular to the position vector of the particle at time t. To do this, we compute the dot product of $\vec{v}$ and $\vec{r}$:

$$\vec{v} \cdot \vec{r} = (-5\pi \sin(\pi t)\vec{i} + 5\pi \cos(\pi t)\vec{j}) \cdot (5\cos(\pi t)\vec{i} + 5\sin(\pi t)\vec{j})$$
$$= -25\pi \sin(\pi t) \cos(\pi t) + 25\pi \cos(\pi t) \sin(\pi t) = 0.$$

So the velocity vector, $\vec{v}$, is perpendicular to $\vec{r}$ and hence tangent to the circle. (See Figure 17.3.)

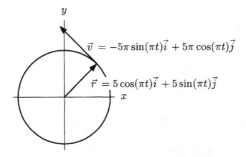

Figure 17.3: Velocity and radius vector of motion around a circle

Velocity Vectors and Tangent Lines

Since the velocity vector is tangent to the path of motion, it can be used to find parametric equations for the tangent line, if there is one.

Example 3   Find the tangent line at the point $(1, 3)$ to the curve defined by the parametric equation

$$\vec{r}(t) = t^2\vec{i} + 3t\vec{j}.$$

Solution   At time $t = 1$ the particle is at the point $(1, 3)$ with position vector $\vec{r}_0 = \vec{i} + 3\vec{j}$. The velocity vector at time t is $\vec{r}\,'(t) = 2t\vec{i} + 3\vec{j}$, so at time $t = 1$ the velocity is $\vec{v} = \vec{r}\,'(1) = 2\vec{i} + 3\vec{j}$. The tangent line passes through $(1, 3)$ in the direction of $\vec{v}$, so it has the parametric equation

$$\vec{r}(t) = \vec{r}_0 + t\vec{v} = (\vec{i} + 3\vec{j}) + t(2\vec{i} + 3\vec{j}).$$

The Acceleration Vector

Just as the velocity of a particle moving in 2-space is a vector quantity, so is the rate of change of the velocity of the particle, namely its acceleration. Figure 17.4 shows a particle at time t with velocity vector $\vec{v}(t)$ and then a little later at time $t + \Delta t$. The vector $\Delta\vec{v} = \vec{v}(t + \Delta t) - \vec{v}(t)$ is the change in velocity and points approximately in the direction of the acceleration. So,

$$\text{Average acceleration} = \frac{\Delta\vec{v}}{\Delta t}.$$

In the limit as $\Delta t \to 0$, we have the instantaneous acceleration at time t:

The **acceleration vector** of an object moving with velocity $\vec{v}(t)$ at time t is

$$\vec{a}(t) = \lim_{\Delta t \to 0} \frac{\Delta\vec{v}}{\Delta t} = \lim_{\Delta t \to 0} \frac{\vec{v}(t + \Delta t) - \vec{v}(t)}{\Delta t},$$

if the limit exists. We use the notation $\vec{a} = \dfrac{d\vec{v}}{dt} = \dfrac{d^2\vec{r}}{dt^2} = \vec{r}\,''(t)$.

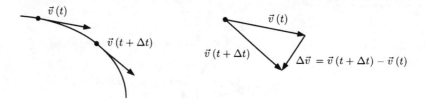

Figure 17.4: Computing the difference between two velocity vectors

Components of the Acceleration Vector

If we represent a curve in space parametrically by $x = f(t)$, $y = g(t)$, we can express the acceleration in components. The velocity vector $\vec{v}(t)$ is given by

$$\vec{v}(t) = f'(t)\vec{i} + g'(t)\vec{j}.$$

From the definition of the acceleration vector, we have

$$\vec{a}(t) = \lim_{\Delta t \to 0} \frac{\vec{v}(t + \Delta t) - \vec{v}(t)}{\Delta t} = \frac{d\vec{v}}{dt}.$$

Using the same method to compute $d\vec{v}/dt$ as we used to compute $d\vec{r}/dt$ on page 306, we obtain

The **components of the acceleration vector**, $\vec{a}(t)$, at time t of a particle moving in space with position vector $\vec{r}(t) = f(t)\vec{i} + g(t)\vec{j}$ at time t are given by

$$\vec{a}(t) = f''(t)\vec{i} + g''(t)\vec{j} = \frac{d^2x}{dt^2}\vec{i} + \frac{d^2y}{dt^2}\vec{j}.$$

Motion In a Circle and Along a Line

We now consider the velocity and acceleration vectors for two basic motions: uniform motion around a circle, and motion along a straight line.

Example 4   Find the acceleration vector for the child on the ferris wheel in Examples 1 and 2.

Solution   The child's position vector is given by $\vec{r}(t) = 5\cos(\pi t)\vec{i} + 5\sin(\pi t)\vec{j}$. In Example 2 we saw that the velocity vector is

$$\vec{v}(t) = \frac{dx}{dt}\vec{i} + \frac{dy}{dt}\vec{j} = -5\pi\sin(\pi t)\vec{i} + 5\pi\cos(\pi t)\vec{j}.$$

Thus, the acceleration vector is

$$\vec{a}(t) = \frac{d^2x}{dt^2}\vec{i} + \frac{d^2y}{dt^2}\vec{j} = -(5\pi)\cdot\pi\cos(\pi t)\vec{i} - (5\pi)\cdot\pi\sin(\pi t)\vec{j}$$
$$= -5\pi^2\cos(\pi t)\vec{i} - 5\pi^2\sin(\pi t)\vec{j}.$$

Notice that $\vec{a}(t) = -\pi^2\vec{r}(t)$. Thus, the acceleration vector is a multiple of $\vec{r}(t)$ and points toward the origin.

The motion of the child on the ferris wheel is an example of uniform circular motion, whose properties follow.

Uniform Circular Motion: For a particle whose motion is described by

$$\vec{r}(t) = R\cos(\omega t)\vec{i} + R\sin(\omega t)\vec{j}$$

- Motion is in a circle of radius R with period $2\pi/\omega$.
- Velocity, $\vec{v}$, is tangent to the circle and speed is constant $\|\vec{v}\| = \omega R$.
- Acceleration, $\vec{a}$, points toward the center of the circle with $\|\vec{a}\| = \|\vec{v}\|^2/R$.

In uniform circular motion, the acceleration vector is perpendicular to the velocity vector because the velocity vector does not change in magnitude, only in direction. We now look at straight line motion in which the velocity vector always has the same direction but its magnitude changes. In straight line motion, the acceleration vector points in the same direction as the velocity vector if the speed is increasing and in the opposite direction to the velocity vector if the speed is decreasing.

Example 5   Consider the motion given by the vector equation

$$\vec{r}(t) = 2\vec{i} + 6\vec{j} + (t^3 + t)(4\vec{i} + 3\vec{j}).$$

Show that this is straight line motion in the direction of the vector $4\vec{i} + 3\vec{j}$ and relate the acceleration vector to the velocity vector.

Solution   The velocity vector is

$$\vec{v} = (3t^2 + 1)(4\vec{i} + 3\vec{j}).$$

Since $(3t^2 + 1)$ is a positive scalar, the velocity vector $\vec{v}$ always points in the direction of the vector $4\vec{i} + 3\vec{j}$. In addition,

$$\text{Speed} = \|\vec{v}\| = (3t^2 + 1)\sqrt{4^2 + 3^2} = 5(3t^2 + 1).$$

Notice that the speed is decreasing until $t = 0$, then starts increasing. [The graph of speed $= f(t)$ is a parabola opening up with its vertex at $(0, 1)$.] The acceleration vector is

$$\vec{a} = 6t(4\vec{i} + 3\vec{j}).$$

For $t > 0$, the acceleration vector points in the same direction as $4\vec{i} + 3\vec{j}$, which is the same direction as $\vec{v}$. This makes sense because the object is speeding up. For $t < 0$, the acceleration vector $6t(4\vec{i} + 3\vec{j})$ points in the opposite direction to $\vec{v}$ because the object is slowing down.

The Length of a Curve

The speed of a particle is the magnitude of its velocity vector:

$$\text{Speed} = \|\vec{v}\| = \sqrt{\left(\frac{dx}{dt}\right)^2 + \left(\frac{dy}{dt}\right)^2}.$$

As in one dimension, we can find the distance traveled by a particle along a curve by integrating its speed. Thus,

$$\text{Distance traveled} = \int_a^b \|\vec{v}(t)\|\, dt.$$

If the particle never stops or reverses its direction as it moves along the curve, the distance it travels will be the same as the length of the curve. This suggests the following formula, which is justified in Problem 23:

If the curve C is given parametrically for $a \leq t \leq b$ by smooth functions and if the velocity vector $\vec{v}$ is not $\vec{0}$ for $a < t < b$, then

$$\text{Length of } C = \int_a^b \|\vec{v}\|\, dt.$$

Example 6 Find the circumference of the ellipse given by the parametric equations

$$x = 2\cos t, \quad y = \sin t, \quad 0 \leq t \leq 2\pi.$$

Solution The circumference of this curve is given by an integral which must be calculated numerically:

$$\text{Circumference} = \int_0^{2\pi} \sqrt{\left(\frac{dx}{dt}\right)^2 + \left(\frac{dy}{dt}\right)^2}\, dt = \int_0^{2\pi} \sqrt{(-2\sin t)^2 + (\cos t)^2}\, dt$$

$$= \int_0^{2\pi} \sqrt{4\sin^2 t + \cos^2 t}\, dt = 9.69.$$

Since the ellipse is inscribed in a circle of radius 2 and circumscribes a circle of radius 1, we would expect the length of the ellipse to be between $2\pi(2) \approx 12.57$ and $2\pi(1) \approx 6.28$, so the value of 9.69 is reasonable.

Problems on Motion, Velocity, and Acceleration

Exercises

For Exercises 1–2, find the velocity $\vec{v}(t)$ and the speed $\|\vec{v}(t)\|$. Find any times at which the particle stops.

1. $x = 3t^2, \quad y = t^3 + 1$
2. $x = 3\sin(t^2) - 1, \quad y = 3\cos(t^2)$

In Exercises 3–4, find the velocity and acceleration vectors.

3. $x = 3\cos t, y = 4\sin t$
4. $x = t, y = t^3 - t$
5. Find the position, velocity vector, and speed, at $t = 3$, of the particle whose motion is given by
$$x = t^3 - 8t + 1, \quad y = t^2 - 4.$$

6. A particle moves with $x = 3\cos 2t, y = 3\sin 2t$. Describe the motion in words and sketch the particle's path. Find the particle's position, velocity, and acceleration vectors at $t = 0$, and add these vectors to your sketch.

In Exercises 7–8, find the velocity and acceleration vectors of the straight line motion. Check that the acceleration vector points in the same direction as the velocity vector if the speed is increasing and in the opposite direction if the speed is decreasing.

7. $x = 2 + t^2, y = 3 - 2t^2$
8. $x = -2t^3 - 3t + 1, y = 4t^3 + 6t - 5$

Find the length of the curves in Exercises 9–11.

9. $x = 3 + 5t, y = 1 + 4t$ for $1 \le t \le 2$. Explain your answer.
10. $x = \cos(e^t), y = \sin(e^t)$ for $0 \le t \le 1$. Explain why your answer is reasonable.
11. $x = \cos 3t, y = \sin 5t$ for $0 \le t \le 2\pi$.

Problems

12. Using time increments of 0.01, give a table of values near $t = 1$ for the position vector of the circular motion
$$\vec{r}(t) = (\cos t)\vec{i} + (\sin t)\vec{j}.$$

Use the table to approximate the velocity vector, $\vec{v}$, at time $t = 1$. Show that $\vec{v}$ is perpendicular to the radius from the origin at $t = 1$.

13. The table gives x and y coordinates of a particle in the plane at time t. Assuming the path is smooth, estimate the following quantities:

   (a) The velocity vector and speed at time $t = 2$.
   (b) Any times when the particle is moving parallel to the y-axis.
   (c) Any times when the particle has come to a stop.

t	0	0.5	1.0	1.5	2.0	2.5	3.0	3.5	4.0
x	1	4	6	7	6	3	2	3	5
y	3	2	3	5	8	10	11	10	9

14. (a) Sketch the parameterized curve $x = t\cos t, y = t\sin t$ for $0 \le t \le 4\pi$.
   (b) Use difference quotients to approximate the velocity vectors $\vec{v}(t)$ for $t = 2, 4$, and 6.
   (c) Compute the velocity vectors $\vec{v}(t)$ for $t = 2, 4$, and 6, exactly and sketch them on the graph of the curve.

In Problems 15–16, find all values of t for which the particle is moving parallel to the x-axis and to the y-axis. Determine the end behavior and graph the particle's path.

15. $x = t^3 - 12t, \quad y = t^2 + 10t$
16. $x = t^2 - 6t, \quad y = t^3 - 3t$

17. Find parametric equations for a particle moving along the line $y = -2x + 5$ with speed 3.

18. A particle moves on a circle of radius 5 cm, centered at the origin, in the xy-plane (x and y measured in centimeters). It starts at the point $(0, 5)$ and moves counterclockwise, going once around the circle in 8 seconds.

   (a) Write a parameterization for the particle's motion.
   (b) What is the particle's speed? Give units.

19. Emily is standing on the outer edge of a merry-go-round, 10 meters from the center. The merry-go-round completes one full revolution every 20 seconds. As Emily passes over a point P on the ground, she drops a ball from 3 meters above the ground. How fast is Emily going?

20. An ant crawls along the radius from the center to the edge of a circular disk of radius 1 meter, moving at a constant rate of 1 cm/sec. Meanwhile, the disk is turning counterclockwise about its center at 1 revolution per second.

   (a) Parameterize the motion of the ant.
   (b) Find the velocity and speed of the ant.
   (c) Determine the acceleration and magnitude of the acceleration of the ant.

311

21. How do the motions of objects A and B differ, if A has position vector $\vec{r}_A(t)$ and B has position vector $\vec{r}_B(t) = \vec{r}_A(2t)$ for $t \geq 0$. Illustrate your answer with $\vec{r}_A(t) = t\vec{i} + t^2\vec{j}$.

22. How does the motion of objects A and B differ if A has position vector $\vec{r}_A(t)$ and B has position vector $\vec{r}_B(t) = \vec{r}_A(t-2)$? Illustrate your answer with $\vec{r}_A(t) = t\vec{i} + t^2\vec{j}$.

23. In this problem we justify the formula for the length of a curve given on page 310. Suppose the curve C is given by smooth parametric equations $x = x(t)$, $y = y(t)$ for $a \leq t \leq b$. By dividing the parameter interval $a \leq t \leq b$ at points $t_1, \ldots, t_{n-1}$ into small segments of length $\Delta t = t_{i+1} - t_i$, we get a corresponding division of the curve C into small pieces. See Figure 17.5, where the points $P_i = (x(t_i), y(t_i))$ on the curve C correspond to parameter values $t = t_i$. Let C_i be the portion of the curve C between P_i and P_{i+1}.

(a) Use local linearity to show that

$$\text{Length of } C_i \approx \sqrt{x'(t_i)^2 + y'(t_i)^2}\,\Delta t.$$

(b) Use part (a) and a Riemann sum to explain why

$$\text{Length of } C = \int_a^b \sqrt{x'(t)^2 + y'(t)^2}\,dt.$$

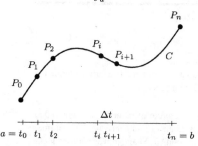

Figure 17.5: A subdivision of the parameter interval and the corresponding subdivision of the curve C

24. At time $t = 0$ an object is moving with velocity vector $\vec{v} = 2\vec{i} + \vec{j}$ and acceleration vector $\vec{a} = \vec{i} + \vec{j}$. Can it be in uniform circular motion about some point in the plane?

25. Figure 17.6 shows the velocity and acceleration vectors of an object in uniform circular motion about a point in the plane at a particular moment. Is it moving round the circle in the clockwise or counterclockwise direction?

Figure 17.6

Solutions to Problems on Motion, Velocity, and Acceleration

Exercises

1. To find $\vec{v}\,(t)$ we first find $dx/dt = 6t$ and $dy/dt = 3t^2$. Therefore, the velocity vector is $\vec{v} = 6t\vec{i} + 3t^2\vec{j}$. The speed of the particle is given by the magnitude of the vector,

$$\|\vec{v}\| = \sqrt{\left(\frac{dx}{dt}\right)^2 + \left(\frac{dy}{dt}\right)^2} = \sqrt{(6t)^2 + (3t^2)^2} = 3|t| \cdot \sqrt{4 + t^2}.$$

The particle stops when $\vec{v} = \vec{0}$, so when $6t = 3t^2 = 0$. Therefore, the particle stops when $t = 0$.

2. To find $\vec{v}\,(t)$ we first find $dx/dt = 6t\cos(t^2)$ and $dy/dt = -6t\sin(t^2)$. Therefore, the velocity is $\vec{v} = 6t\cos(t^2)\vec{i} - 6t\sin(t^2)\vec{j}$. The speed of the particle is given by

$$\begin{aligned}
\|\vec{v}\| &= \sqrt{(6t\cos(t^2))^2 + (-6t\sin(t^2))^2} \\
&= \sqrt{36t^2(\cos(t^2))^2 + 36t^2(\sin(t^2))^2} \\
&= 6|t|\sqrt{\cos^2(t^2) + \sin^2(t^2)} \\
&= 6|t|.
\end{aligned}$$

The particle comes to a complete stop when speed is 0, that is, if $6|t| = 0$, and so when $t = 0$.

3. The velocity vector $\vec{v}$ is given by:

$$\vec{v} = \frac{d}{dt}(3\cos t)\vec{i} + \frac{d}{dt}(4\sin t)\vec{j} = -3\sin t\vec{i} + 4\cos t\vec{j}.$$

The acceleration vector $\vec{a}$ is given by:

$$\vec{a} = \frac{d\vec{v}}{dt} = \frac{d}{dt}(-3\sin t)\vec{i} + \frac{d}{dt}(4\cos t)\vec{j} = -3\cos t\vec{i} - 4\sin t\vec{j}.$$

4. The velocity vector $\vec{v}$ is given by:

$$\vec{v} = \frac{d(t)}{dt}\vec{i} + \left(\frac{d}{dt}(t^3 - t)\right)\vec{j} = \vec{i} + (3t^2 - 1)\vec{j}.$$

The acceleration vector $\vec{a}$ is given by:

$$\vec{a} = \frac{d\vec{v}}{dt} = \frac{d(1)}{dt}\vec{i} + \left(\frac{d}{dt}(3t^2 - 1)\right)\vec{j} = 6t\vec{j}.$$

5. At $t = 3$, the particle is at the point $(4, 5)$ since $x = 3^3 - 8 \cdot 3 + 1 = 4$ and $y = 3^2 - 4 = 5$. The velocity vector is

$$\vec{v} = \frac{dx}{dt}\vec{i} + \frac{dy}{dt}\vec{j} = (3t^2 - 8)\vec{i} + (2t)\vec{j}.$$

When $t = 3$, the velocity vector is $\vec{v} = 19\vec{i} + 6\vec{j}$. The speed of the particle at $t = 3$ is given by

$$\text{Speed} = \|\vec{v}\| = \sqrt{19^2 + 6^2} = \sqrt{397} = 19.92.$$

6. The motion is circular, in a counterclockwise direction, around a circle centered at the origin of radius 3. At time $t = 0$, the particle is at point $(3, 0)$. The velocity vector is

$$\vec{v} = (-6\sin 2t)\vec{i} + (6\cos 2t)\vec{j}.$$

At $t = 0$, the velocity is $\vec{v} = 6\vec{j}$. The acceleration vector is

$$\vec{a} = (-12\cos 2t)\vec{i} + (-12\sin 2t)\vec{j}.$$

At $t = 0$, the acceleration is $\vec{a} = -12\vec{i}$. The vectors $\vec{v} = 6\vec{j}$ and $\vec{a} = -12\vec{i}$ are shown in Figure 17.7.

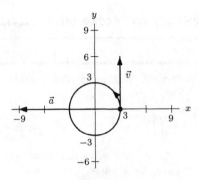

Figure 17.7

7. In vector form the parameterization is

$$\vec{r} = 2\vec{i} + 3\vec{j} + t^2(\vec{i} - 2\vec{j}).$$

Thus the motion is along the straight line through $(2, 3)$ in the direction of $\vec{i} - 2\vec{j}$. The velocity vector $\vec{v}$ is

$$\vec{v} = \frac{dx}{dt}\vec{i} + \frac{dy}{dt}\vec{j} = 2t(\vec{i} - 2\vec{j})$$

The acceleration vector $\vec{a}$ is

$$\vec{a} = \frac{d^2x}{dt^2}\vec{i} + \frac{d^2y}{dt^2}\vec{j} = 2(\vec{i} - 2\vec{j}).$$

The speed is

$$\|\vec{v}\| = 2|t|\|\vec{i} - 2\vec{j}\| = 2\sqrt{5}|t|.$$

The acceleration vector is constant and points in the direction of $\vec{i} - 2\vec{j}$. When $t < 0$ the absolute value $|t|$ is decreasing, hence the speed is decreasing. Also, when $t < 0$ the velocity vector $2t(\vec{i} - 2\vec{j})$ points in the direction opposite to $\vec{i} - 2\vec{j}$. When $t > 0$ the absolute value $|t|$ is increasing and hence the speed is increasing. Also, when $t > 0$ the velocity vector points in the same direction as $\vec{i} - 2\vec{j}$.

8. In vector form the parameterization is

$$\vec{r} = \vec{i} + -5\vec{j} + (2t^3 + 3t)(-\vec{i} + 2\vec{j}).$$

Thus the motion is along the straight line through $(1, -5)$ in the direction of $-\vec{i} + 2\vec{j}$. The velocity vector $\vec{v}$ is

$$\vec{v} = \frac{dx}{dt}\vec{i} + \frac{dy}{dt}\vec{j} = (6t^2 + 3)(-\vec{i} + 2\vec{j})$$

The acceleration vector $\vec{a}$ is

$$\vec{a} = \frac{d^2x}{dt^2}\vec{i} + \frac{d^2y}{dt^2}\vec{j} = 12t(-\vec{i} + 2\vec{j}).$$

The speed is

$$\|\vec{v}\| = |6t^2 + 3|\|-\vec{i} + 2\vec{j}\| = 3\sqrt{5}|2t^2 + 1| = 3\sqrt{5}(2t^2 + 1).$$

The graph of the speed is a parabola opening upward with vertex at $t = 0$. Thus the speed is decreasing when $t < 0$ and increasing when $t > 0$. The velocity vector always points in the same direction $-\vec{i} + 2\vec{j}$, since $6t^2 + 3$ is always positive. The acceleration vector points in the opposite direction to $-\vec{i} + 2\vec{j}$ when $t < 0$ and in the same direction when $t > 0$. Thus the acceleration vector points in the opposite direction to the speed when $t < 0$ and in the same direction when $t > 0$.

9. We have

$$\text{Length} = \int_1^2 \sqrt{(x'(t))^2 + (y'(t))^2}\, dt = \int_1^2 \sqrt{5^2 + 4^2}\, dt = \sqrt{41}.$$

This is the length of a straight line from the point $(8, 5)$ to $(13, 9)$.

10. We have

$$\text{Length} = \int_0^1 \sqrt{(-e^t \sin(e^t))^2 + (e^t \cos(e^t))^2}\, dt$$

$$= \int_0^1 \sqrt{e^{2t}}\, dt = \int_0^1 e^t\, dt$$

$$= e - 1.$$

This is the length of the arc of a unit circle from the point $(\cos 1, \sin 1)$ to $(\cos e, \sin e)$—in other words between the angles $\theta = 1$ and $\theta = e$. The length of this arc is $(e - 1)$.

11. We have

$$\text{Length} = \int_0^{2\pi} \sqrt{(-3 \sin 3t)^2 + (5 \cos 5t)^2}\, dt.$$

We cannot find this integral symbolically, but numerical methods show Length ≈ 24.6.

Problems

12. Table 17.1 shows values near $t = 1$ with t changing by increments of 0.01.

Table 17.1 *Values for the position vector $\vec{r}(t) = \cos t \vec{i} + \sin t \vec{j}$ near $t = 1$*

t	$\vec{r}$
0.98	$0.5570\vec{i} + 0.8305\vec{j}$
0.99	$0.5487\vec{i} + 0.8360\vec{j}$
1.00	$0.5403\vec{i} + 0.8415\vec{j}$
1.01	$0.5319\vec{i} + 0.8468\vec{j}$
1.02	$0.5234\vec{i} + 0.8521\vec{j}$

As we go down the table, the x-values are decreasing by about 0.0084 and the y-values are increasing by about 0.0054. Thus, a change in time of $\Delta t = 0.01$ produces the change in position vector $\Delta x \vec{i} + \Delta y \vec{j} \approx -0.0084\vec{i} + 0.0054\vec{j}$. So, the velocity vector is approximately

$$\vec{v} \approx \frac{1}{\Delta t}\left(\Delta x \vec{i} + \Delta y \vec{j}\right) \approx -0.84\vec{i} + 0.54\vec{j}.$$

Note that this velocity vector is perpendicular to the radius vector from the origin $(0,0)$ to the position $(0.54, 0.84)$ at time $t = 1$. Finally, the x and y-values in the table are almost indistinguishable from those of linear motion given by $x = 0.5403 - 0.84(t - 1)$, $y = 0.8415 + 0.54(t - 1)$, which are the parametric equations for the tangent line through the point $(0.5403, 0.8415)$.

13. Plotting the positions on the xy plane and noting their times gives the graph shown in Figure 17.8.

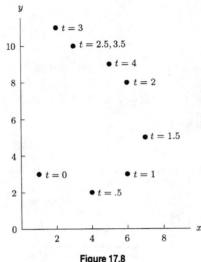

Figure 17.8

(a) We approximate dx/dt by $\Delta x/\Delta t$ calculated between $t = 1.5$ and $t = 2.5$:

$$\frac{dx}{dt} \approx \frac{\Delta x}{\Delta t} = \frac{3 - 7}{2.5 - 1.5} = \frac{-4}{1} = -4.$$

Similarly,

$$\frac{dy}{dt} \approx \frac{\Delta y}{\Delta t} = \frac{10 - 5}{2.5 - 1.5} = \frac{5}{1} = 5.$$

So,

$$\vec{v}(2) \approx -4\vec{i} + 5\vec{j} \quad \text{and} \quad \text{Speed} = \|\vec{v}\| = \sqrt{41}.$$

(b) The particle is moving vertically at about time $t = 1.5$.

(c) The particle stops at about time $t = 3$ and reverses course.

14. (a) The curve is a spiral as shown in Figure 17.10.

(b) We have:

$$\vec{v}(2) \approx \frac{2.001 \cos 2.001 - 2 \cos 2}{0.001}\vec{i} + \frac{2.001 \sin 2.001 - 2 \sin 2}{0.001}\vec{j}$$
$$= -2.24\vec{i} + 0.08\vec{j},$$
$$\vec{v}(4) \approx \frac{4.001 \cos 4.001 - 4 \cos 4}{0.001}\vec{i} + \frac{4.001 \sin 4.001 - 4 \sin 4}{0.001}\vec{j}$$
$$= 2.38\vec{i} - 3.37\vec{j},$$
$$\vec{v}(6) \approx \frac{6.001 \cos 6.001 - 6 \cos 6}{0.001} + \frac{6.001 \sin 6.001 - 6 \sin 6}{0.001}\vec{j}$$
$$= 2.63\vec{i} + 5.48\vec{j}.$$

(c) Evaluating the exact formula $\vec{v}(t) = (\cos t - t \sin t)\vec{i} + (\sin t + t \cos t)\vec{j}$ gives :

$$\vec{v}(2) = -2.235\vec{i} + 0.077\vec{j},$$
$$\vec{v}(4) = 2.374\vec{i} - 3.371\vec{j},$$
$$\vec{v}(6) = 2.637\vec{i} + 5.482\vec{j}.$$

See Figure 17.9.

316

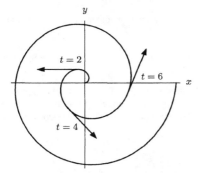

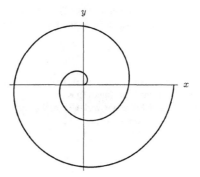

Figure 17.9: The spiral
$x = t \cos t, y = t \sin t$ and three velocity
vectors

Figure 17.10: The spiral
$x = t \cos t, y = t \sin t$ for $0 \le t \le 4\pi$

15. The velocity vector for this motion is

$$\vec{v} = \frac{dx}{dt}\vec{i} + \frac{dy}{dt}\vec{j} = (3t^2 - 12)\vec{i} + (2t + 10)\vec{j}.$$

The motion is vertical when the component in the $\vec{i}$ direction is 0 and motion in $\vec{j}$ direction is not 0. Motion in $\vec{i}$ direction is 0 when

$$3t^2 - 12 = 0,$$
$$t = 2, -2.$$

At these times, motion in $\vec{j}$ direction is not 0. The motion is horizontal when the component in the $\vec{j}$ direction is 0 and motion in $\vec{i}$ direction is not 0. Motion in $\vec{j}$ direction is 0 when

$$2t + 10 = 0,$$
$$t = -5.$$

At this time, the motion in $\vec{i}$ direction is not 0. To determine the end behavior, recall that a polynomial is approximated by its highest powered term for large values (positive or negative) of the independent variable. Thus, as $t \to \pm\infty$, we have $x \approx t^3$ and $y \approx t^2$. The end behavior, and the x and y coordinates when the motion is vertical or horizontal, are shown in Table 17.2. The graph is shown in Figure 17.11.

Table 17.2

t	x	y
$-\infty$	$-\infty$	$+\infty$
-5	-65	-25
-2	16	-16
2	-16	24
$+\infty$	$+\infty$	$+\infty$

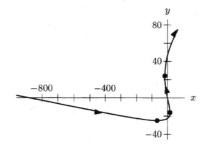

Figure 17.11

16. The velocity vector for this motion is

$$\vec{v} = (2t - 6)\vec{i} + (3t^2 - 3)\vec{j}.$$

The motion is vertical when the component in the $\vec{i}$ direction is 0 and motion in $\vec{j}$ direction is not 0. Motion in $\vec{i}$ direction is 0 when

$$2t - 6 = 0,$$
$$t = 3.$$

317

At that time, motion in $\vec{j}$ direction is not 0. The motion is horizontal when the component in the $\vec{j}$ direction is 0 and motion in $\vec{i}$ direction is not 0. Motion in $\vec{j}$ direction is 0 when

$$3t^2 - 3 = 0,$$
$$t = 1, -1.$$

At these times, motion in $\vec{i}$ direction is not 0. To determine the end behavior, recall that a polynomial is approximated by its highest powered term for large values (positive or negative) of the independent variable. Thus, as $t \to \pm\infty$, we have $x \approx t^2$ and $y \approx t^3$. The end behavior, and the x and y coordinates when the motion is vertical or horizontal, are shown in Table 17.3. The graph is shown in Figure 17.12.

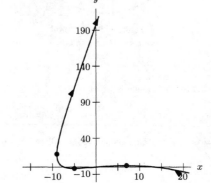

Table 17.3

t	x	y
$-\infty$	$+\infty$	$-\infty$
-1	7	2
1	-5	-2
3	-9	18
$+\infty$	$+\infty$	$+\infty$

Figure 17.12

17. Parametric equations for a line in 2-space are

$$x = x_0 + at$$
$$y = y_0 + bt$$

where (x_0, y_0) is a point on the line and $\vec{v} = a\vec{i} + b\vec{j}$ is the direction of motion. Notice that the slope of the line is equal to $\Delta y/\Delta x = b/a$, so in this case we have

$$\frac{b}{a} = \text{Slope} = -2,$$
$$b = -2a.$$

In addition, the speed is 3, so we have

$$\|\vec{v}\| = 3$$
$$\sqrt{a^2 + b^2} = 3$$
$$a^2 + b^2 = 9.$$

Substituting $b = -2a$ gives

$$a^2 + (-2a)^2 = 9$$
$$5a^2 = 9$$
$$a = \frac{3}{\sqrt{5}}, -\frac{3}{\sqrt{5}}.$$

If we use $a = 3/\sqrt{5}$, then $b = -2a = -6/\sqrt{5}$. The point (x_0, y_0) can be any point on the line: we use $(0, 5)$. The parametric equations are

$$x = \frac{3}{\sqrt{5}}t, \quad y = 5 - \frac{6}{\sqrt{5}}t.$$

Alternatively, we can use $a = -3/\sqrt{5}$ giving $b = 6/\sqrt{5}$. An alternative answer, which represents the particle moving in the opposite direction is

$$x = -\frac{3}{\sqrt{5}}t, \quad y = 5 + \frac{6}{\sqrt{5}}t.$$

18. (a) For any positive constant k, the parameterization

$$x = -5\sin(kt) \quad y = 5\cos(kt)$$

moves counterclockwise on a circle of radius 5 starting at the point $(0, 5)$. We choose k to make the period 8 seconds. If $k \cdot 8 = 2\pi$, then $k = \pi/4$ and the parameterization is

$$x = -5\sin\left(\frac{\pi t}{4}\right) \qquad y = 5\cos\left(\frac{\pi t}{4}\right).$$

(b) Since it takes 8 seconds for the particle to go around the circle

$$\text{Speed} = \frac{\text{Circumference of circle}}{8} = \frac{2\pi(5)}{8} = \frac{5\pi}{4} \text{ cm/sec.}$$

19. The parametric equation describing Emily's motion is

$$x = 10\cos\left(\frac{2\pi}{20}t\right) = 10\cos\left(\frac{\pi}{10}t\right), \quad y = 10\sin\left(\frac{2\pi}{20}t\right) = 10\sin\left(\frac{\pi}{10}t\right).$$

Her velocity vector is

$$\vec{v} = \frac{dx}{dt}\vec{i} + \frac{dy}{dt}\vec{j} = -\pi\sin\left(\frac{\pi}{10}t\right)\vec{i} + \pi\cos\left(\frac{\pi}{10}t\right)\vec{j}.$$

Her speed is given by:

$$\|\vec{v}\| = \sqrt{\left(-\pi\sin\left(\frac{\pi}{10}t\right)\right)^2 + \left(\pi\cos\left(\frac{\pi}{10}t\right)\right)^2}$$

$$= \pi\sqrt{\sin^2\left(\frac{\pi}{10}t\right) + \cos^2\left(\frac{\pi}{10}t\right)}$$

$$= \pi\sqrt{1} = \pi \text{ m/sec,}$$

which is independent of time (as we expected). This is certainly the long way to solve this problem though, since we could have simply divided the circumference of the circle (20π) by the time taken for a single rotation (20 seconds) to arrive at the same answer.

20. (a) Let the ant begin the trip at time $t = 0$, and let's place the origin of our coordinate system at the center of the disk. We align the axes so that at time $t = 0$ the radius along which the ant crawls falls on the positive x-axis. At time t seconds, the ant is at a distance of $r = t$ cm from the origin and at angle $\theta = 2\pi t$ radians from the positive x-axis. The Cartesian coordinates of this point are $(x, y) = (r\cos\theta, r\sin\theta) = (t\cos(2\pi t), t\sin(2\pi t))$. We can write the parametric equations of the ant's motion in vector form as

$$\vec{r}(t) = t\cos(2\pi t)\vec{i} + t\sin(2\pi t)\vec{j}, 0 \leq t \leq 100.$$

(b) The velocity vector of the ant is the derivative

$$\vec{v}(t) = \vec{r}\,'(t) = (\cos(2\pi t) - 2\pi t\sin(2\pi t))\vec{i} + (\sin(2\pi t) + 2\pi t\cos(2\pi t))\vec{j}.$$

The speed is the magnitude of the velocity vector

$$\|\vec{v}\| = ((\cos(2\pi t) - 2\pi t\sin(2\pi t))^2 + (\sin(2\pi t) + 2\pi t\cos(2\pi t))^2)^{1/2}$$

$$= (1 + 4\pi^2 t^2)^{1/2} \text{ cm/sec.}$$

Observe that the speed of the ant is increasing. Even though the ant is crawling at constant rate on the disk, the turning of the disk moves the ant faster and faster as it gets closer to the edge.

(c) The acceleration vector is

$$\vec{a} = \vec{v}\,'(t) = (-4\pi\sin(2\pi t) - 4\pi^2 t\cos(2\pi t))\vec{i} + (4\pi\cos(2\pi t) - 4\pi^2 t\sin(2\pi t))\vec{j}.$$

The magnitude of the acceleration is

$$\|\vec{a}\| = ((-4\pi\sin(2\pi t) - 4\pi^2 t\cos(2\pi t))^2 + (4\pi\cos(2\pi t) - 4\pi^2 t\sin(2\pi t))^2)^{1/2}$$

$$= 4\pi(1 + \pi^2 t^2)^{1/2} \text{ cm/sec}^2.$$

21. At time t object B is at the point with position vector $\vec{r}_B(t) = \vec{r}_A(2t)$, which is exactly where object A is at time $2t$. Thus B visits the same points as A, but does so at different times; A gets there later. While B covers the same path as A, it moves twice as fast. To see this, note for example that between $t = 1$ and $t = 3$, object B moves along the path from $\vec{r}_B(1) = \vec{r}_A(2)$ to $\vec{r}_B(3) = \vec{r}_A(6)$ which is traversed by object A during the time interval from $t = 2$ to $t = 6$. It takes A twice as long to cover the same ground.

In the case where $\vec{r}_A(t) = t\vec{i} + t^2\vec{j}$, both objects move on the parabola $y = x^2$. Both A and B are at the origin at time $t = 0$, but B arrives at the point $(2, 4)$ at time $t = 1$, whereas A does does not get there until $t = 2$.

22. At time t object B is at the point with position vector $\vec{r}_B(t) = \vec{r}_A(t-2)$, which is exactly where object A was two time units earlier, at time $t - 2$. Thus B visits the same points as A, but does so 2 time units later. In other words, B follows 2 time units behind A.

In the case where $\vec{r}_A(t) = t\vec{i} + t^2\vec{j}$, both objects move on the parabola $y = x^2$, but, for example, A is at the origin at time $t = 0$ whereas B does not get to the origin until time $t = 2$.

23. (a) If $\Delta t = t_{i+1} - t_i$ is small enough so that C_i is approximately a straight line, then we can make the linear approximations

$$x(t_{i+1}) \approx x(t_i) + x'(t_i)\Delta t,$$
$$y(t_{i+1}) \approx y(t_i) + y'(t_i)\Delta t,$$

and so

$$\text{Length of } C_i \approx \sqrt{(x(t_{i+1}) - x(t_i))^2 + (y(t_{i+1}) - y(t_i))^2}$$
$$\approx \sqrt{x'(t_i)^2(\Delta t)^2 + y'(t_i)^2(\Delta t)^2}$$
$$= \sqrt{x'(t_i)^2 + y'(t_i)^2}\,\Delta t.$$

(b) From point (a) we obtain the approximation

$$\text{Length of } C = \sum \text{length of } C_i$$
$$\approx \sum \sqrt{x'(t_i)^2 + y'(t_i)^2}\,\Delta t.$$

The approximation gets better and better as Δt approaches zero, and in the limit the sum becomes a definite integral:

$$\text{Length of } C = \lim_{\Delta t \to 0} \sum \sqrt{x'(t_i)^2 + y'(t_i)^2}\,\Delta t$$
$$= \int_a^b \sqrt{x'(t)^2 + y'(t)^2}\,dt.$$

24. In uniform circular motion the velocity vector is tangent to the circle of motion and the acceleration vector is directed toward the center of the circle. At all times the velocity $\vec{v}$ and acceleration $\vec{a}$ are perpendicular. Since $\vec{v} \cdot \vec{a} = (2\vec{i} + \vec{j}) \cdot (\vec{i} + \vec{j}) = 3 \neq 0$, $\vec{v}$ and $\vec{a}$ are not perpendicular, and so the object can not be in uniform circular motion.

25. The acceleration vector points from the object to the center of the orbit, and the velocity vector points from the object tangent to the circle in the direction of motion. From Figure 17.13 we see that the movement is counterclockwise.

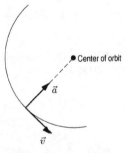

Figure 17.13

320